THE
GAMBLER'S
COMPANION

THE GAMBLER'S COMPANION

compiled and edited by
George G. Blakey

With cartoons by Enzo Apicella

PADDINGTON
PRESS LTD
NEW YORK & LONDON

To Kristin

Library of Congress Cataloging in Publication Data
Main Entry under title:
The Gambler's companion.
　　1. Gambling—Fiction　I. Blakey, George G.,
　　1934—
　　PZ1.G2325　(PN6071.G24)　813'.01　78-27529
ISBN 0 448 22071 7 (U.S. and Canada only)
ISBN 0 7092 0049 8

Filmset in England by Tradespools Ltd., Frome, Somerset
Printed and bound in the United States
Designed by Sandra Shafee

IN THE UNITED STATES
PADDINGTON PRESS
Distributed by
GROSSET & DUNLAP

IN THE UNITED KINGDOM
PADDINGTON PRESS

IN CANADA
Distributed by
RANDOM HOUSE OF CANADA LTD.

IN SOUTHERN AFRICA
Distributed by
ERNEST STANTON (PUBLISHERS) (PTY.) LTD.

IN AUSTRALIA AND NEW ZEALAND
Distributed by
A. H. & A. W. REED

Contents

ACKNOWLEDGMENTS

"Children" is reprinted in the US by permission of Macmillan Publishing Co., Inc. from *The Cook's Wedding and Other Stories* by Anton Chekhov. Translated from the Russian by Constance Garnett. Copyright ©1922 byMacmillan Publishing Co., Inc., renewed 1950 by David Garnett. Reprinted in the UK and British Commonwealth by permission of David Garnett and Chatto & Windus Ltd.

"Rory and Bran" excerpted from the book *Rory and Bran* by Lord Dunsany. Reprinted by permission of Curtis Brown Ltd., London, on behalf of the Estate of Lord Dunsany.

"After the Race" from *The Dubliners* by James Joyce, originally published by B.W. Huebsch Inc. in 1916, copyright ©1967 by the Estate of James Joyce. All rights reserved. Reprinted in the US and Canada by permission of Viking Penguin Inc. Reprinted in the UK and British Commonwealth by permission of the Executors of the James Joyce Estate and Jonathan Cape Ltd.

"Monte" by Arnold Bennett from *Paris Nights and Other Impressions of Places and Peoples*. Copyright ©1913 by George H. Doran Company. Reprinted in the US by permission of Doubleday & Company, Inc., and in the UK and British Commonwealth by permission of the Estate of the late Mrs. D. Cheston Bennett.

"The Great Sermon Handicap" by P.G. Wodehouse from the *Jeeves Omnibus* is reprinted in the US by permission of the Estate of the late P.G. Wodehouse and Scott Meredith Literary Agency Inc., and in the UK and British Commonwealth by permission of the Estate of the late P.G. Wodehouse and Barrie and Jenkins Ltd.

"How to Win While Losing" by William Saroyan from *Here Comes, There Goes, You know Who*. Copyright ©1961 by William Saroyan. Reprinted by permission of Simon & Schuster, a Division of Gulf & Western Corporation

"Rien ne va plus" by Alexander Woollcott from *The Portable Woollcott*, edited by Joseph P. Hennessey, is reprinted by permission of the Viking Press.

INTRODUCTION

"THE URGE TO GAMBLE is so universal and its practice so pleasurable that I assume it must be evil" wrote the American columnist Heywood Broun, neatly classifying gambling along with sex as one of those intensely human activities that seems to invite universal condemnation despite universal participation. Indeed no one can in all honesty totally disapprove of gambling any more than they can of sex since life itself is the biggest gamble of all, beginning with the lottery of birth. All our decisions whether in business or private life, however carefully judged, inevitably contain an element of chance. They are a step into the unknown. What the gambling table does is to bring us face to face with fate, allowing us to play the game of life in microcosm by seeing in an instant the consequences of our actions. The zero on the roulette wheel becomes the representation of fire, flood or sudden death while the unexpected fistful of aces is the equivalent of the freak wave that snatches the sailor from the maelstrom and deposits him safe but terrified back on his deck.

But like most things in life, gambling can be abused. Too often it becomes no longer just a game for entertainment and relaxation, but a deadly serious pursuit. Instead of being a microcosm of life, it becomes more important than life itself. The poor gambler sees the chance to redress the lottery of birth that made him poor, the rich gambler, the chance to flirt with the danger from which his wealth had so long insulated him. To both, the gaming table provides in a relatively secure age the terror and excitement of the jungle that their ancestors knew. The gaming table is the common meeting ground – or killing ground. The dice hold the balance between life and death. Indeed, one seventeenth-century English writer was moved to question "whether men in ships were to be accounted among the living or the dead because there were but few inches betwixt them and drowning, so the same query may be made of gamesters . . . whether they are to be esteemed rich or poor since there are but a few casts of dice betwixt a person of fortune and a beggar."

It is this razor's edge between success and disaster that has fascinated the world's great writers perhaps more than any other aspect of gambling, and it is not difficult to distinguish the broadly different attitudes to gambling by the nationality of the writers. The Russian gambler of Lermontov or Dostovevsky is perpetually anguished and fatalistic; Bourget's French gambler is equally anguished but more moralistic, while by contrast the English and American writers have adopted a much more sensible approach in regarding gambling as more within the realm of free will than of fate. And yet there is a further difference between these two nationalities. For an English writer like Saki or Wodehouse, gambling is a pleasant pastime rather like cricket or golf but with a small monetary stake added for excitement, and for Benson it is a serious business to which the laws of probability must be applied. Unlike a Russian, an English gambler nearly always has the sense to quit when he is ahead or even when he is behind to an acceptable extent.

As for an American, it may be that the race memory of the hazards of nineteenth-century pioneer life is too strong to allow for a totally rational and unemotional approach to gambling. The terrible risks that the American gambler assumes, often against all the odds, argue for a degree of courage in his make-up that has to be admired and respected. The psychologists may talk about masochism and the death wish but the courage that impels a gambler to bet the deeds of his plantation on the turn of a card can be of the same order as that which in time of war will prompt him to charge an enemy machine gun post with his bare hands. This is the gambler we read about in the pages of Bret Harte, Stephen Crane or William Saroyan.

But fortunately we are not all desperate gamblers ready to stake our very lives on a throw of the dice or a spin of the wheel, and there remains a lighter side of gambling capable of providing almost infinite scope for the imagination of the writer. For every one of Lermontov's hussars with a pistol to his head there is a Bertie Wooster betting on the length of a sermon at a country church, or a jumping frog making a sucker out of the smartest gambler in Calaveras County. Frank Hardy's account of crooked racing in Australia is rivaled by Lord Dunsany's tale of a chaotic Irish race meeting. Chekhov's solitary prisoner who gambled away his freedom contrasts with Richard Condon's Captain Huntingdon who, having nothing left to bet with, stakes the services of his cook. And the Australian financier in *Mammon & Co.* plan to make a million out of rigging the market in Carmel gold mining stock while the town barber in *Mariposa* is being taken to the cleaners by the gentlemen of the Cuban Lands Company.

But for most of us gambling will remain a pleasant diversion with only the occasional painful loss to make us resolve never to touch a card or call our bookmaker or stockbroker ever again–at least until the next time–but the stories that follow deal as much with the pain as with the pleasure of gambling. Indeed, reading some of the more tragic tales should prove as effective as a course in aversion therapy for the would-be high roller, making unnecessary a painful loss to point out the folly of betting too heavily. Five minutes with Tolstoy's *Recollections of a Scorer* is guaranteed to save the reader thousands the next time he or she is challenged to a game of billiards, and even the briefest acquaintance with Benson's Mr. Alington or Hemyng's Mr. John Jeffries will make sure everyone stays away from speculative mining stocks for ever!

GEORGE G. BLAKEY
London
January 1979

BEGINNER'S LUCK

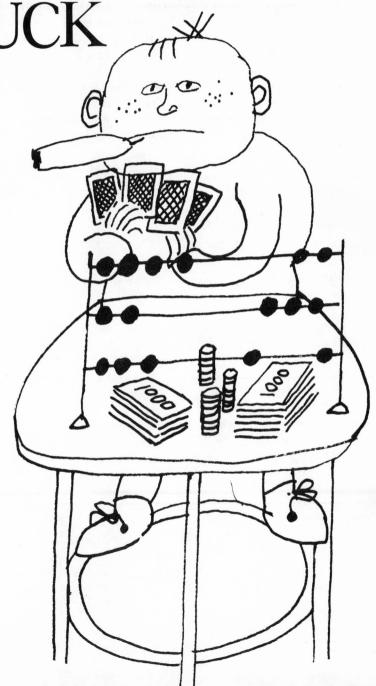

THE DIARY OF A NOBODY

George Grossmith

George Grossmith was not only an actor, comedian and singer but also the producer and manager credited with introducing the revue to the theater of Edwardian London. Neither was he without literary ambitions and he is undoubtedly best remembered today as the author of *The Diary of a Nobody*, that unique chronicle of lower middle class daily life of the period.

In this extract from the diary, Mr Pooter is persuaded by his son Lupin to undertake his first speculative venture in the stock market. The outcome makes him resolve that it will also be his last.

JANUARY 5. – I can scarcely write the news. Mr Perkupp told me my salary would be raised £100! I stood gaping for a moment unable to realise it. I annually get £10 rise, and I thought it might be £15 or even £20; but £100 surpasses all belief. Carrie and I both rejoiced over our good fortune. Lupin came home in the evening in the utmost good spirits. I sent Sarah quietly round to the grocer's for a bottle of champagne, the same as we had before, "Jackson Frères." It was opened at supper, and I said to Lupin: "This is to celebrate some good news I have received today." Lupin replied: "Hooray, Guv.! And I have some good news, also; a double event, eh?" I said: "My boy, as a result of twenty-one years' industry and strict attention to the interest of my superiors in office, I have been rewarded with promotion and a rise in salary of £100."

Lupin gave three cheers, and we rapped the tables furiously, which brought in Sarah to see what the matter was. Lupin ordered us to "fill up" again, and addressing us upstanding, said: "Having been in the firm of Job Cleanands, stock and share-brokers, a few weeks, and *not* having paid particular attention to the interests of my superiors in office, my Guv'nor, as a reward to me, allotted me £5 worth of shares in a really good thing.

The result is, to-day I have made £200." I said : "Lupin, you are joking."
"No, Guv., it's the good old truth; Job Cleanands *put me on to Chlorates.*"

JANUARY 21. – I am very much concerned at Lupin having started a pony-trap. I said : "Lupin, are you justified in this outrageous extravagance?" Lupin replied : "Well, one must get to the City somehow. I've only hired it, and can give it up any time I like." I repeated my question : "Are you justified in this extravagance?" He replied : "Look here, Guv.; excuse my saying so, but you're a bit out of date. It does not pay nowadays, fiddling about over small things. I don't mean anything personal, Guv'nor. My boss says if I take his tip, and stick to big things, I can make big money !" I said I thought the very idea of speculation most horrifying. Lupin said : "It is not speculation, it's a dead cert." I advised him, at all events, not to continue the pony and cart; but he replied : "I made £200 in one day; now suppose I only make £200 in a month, or put it at £100 a month, which is ridiculously low – why, that is £1250 a year. What's a few pounds a week for a trap?"

I did not pursue the subject further, beyond saying that I should feel glad when the autumn came, and Lupin would be of age and responsible for his own debts. He answered : "My dear Guv., I promise you faithfully that I will never speculate with what I have not got. I shall only go on Job Cleanands' tips, and as he is in the 'know' it is pretty safe sailing." I felt somewhat relieved. Gowing called in the evening and, to my surprise, informed me that, as he had made £10 by one of Lupin's tips, he intended asking us and the Cummings' round next Saturday. Carrie and I said we should be delighted.

FEBRUARY 18. – Carrie has several times recently called attention to the thinness of my hair at the top of my head, and recommended me to get it seen to. I was this morning trying to look at it by the aid of a small hand-glass, when somehow my elbow caught against the edge of the chest of drawers and knocked the glass out of my hand and smashed it. Carrie was in an awful way about it, as she is rather absurdly superstitious. To make matters worse, my large photograph in the drawing-room fell during the night, and the glass is cracked.

Carrie said : "Mark my words, Charles, some misfortune is about to happen."

I said : "Nonsense, dear."

In the evening Lupin arrived home early, and seemed a little agitated. I said: "What's up, my boy?" He hesitated a good deal, and then said: "You know those Parachikka Chlorates I advised you to invest £20 in?" I replied: "Yes, they are all right, I trust?" He replied: "Well, no! To the surprise of everybody, they have utterly collapsed."

My breath was so completely taken away, I could say nothing. Carrie looked at me, and said: "What did I tell you?" Lupin, after a while, said: "However, you are specially fortunate. I received an early tip, and sold out yours immediately, and was fortunate to get £2 for them. So you get something after all."

I gave a sigh of relief. I said: "I was not so sanguine as to suppose, as you predicted, that I should get six or eight times the amount of my investment; still a profit of £2 is a good percentage for such a short time." Lupin said, quite irritably: "You don't understand. I sold your £20 shares for £2; you therefore lose £18 on the transaction, whereby Cummings and Gowing will lose the whole of theirs."

FEBRUARY 19. – Lupin, before going to town, said: "I am very sorry about those Parachikka Chlorates; it would not have happened if the boss, Job Cleanands, had been in town. Between ourselves, you must not be surprised if something goes wrong at our office. Job Cleanands has not been seen the last few days, and it strikes me several people *do* want to see him very particularly."

In the evening Lupin was just on the point of going out to avoid a collision with Gowing and Cummings, when the former entered the room, without knocking, but with his usual trick of saying, "May I come in?"

He entered, and to the surprise of Lupin and myself, seemed to be in the best of spirits. Neither Lupin nor I broached the subject to him, but he did so of his own accord. He said: "I say, those Parachikka Chlorates have gone an awful smash! You're a nice one, Master Lupin. How much do you lose?" Lupin, to my utter astonishment, said: "Oh! I had nothing in them. There was some informality in my application – I forgot to enclose the cheque, or something, and I didn't get any. The Guv. loses £18." I said: "I quite understood you were in it, or nothing would have induced me to speculate." Lupin replied: "Well, it can't be helped; you must go double on the next tip." Before I could reply, Gowing said: "Well, I lose nothing, fortunately. From what I heard, I did not quite believe in them, so I persuaded Cummings to take my £15 worth, as he had more faith in them than I had."

Lupin burst out laughing, and, in the most unseemly manner, said:

"Alas, poor Cummings! He'll lose £35." At that moment there was a ring at the bell. Lupin said: "I don't want to meet Cummings." If he had gone out of the door he would have met him in the passage, so as quickly as possible Lupin opened the parlour window and got out. Gowing jumped up suddenly, exclaiming: "I don't want to see him either!" and, before I could say a word, he followed Lupin out of the window.

For my own part, I was horrified to think my own son and one of my most intimate friends should depart from the house like a couple of interrupted burglars. Poor Cummings was very upset, and of course was naturally very angry both with Lupin and Gowing. I pressed him to have a little whisky, and he replied that he had given up whisky; but would like a little "Unsweetened," as he was advised it was the most healthy spirit. I had none in the house, but sent Sarah round to Lockwood's for some.

FEBRUARY 20. – The first thing that caught my eye on opening the *Standard* was – "Great Failure of Stock and Share Dealers! Mr Job Cleanands Absconded!" I handed it to Carrie, and she replied: "Oh! perhaps it's for Lupin's good. I never did think it a suitable situation for him." I thought the whole affair very shocking.

Lupin came down to breakfast, and seeing he looked painfully distressed, I said: "We know the news, my dear boy, and feel very sorry for you." Lupin said: "How did you know? who told you?" I handed him the *Standard*. He threw the paper down, and said: "Oh, I don't care a button for that! I expected that, but I did not expect this." He then read a letter from Frank Mutlar, announcing, in a cool manner, that Daisy Mutlar is to be married next month to Murray Posh. I exclaimed: "Murray Posh! Is not that the very man Frank had the impudence to bring here last Tuesday week?" Lupin said: "Yes; the '*Posh's-three-shilling-hats*' chap."

We all then ate our breakfast in dead silence.

In fact, I could eat nothing. I was not only too worried, but I cannot and will not eat cushion of bacon. If I cannot get streaky bacon, I will do without anything.

When Lupin rose to go I noticed a malicious smile creep over his face. I asked him what it meant. He replied: "Oh! only a little consolation – still it is a consolation. I have just remembered that, by *my* advice, Mr Murray Posh has invested £600 in Parachikka Chlorates!"

THE SOCIETY
FOR THE REFORMATION OF
POKER PLAYERS

Robert Barr

Journalist, novelist and detective story writer, Robert Barr was born in Scotland in 1850 but spent most of the first thirty years of his life in Canada and the U.S.A. His journalistic career began on the Detroit Free Press in 1876 where he quickly gained a reputation as a reporter who would stop at nothing to get a story. In 1881 Barr came to England and started *The Idler* in partnership with Jerome K. Jerome of *Three Men in a Boat* fame.

Best known for his short stories and extravagant historical romances – many of them written under the pseudonym, Luke Sharp – Barr had a keen but sympathetic eye for the foibles of humanity. In this story from a collection entitled *In a Steamer Chair*, he relates how a group of friends contrive to prevent one of their number being ruined by a professional gambler.

> *O Unseen Hand that ever makes and deals us,*
> *And plays our game !*
> *That now obscures and then to light reveals us,*
> *Serves blanks or fame.*
> *How vain our shuffling, bluff and weak pretending !*
> *'Tis Thou alone can name the final ending.*

THE SEDUCTIVE GAME of poker is one that I do not understand. I do not care to understand it, because it cannot be played without the putting up of a good deal of the coin of the realm, and although I have nothing to say against betting, my own theory of conduct in the matter is this, that I want no man's money which I do not earn, and I do not want any man to get my money unless he earns it. So it happens, in the matter of cards, I content myself with eucre and other games which do not require the wagering of money.

On board the Atlantic steamers there is always more or less gambling. I have heard it said that men make trips to and fro merely for the purpose of fleecing their fellow-passengers; but, except in one instance, I never had any experience with this sort of thing.

Our little society for the reformation of poker players, or to speak more correctly, for the reformation of one particular poker player, was formed one bright starlight night, latitude such a number, and longitude something else, as four of us sat on a seat at the extreme rear end of the great steamer. We four, with one other, sat at a small table in the saloon. One of the small tables on a Transatlantic steamer is very pleasant if you have a nice crowd with you. A seat at a small table compares with a seat at the large table as living in a village compares with living in a city. You have some individuality at the short table; you are merely one of a crowd at the long table. Our small table was not quite full. I had the honour of sitting at the head of it, and on each side of me were two young fellows, making five altogether. We all rather prided ourselves on the fact that there were no ladies at our little table.

The young Englishman who sat at my right hand at the corner of the table was going out to America to learn farming. I could, myself, have taught him a good deal about it, but I refrained from throwing cold water on his enthusiastic ideas about American agriculture. His notion was that it was an occupation mostly made up of hunting and fishing, and having a good time generally. The profits, he thought, were large and easily acquired. He had guns with him, and beautiful fishing-rods, and things of that sort. He even had a vague idea that he might be able to introduce fox-hunting in the rural district to which he was going. He understood, and regretted the fact, that we in the United States were rather behindhand in the matter of fox-hunting. He had a good deal of money with him, I understood, and he had already paid a hundred pounds to a firm in England that had agreed to place him on a farm in America. Of course, now that the money had been paid, there was no use in telling the young man he had been a fool. He would find that out soon enough when he got to America. Henry Storm was his name, and a milder mannered man with a more unsuitable name could hardly be found. The first two or three days out he was the life of our party. We all liked him, in fact, nobody could help liking him; but, as the voyage progressed, he grew more and more melancholy, and, what was really serious, took little food, which is not natural in an Englishman. I thought somebody had been telling him what a fool he had been to pay away his hundred pounds before leaving England, but young Smith of Rochester, who sat at my left, told me what the trouble was one day as we walked the deck.

"Do you know," he began, "that Henry Storm is being robbed?"

"Being robbed?" I answered; "you mean he has been robbed."

"Well, has been, and is being, too. The thing is going on yet. He is playing altogether too much poker in the smoking-room, and has lost a pile of money – more, I imagine, than he can well afford."

"That's what's the trouble with him, is it? Well, he ought to know better than to play for bigger stakes than he can afford to lose."

"Oh, it's easy to say that; but he's in the hands of a swindler, of a professional gambler. You see that man?" He lowered his voice as he spoke, and I looked in the direction of his glance. By this time we knew, in a way, everybody on board the ship. The particular man Smith pointed out was a fellow I had noticed a good deal, who was very quiet and gentlemanly, interfering with nobody, and talking with few. I had spoken to him once, but he had answered rather shortly, and, apparently to his relief, and certainly to my own, our acquaintance ceased where it began. He had jet black beard and hair, both rather closely clipped; and he wore a fore and aft cap, which never improves a man's appearance very much.

"That man," continued Smith, as he passed us, "was practically under arrest for gambling on the steamer in which I came over. It seems that he is a regular professional gambler, who does nothing but go across the ocean and back again, fleecing young fellows like Storm."

"Does he cheat?" I asked.

"He doesn't need to. He plays poker. An old hand, and a cool one, has no occasion to cheat at that game to get a young one's money away from him."

"Then why doesn't some one warn young Storm?"

"Well, that's just what I wanted to speak to you about. I think it ought to be done. I think we should call a meeting of our table, somewhere out here in the quiet, and have a talk over it, and make up our minds what is to be done. It's a delicate matter, you know, and I am afraid we are a little late as it is. I do believe young Storm has lost nearly all his money to that fellow."

"Can't he be made to disgorge?"

"How? The money has been won fairly enough, as that sort of thing goes. Other fellows have played with them. It isn't as if he had been caught cheating – he hasn't, and won't be. He doesn't cheat – he doesn't need to, as I said before. Now that gambler pretends he is a commercial traveller from Buffalo. I know Buffalo down to the ground, so I took him aside yesterday and said plumply to him, 'What firm in Buffalo do you represent?' He answered shortly that his business was his own affair. I said, 'Certainly it is, and you are quite right in keeping it dark. When I was coming over to Europe, I saw a man in your line of business who looked very much like you, practically put under arrest by the purser for gambling. You were travelling for a St Louis house then.'"

"What did he say to that?"

"Nothing; he just gave me one of those sly, sinister looks of his, turned on his heel, and left me."

The result of this conversation was the inauguration of the Society for the Reforming of a Poker Player. It was agreed between us that if young Storm had lost all his money we would subscribe enough as a loan to take care of him until he got a remittance from home. Of course we knew that any young fellow who goes out to America to begin farming, does not, as a general rule, leave people in England exceedingly well off, and probably this fact, more than any other, accounted for the remorse visible on Storm's countenance. We knew quite well that the offering of money to him would be a very delicate matter, but it was agreed that Smith should take this in hand if we saw the offer was necessary. Then I, as the man who sat at the head of the table, was selected to speak to young Storm, and, if possible, get him to abandon poker. I knew this was a somewhat impudent piece of business on my part, and so I took that evening to determine how best to perform the task set for me. I resolved to walk the deck with him in the morning, and have a frank talk over the matter.

When the morning came, I took young Storm's arm and walked two or three turns up and down the deck, but all the while I could not get up courage enough to speak with him in relation to gambling. When he left me, I again thought over the matter. I concluded to go into the smoking-room myself, sit down beside him, see him lose some money and use that fact as a text for my coming discourse on the evils of gambling. After luncheon I strolled into the smoking-room, and there sat this dark-faced man with his half-closed eyes opposite young Storm, while two others made up the four-handed game of poker.

Storm's face was very pale, and his lips seemed dry, for he moistened them every now and then as the game went on. He was sitting on the sofa, and I sat down beside him, paying no heed to the dark gambler's look of annoyance. However, the alleged Buffalo man said nothing, for he was not a person who did much talking. Storm paid no attention to me as I sat down beside him. The gambler had just dealt. It was very interesting to see the way he looked at his hand. He allowed merely the edges of the cards to show over each other, and then closed up his hand and seemed to know just what he had. When young Storm looked at his hand he gave a sort of gasp, and for the first time cast his eyes upon me. I had seen his hand, but did not know whether it was a good one or not. I imagined it was not very good, because all the cards were of a low denomination. Threes or fours I think, but four of the cards had a like number of spots. There was some money in the centre of the table. Storm pushed a half-crown in front of him, and the next man did the same. The gambler put down a half-sovereign, and the man at his left, after a moment's hesitation, shoved out an equal amount from the pile of gold in front of him.

Young Storm pushed out a sovereign.

"I'm out," said the man whose next bet it was, throwing down his cards.

The gambler raised it a sovereign, and the man at his left dropped out. It now rested between Storm and the gambler. Storm increased the bet a sovereign. The gambler then put on a five-pound note.

Storm said to me huskily, "Have you any money?"

"Yes," I answered him.

"Lend me five pounds if you can."

Now, the object of my being there was to stop gambling, not to encourage it. I was the president *pro tem.* of the Society for the Reformation of Poker Players, yet I dived into my pocket, pulled out my purse under the table and slipped a five-pound note into his hand. He put that on the table as if he had just taken it from his own pocket.

"I call you," he said.

"What have you got?" asked the gambler.

"Four fours," said Storm, putting down his hand.

The gambler closed up his and threw the cards over to the man who was to deal. Storm paused a moment and then pulled towards him the money in the centre of the table and handed me my five-pound note.

When the cards were next dealt, Storm seemed to have rather an ordinary hand, so apparently had all the rest, and there was not much money in the pile. But, poor as Storm's hand was, the rest appeared to be poorer, and he raked in the cash. This went on for two or three deals, and finding that, as Storm was winning all the time, although not heavily, I was not getting an object lesson against gambling, I made a move to go.

"Stay where you are," whispered Storm to me, pinching my knee with his hand so hard that I almost cried out.

Then it came to the gambler's turn to deal again. All the time he deftly shuffled the cards he watched the players with that furtive glance of his from out his half-shut eyes.

Storm's hand was a remarkable one, after he had drawn two cards, but I did not know whether it had any special value or not. The other players drew three cards each, and the gambler took one.

"How much money have you got?" whispered Storm to me.

"I don't know," I said, "perhaps a hundred pounds."

"Be prepared to lend me every penny of it," he whispered.

I said nothing; but I never knew the president of a society for the suppression of gambling to be in such a predicament.

Storm bet a sovereign. The player to his left threw down his hand. The gambler pushed out two sovereigns. The other player went out.

Storm said, "I see your bet, and raise you another sovereign." The gambler, without saying a word, shoved forward some more gold.

"Get your money ready," whispered Storm to me.

I did not quite like his tone, but I made allowance for the excitement under which he was evidently labouring.

He threw on a five-pound note. The gambler put down another five-pound note, and then, as if it were the slightest thing possible, put a ten-pound note on top of that, which made the side players gasp. Storm had won sufficient to cover the bet and raise it. After that I had to feed in to him five-pound notes, keeping count of their number on my fingers as I did so. The first to begin to hesitate about putting money forward was the gambler. He shot a glance now and again from under his eyebrows at the young man opposite. Finally, when my last five-pound note had been thrown on the pile, the gambler spoke for the first time.

"I call you," he said.

"Put down another five-pound note," cried the young man.

"I have called you," said the gambler.

Henry Storm half rose from his seat in his excitement. "Put down another five-pound note, if you dare."

"That isn't poker," said the gambler. "I have called you. What have you got?"

"Put down another five-pound note, and I'll put a ten-pound note on top of it."

"I say that isn't poker. You have been called. What have you got?"

"I'll bet you twenty pounds against your five-pound note, if you dare put it down."

By this time Storm was standing up, quivering with excitement, his cards tightly clenched in his hand. The gambler sat opposite him calm and imperturbable.

"What have you got?" said Storm.

"I called you," said the gambler, "show your hand."

"Yes; but when I called you, you asked me what I had, and I told you. What have *you* got?"

"I am not afraid to show my hand," said the gambler, and he put down on the table four aces.

"There's the king of hearts," said Storm, putting it down on the table. "There's the queen of hearts, there's the knave of hearts, there's the ten of hearts. Now," he cried, waving his other card in the air, "can you tell me what this card is?"

"I am sure I don't know," answered the gambler, quietly, "probably the nine of hearts."

"It *is* the nine of hearts," shouted Storm, placing it down beside the others.

The gambler quietly picked up the cards, and handed them to the man who was to deal. Storm's hands were trembling with excitement as he pulled the pile of bank notes and gold towards him. He counted out what I had given him, and passed it to me under the table. The rest he thrust into his pocket.

"Come," I said, "it is time to go. Don't strain your luck."

"Another five pounds," he whispered; "sit where you are."

"Nonsense," I said, "another five pounds will certainly mean that you lose everything you have won. Come away, I want to talk with you."

"Another five pounds, I have sworn it."

"Very well, I shall not stay here any longer."

"No, no," he cried eagerly; "sit where you are, sit where you are."

There was a grim thin smile on the lips of the gambler as this whispered conversation took place.

When the next hand was dealt around and Storm looked at his cards, he gave another gasp of delight. I thought that a poker player should not be so free with his emotions; but of course I said nothing. When it came his time to bet, he planked down a five-pound note on the table. The other two, as was usual, put down their cards. They were evidently very timorous players. The gambler hesitated for a second, then he put a ten-pound note on Storm's five pounds. Storm at once saw him, and raised him ten. The gambler hesitated longer this time, but at last he said, "I shall not bet. What have you got?"

"Do you call me?" asked Storm. "Put up your money if you do."

"No, I do not call you."

Storm laughed and threw his cards face up on the table. "I have nothing," he said, "I have bluffed you for once."

"It is very often done," answered the gambler, quietly, as Storm drew in his pile of money, stuffing it again in his coat pocket. "Your deal, Storm."

"No, sir," said the young man, rising up; "I'll never touch a poker hand again. I have got my own money back and five or ten pounds over. I know when I've had enough."

Although it was Storm's deal, the gambler had the pack of cards in his hand idly shuffling them to and fro.

"I have often heard," he said slowly without raising his eyes, "that when one fool sits down beside another fool at poker, the player has the luck of two fools – but I never believed it before."

VAN BIBBER AT THE RACES

R.H.Davis

Richard Harding Davis was perhaps the most famous and romantic of the American war correspondents who flourished around the turn of the century. He covered six wars for Hearst Newspapers and his celebrated despatch, *The Death of Rodriguez*, describing in moving terms the execution of the Cuban rebel leader in 1898, is credited with having helped to start the Spanish–American War.

Although best known for his work as a war correspondent, Davis also wrote a number of adventure stories, many of them concerned with gambling. This one is from a collection of stories about one of his most popular characters, the young man about town, Van Bibber, and describes his adventures at a race meeting one Fourth of July.

Y OUNG V AN B IBBER had never spent a Fourth of July in the city, as he had always understood it was given over to armies of small boys on that day, who sat on all the curbstones and set off fire-crackers, and that the thermometer always showed ninety degrees in the shade, and cannon boomed and bells rang from daybreak to midnight. He had refused all invitations to join any Fourth-of-July parties at the sea-shore or on the Sound or at Tuxedo, because he expected his people home from Europe, and had to be in New York to meet them. He was accordingly greatly annoyed when he received a telegram saying they would sail in a boat a week later.

He finished his coffee at the club on the morning of the Fourth about ten o'clock, in absolute solitude, and with no one to expect and nothing to anticipate; so he asked for a morning paper, and looked up the amusements offered for the Fourth. There were plenty of excursions with brass bands, and refreshments served on board, baseball matches by the hundred, athletic meetings and picnics by the dozen, but nothing that seemed to exactly please him.

The races sounded attractive, but then he always lost such a lot of money, and the crowd pushed so, and the sun and the excitement made his head ache between the eyes and spoiled his appetite for dinner. He had vowed again and again that he would not go to the races ; but as the day wore on and the solitude of the club became oppressive, and the silence of the Avenue began to tell on him, he changed his mind, and made his preparations accordingly.

First, he sent out after all the morning papers and read their tips on the probable winners. Very few of them agreed, so he took the horse which most of them seemed to think was best, and determined to back it, no matter what might happen or what new tips he might get later. Then he put two hundred dollars in his pocket-book to bet with, and twenty dollars for expenses, and sent around for his field-glasses.

He was rather late in starting, and he made up his mind on the way to Morris Park that he would be true to the list of winners he had written out, and not make any side bets on any suggestions or inside information given him by others. He vowed a solemn vow on the rail of the boat to plunge on each of the six horses he had selected from the newspaper tips, and on no others. He hoped in this way to win something. He did not care so much to win, but he hated to lose. He always felt so flat and silly after it was over; and when it happened, as it often did, that he had paid several hundred dollars for the afternoon's sport, his sentiments did him credit.

"I shall probably, or rather certainly, be tramped on and shoved," soliloquised Van Bibber. "I shall smoke more cigars than are good for me, and drink more than I want, owing to the unnatural excitement and heat, and I shall be late for my dinner. And for all this I shall probably pay two hundred dollars. It really seems as if I were a young man of little intellect, and yet thousands of others are going to do exactly the same thing."

The train was very late. One of the men in front said they would probably just be able to get their money up in time for the first race. A horse named Firefly was Van Bibber's choice, and he took one hundred dollars of his two hundred to put up on her. He had it already in his hand when the train reached the track, and he hurried with the rest towards the bookmakers to get his one hundred on as quickly as possible. But while he was crossing the lawn back of the stand, he heard cheers and wild yells that told him they were running the race at that moment.

"Raceland!" "Raceland!" "Raceland by a length!" shouted the crowd.

"Who's second?" a fat man shouted at another fat man.

"Firefly," called back the second joyously, "and I've got her for a place and I win eight dollars."

"Ah!" said Van Bibber, as he slipped his one hundred dollars back in his pocket, "good thing I got here a bit late."

"What'd you win, Van Bibber?" asked a friend who rushed past him, clutching his tickets as though they were precious stones.

"I win one hundred dollars," answered Van Bibber calmly, as he walked on up into the boxes. It was delightfully cool up there, and to his satisfaction and surprise he found several people there whom he knew. He went into Her box and accepted some *pâté* sandwiches and iced champagne, and chatted and laughed with Her so industriously, and so much to the exclusion of all else, that the horses were at the starting-post before he was aware of it, and he had to excuse himself hurriedly and run to put up his money on Bugler, the second on his list. He decided that as he had won one hundred dollars on the first race he could afford to plunge on this one, so he counted out fifty more, and putting this with the original one hundred dollars, crowded into the betting-ring and said, "A hundred and fifty on Bugler straight."

"Bugler's just been scratched," said the bookie, leaning over Van Bibber's shoulder for a greasy five-dollar bill.

"Will you play anything else?" he asked, as the young gentleman stood there irresolute.

"No, thank you," said Van Bibber, remembering his vow, and turning hastily away. "Well," he mused, "I'm one hundred and fifty dollars better off than I might have been if Bugler hadn't been scratched and hadn't won. One hundred and fifty dollars added to one hundred makes two hundred and fifty dollars. That puts me 'way ahead of the game. I am fifty dollars better off than when I left New York. I'm playing in great luck." So, on the strength of this, he bought out the man who sells bouquets, and ordered more champagne to be sent up to the box where She was sitting, and they all congratulated him on his winnings, which were suggested by his generous and sudden expenditures.

"You must have a great eye for picking a winner," said one of the older men grudgingly.

"Y-e-s," said Van Bibber modestly. "I know a horse when I see it, I think; and," he added to himself, "that's about all."

His horse for the third race was Rover, and the odds were five to one against him. Van Bibber wanted very much to bet on Pirate King instead, but he remembered his vow to keep to the list he had originally prepared, whether he lost or won. This running after strange gods was always a losing business. He took one hundred dollars in five-dollar bills, and went down to the ring and put the hundred up on Rover and returned to the box. The horses had been weighed in and the bugle had sounded, and three of the racers were making their way up the track, when one of them plunged suddenly forward and went down on his knees and then stretched out dead. Van Bibber was confident it was Rover, although he had no idea which the horse was, but he knew his horse would not run. There was a great deal of excitement, and people who did not know the rule which requires the return of all money if any accident happens to a horse on the race-track between the time of weighing in and arriving at the post, were needlessly alarmed. Van Bibber walked down to the ring and received his money back with a smile.

"I'm just one hundred dollars better off than I was three minutes ago," he said. "I've really had a most remarkable day."

Mayfair was his choice for the fourth race, and she was selling at three to one. Van Bibber determined to put one hundred and seventy-five dollars up on her, for, as he said, he had not lost on any one race yet. The girl in the box was very interesting, though, and Van Bibber found a great deal to say to her. He interrupted himself once to call to one of the messenger-boys who ran with bets, and gave him one hundred and seventy-five dollars to put on Mayfair.

Several other gentlemen gave the boy large sums as well, and Van

Bibber continued to talk earnestly with the girl. He raised his head to see Mayfair straggle in a bad second, and shrugged his shoulders. "How much did you lose?" she asked.

"Oh, 'bout two hundred dollars," said Van Bibber; "but it's the first time I've lost to-day, so I'm still ahead." He bent over to continue what he was saying, when a rude commotion and loud talking caused those in the boxes to raise their heads and look around. Several gentlemen were pointing out Van Bibber to one of the Pinkerton detectives, who had a struggling messenger boy in his grasp.

"These gentlemen say you gave this boy some money, sir," said the detective. "He tried to do a welsh with it, and I caught him just as he was getting over the fence. How much and on what horse, sir?"

Van Bibber showed his memoranda, and the officer handed him over one hundred and seventy-five dollars.

"Now, let me see," said Van Bibber, shutting one eye and calculating intently, "one hundred and seventy-five to three hundred and fifty dollars makes me a winner by five hundred and twenty-five dollars. That's purty good, isn't it? I'll have a great dinner at Delmonico's to-night. You'd better all come back with me!"

But She said he had much better come back with her and her party on top of the coach and take dinner in the cool country instead of the hot, close city, and Van Bibber said he would like to, only he did wish to get his one hundred dollars up on at least one race. But they said "no," they must be off at once, for the ride was a long one, and Van Bibber looked at his list and saw that his choice was Jack Frost, a very likely winner, indeed; but, nevertheless, he walked out to the enclosure with them and mounted the coach beside the girl on the back seat, with only the two coachmen behind to hear what he chose to say.

And just as they finally were all harnessed up and the horn sounded, the crowd yelled, "They're off," and Van Bibber and all of them turned on their high seats to look back.

"Magpie wins," said the whip.

"And Jack Frost's last," said another.

"And I win my one hundred dollars," said Van Bibber. "It's really very curious," he added, turning to the girl. "I started out with two hundred dollars to-day, I spent only twenty-five dollars on flowers, I won six hundred and twenty-five dollars, and I have only one hundred and seventy-five dollars to show for it, and yet I've had a very pleasant Fourth."

CHILDREN

Anton Chekhov

One of the great names of Russian literature, Chekhov did not have the same reputation as a gambling man as his equally distinguished contemporaries, Dostoevsky and Tolstoy. However, the subject clearly fascinated him and in "Children", he observes how a group of children portray much the same emotions as their elders when they become involved in a nursery game of loto.

PAPA AND MAMMA and Aunt Nadya are not at home. They have gone to a christening party at the house of that old officer who rides on a little grey horse. While waiting for them to come home, Grisha, Anya, Alyosha, Sonya, and the cook's son, Andrey, are sitting at the table in the dining-room, playing at loto. To tell the truth, it is bedtime, but how can one go to sleep without hearing from mamma what the baby was like at the christening, and what they had for supper? The table, lighted by a hanging lamp, is dotted with numbers, nutshells, scraps of paper, and little bits of glass. Two cards lie in front of each player, and a heap of bits of glass for covering the numbers. In the middle of the table is a white saucer with five kopecks in it. Beside the saucer, a half-eaten apple, a pair of scissors, and a plate on which they have been told to put their nutshells. The children are playing for money. The stake is a kopeck. The rule is: if anyone cheats, he is turned out at once. There is no one in the dining-room but the players, and nurse, Agafya Ivanovna, is in the kitchen, showing the cook how to cut a pattern, while their elder brother, Vasya, a schoolboy in the fifth class, is lying on the sofa in the drawing-room, feeling bored.

They are playing with zest. The greatest excitement is expressed on the face of Grisha. He is a small boy of nine, with a head cropped so that the bare skin shows through, chubby cheeks, and thick lips like a negro's. He is already in the preparatory class, and so is regarded as grown up, and the cleverest. He is playing entirely for the sake of the money. If there had been no kopecks in the saucer, he would have been asleep long ago. His brown eyes stray uneasily and jealously over the other players' cards. The fear that he may not win, envy, and the financial combinations of which his cropped head is full, will not let him sit still and concentrate his mind. He fidgets as though he were sitting on thorns. When he wins, he snatches up the money greedily, and instantly puts it in his pocket. His sister, Anya, a girl of eight, with a sharp chin and clever shining eyes, is also afraid that someone else may win. She flushes and turns pale, and watches the players keenly. The kopecks do not interest her. Success in the game is for her a question of vanity. The other sister Sonya, a child of six with a curly head, and a complexion such as is seen only in very healthy children, expensive dolls, and the faces on bonbon boxes, is playing loto for the process of the game itself. There is bliss all over her face. Whoever wins, she laughs and claps her hands. Alyosha, a chubby, spherical little figure, gasps, breathes hard through his nose, and stares open-eyed at the cards. He is moved neither by covetousness nor vanity. So long as he is not driven out of the room, or sent to bed, he is thankful. He looks phlegmatic, but at heart he is rather a little beast. He is not there so much for the sake of the loto, as for the sake of the misunderstandings which are inevitable in the game. He is greatly delighted if one hits another, or calls him names. He ought to have run off somewhere long ago, but he won't leave the table for a minute, for fear they should steal his counters or his kopecks. As he can only count the units and numbers which end in nought, Anya covers his numbers for him. The fifth player, the cook's son, Andrey, a dark-skinned and sickly looking boy in a cotton shirt, with a copper cross on his breast, stands motionless, looking dreamily at the numbers. He takes no interest in winning, or in the success of the others, because he is entirely engrossed by the arithmetic of the game, and its far from complex theory: "How many numbers there are in the world," he is thinking, "and how is it they don't get mixed up?"

They all shout out the numbers in turn, except Sonya and Alyosha. To vary the monotony, they have invented in the course of time a number of synonyms and comic nicknames. Seven, for instance, is called the "ovenrake," eleven the "sticks," seventy-seven "Semyon Semyonitch," ninety "grandfather," and so on. The game is going merrily.

"Thirty-two," cries Grisha, drawing the little yellow cylinders out of his father's cap. "Seventeen! Ovenrake! Twenty-eight! Lay them straight. . . ."

Anya sees that Andrey has let twenty-eight slip. At any other time she would have pointed it out to him, but now when her vanity lies in the saucer with the kopecks, she is triumphant.

"Twenty-three!" Grisha goes on, "Semyon Semyonitch! Nine!"

"A beetle, a beetle," cries Sonya, pointing to a beetle running across the table. "Aie!"

"Don't kill it," says Alyosha, in his deep bass, "perhaps it's got children. . . ."

Sonya follows the black beetle with her eyes and wonders about its children: what tiny little beetles they must be!

"Forty-three! One!" Grisha goes on, unhappy at the thought that Anya has already made two fours. "Six!"

"Game! I have got the game!" cries Sonya, rolling her eyes coquettishly and giggling.

The players' countenances lengthen.

"Must make sure!" says Grisha, looking with hatred at Sonya.

Exercising his rights as a big boy, and the cleverest, Grisha takes upon himself to decide. What he wants, that they do. Sonya's reckoning is slowly and carefully verified, and to the great regret of her fellow players, it appears that she has not cheated. Another game is begun.

"I did see something yesterday!" says Anya, as though to herself. "Filipp Filippitch turned his eyelids inside out somehow and his eyes looked red and dreadful, like an evil spirit's."

"I saw it too," says Grisha. "Eight! And a boy at our school can move his ears. Twenty-seven!"

Andrey looks up at Grisha, meditates, and says:

"I can move my ears too. . . ."

"Well then, move them."

Andrey moves his eyes, his lips, and his fingers, and fancies that his ears are moving too. Everyone laughs.

"He is a horrid man, that Filipp Filippitch," sighs Sonya. "He came into our nursery yesterday, and I had nothing on but my chemise . . . And I felt so improper!"

"Game!" Grisha cries suddenly, snatching the money from the saucer. "I've got the game! You can look and see if you like."

The cook's son looks up and turns pale.

"Then I can't go on playing any more," he whispers.

"Why not?"

"Because . . . because I have got no more money."

"You can't play without money," says Grisha.

Andrey ransacks his pockets once more to make sure. Finding nothing in them but crumbs and a bitten pencil, he drops the corners of his mouth and begins blinking miserably. He is on the point of crying. . . .

"I'll put it down for you!" says Sonya, unable to endure his look of agony. "Only mind you must pay me back afterwards."

The money is brought and the game goes on.

"I believe they are ringing somewhere," says Anya, opening her eyes wide.

They all leave off playing and gaze open-mouthed at the dark window. The reflection of the lamp glimmers in the darkness.

"It was your fancy."

"At night they only ring in the cemetery," says Andrey. . . .

"And what do they ring there for?"

"To prevent robbers from breaking into the church. They are afraid of the bells."

"And what do robbers break into the church for?" asks Sonya.

"Everyone knows what for: to kill the watchmen."

A minute passes in silence. They all look at one another, shudder, and go on playing. This time Andrey wins.

"He has cheated," Alyosha booms out, apropos of nothing.

"What a lie, I haven't cheated."

Andrey turns pale, his mouth works, and he gives Alyosha a slap on the head! Alyosha glares angrily, jumps up, and with one knee on the table, slaps Andrey on the cheek! Each gives the other a second blow, and both howl. Sonya, feeling such horrors too much for her, begins crying too, and the dining-room resounds with lamentations on various notes. But do not imagine that that is the end of the game. Before five minutes are over the children are laughing and talking peaceably again. Their faces are tear-stained, but that does not prevent them from smiling; Aloysha is positively blissful, there has been a squabble!

Vasya, the fifth form schoolboy, walks into the dining-room. He looks sleepy and disillusioned.

"This is revolting!" he thinks, seeing Grisha feel in his pockets in which the kopecks are jingling. "How can they give children money? And how can they let them play games of chance? A nice way to bring them up, I must say! It's revolting!"

But the children's play is so tempting that he feels an inclination to join them and to try his luck.

"Wait a minute and I'll sit down to a game," he says.

33

"Put down a kopeck!"

"In a minute," he says, fumbling in his pockets. "I haven't a kopeck, but here is a rouble. I'll stake a rouble."

"No, no, no. . . . You must put down a kopeck."

"You stupids. A rouble is worth more than a kopeck anyway," the schoolboy explains. "Whoever wins can give me change."

"No, please! Go away!"

The fifth form schoolboy, shrugs his shoulders, and goes into the kitchen to get change from the servants. It appears there is not a single kopeck in the kitchen.

"In that case, you give me change," he urges Grisha, coming back from the kitchen. "I'll pay you for the change. Won't you? Come, give me ten kopecks for a rouble."

Grisha looks suspiciously at Vasya, wondering whether it isn't some trick, a swindle.

"I won't," he says, holding his pockets.

Vasya begins to get cross, and abuses them, calling them idiots and blockheads.

"I'll put down a stake for you, Vasya!" says Sonya. "Sit down." He sits down and lays two cards before him. Anya begins counting the numbers.

"I've dropped a kopeck!" Grisha announces suddenly, in an agitated voice. "Wait!"

He takes the lamp, and creeps under the table to look for the kopeck. They clutch at nutshells and all sorts of nastiness, knock their heads together, but do not find the kopeck. They begin looking again, and look till Vasya takes the lamp out of Grisha's hands and puts it in its place. Grisha goes on looking in the dark. But at last the kopeck is found. The players sit down at the table and mean to go on playing.

"Sonya is asleep!" Alyosha announces.

Sonya, with her curly head lying on her arms, is in a sweet, sound, tranquil sleep, as though she had been asleep for an hour. She has fallen asleep by accident, while the others were looking for the kopeck.

"Come along, lie on mamma's bed!" says Anya, leading her away from the table. "Come along!"

They all troop out with her, and five minutes later mamma's bed presents a curious spectacle. Sonya is asleep. Alyosha is snoring beside her. With their heads to the others' feet, sleep Grisha and Anya. The cook's son, Andrey too, has managed to snuggle in beside them. Near them lie the kopecks, that have lost their power till the next game. Good-night!

RORY AND BRAN

Lord Dunsany

For a man who by his own estimate spent ninety-seven percent of his time in sport and soldiering, Lord Dunsany was a remarkably prolific writer with an output embracing practically every area of literary activity.

Although best known for his Tolkien-like stories of "never never lands," Lord Dunsany's tales of Irish countryfolk have a dedicated following because of the rare understanding of the Irish character they convey. "Rory and Bran" relates the adventures of two herdsmen on their way to market, and the following extract tells what happens when they run into a jockey called Fagan and are tempted to try their luck at a country race meeting.

IT WAS A CURIOUS FIELD that Rory and Bran and Fagan were coming to now, a field that the night before had been so lonely and still that the feet of rabbits running over the grass, or the sigh of a breeze stirring, were the principal sounds to be heard there by anyone wandering late. Now it was as though a city had suddenly come there, brought down on the field by magic, a city almost instantly throbbing with the full flood of its life. I do not know if in any drawer in a room of any office is a calculation of the amount of money brought to Glenruagh Races, or the number of people that bring it; it is a large sum, that money, and it must take weeks of investigation and hours of calculation to work out what it would be, and it would take men specially trained to that sort of work to deal with the matter at all; and yet there are men to be seen wandering the roads of Ireland for the three or four days before that meeting, and living I know not where for the rest of the year, who with a single glance of the mind's eye seem to know the exact sum, and especially the more important part of it, what may be called the fluid portion, that will change hands at the race-meeting. It is to this sum, perhaps three quarters of the total sum brought to the meeting, that the temples are erected, if we look on the various booths as temples to Chance, Chance duly, and more than duly, ministered to by his priests; or we may consider them as the banks and exchanges of the temporary city whose commerce thrives as actively as in any city I know. By one of these bankers of the money brought to that meeting, Rory and Fagan stopped, and Bran stopped with them. The man seemed to be pouring out the cherished convictions of his soul: with a loud voice and violent emphasis he was saying, "And I tell you that I state without fear of contradiction; and I challenge any man to contradict me, and to make good his assertion before you all; that I am about to show you without any pretence or any deception, and holding back nothing, the most marvellous, the most wonderful and the most stupendous bargain, at the price, that the eye of man has ever been privileged to behold, or will ever behold again, after this opportunity has gone from you, as it will do, ladies and gents, make no mistake about that, as soon as I have retired from this field to go back to my more permanent occupation. For do not suppose, ladies and gents, that this is my way of living. I come her to offer you today a golden and grand opportunity. . . ." Fagan put a hand then on the reins of Veillantif and brought Rory away with him, who was longing to hear more, but Fagan seemed to grudge him to the man with the golden and grand opportunity; and Bran was glad to leave, for he did not believe a word that the man was saying. . . .

Suddenly, as Rory slowly rode through the crowd, he saw written large on a board, 33 to 1; and it started a train of thought. If he put a pound on that horse, whose name was Ratcatcher, he would win £33. That was clear enough. If he put £2 and won, he would get £66. But he had three pounds. He rode to the nearest thorn-tree and dismounted and tied up Veillantif by looping the reins over an upright branch; and saying to Bran "Look after Veillantif while I go and talk to the Bookie," he went back to where he had seen the odds on the board, and asked the owner of it what he would get if he put £3 on Ratcatcher and he won.

"Ninety-nine pounds," said the Bookie.

"It's what I thought," said Rory.

Here then was his chance if Fagan failed him: he could still get a hundred pounds. With the ninety-nine pounds and the three in his pocket, it would be a hundred and two. Of all who were gathered before those high black boards where the odds were written in chalk, Rory and Bran (for Bran was only twenty yards away) were the two that cared least for a hundred pounds ; but Rory was troubled by the thought of going home to his parents with his four pounds lost, if Fagan should not fulfil his promise, whereas it would be a splendid answer when they asked where the four pounds were gone, and why he borrowed three from O'Hara, to show them the hundred pounds. But what if he lost his three pounds too ? That is a calculation unknown to gamblers with wiser heads than Rory's, and it never troubled him either.

So Rory put his £3 on Ratcatcher, and soon watched him going out and cantering down the course. There would be no mistaking him: his jockey wore a jacket of the most brilliant yellow, with sleeves and cap of a brilliant blue : it was like the sun in the very bluest sky that the South and the splendour of summer have to show. Like many other backers, Rory might have put his money on this horse for the colours alone, even were it not that the odds exactly suited him. Meanwhile there was his double chance, if Fagan kept his word ; but he did not know what horse Fagan was choosing, or if it was in this race. Rory drifted with part of the crowd to the first fence, an open ditch from which the hedge had been shaved to the soil, with a flag on each side of the shaving, one red, one white. The crowd lined each side of the course, and a hunt servant in pink on a bay was riding slowly along it. Suddenly the bay plunged at the crowd on the side that Rory was, and the people ran back a little way. "I've known this horse eat a man," said the rider half to himself, but overheard by a group of boys to his left, while his whip was seeking another little group that was pressing forward too much on his right.

Another display by the man-eating horse, and Rory heard someone say, "They're off." Yellow jacket, blue sleeves and cap, was leading. Ratcatcher cleared the fence, and seven more after him. There was a dip in the ground, and hedges soon hid all eight from view. When they appeared again, among the farms, Ratcatcher was still there, but the favourite was level with him now, and blue-and-red hoops were shining beside the yellow jacket. The farms through which they ran were tilted all on a slope, which rose up facing the fields in which the crowd were gathered ; the horses had gone down from these fields and jumped a stream, and had now swung back and were passing in full view of everyone. A chestnut was coming up to join the two leading horses, a horse of so bright a hue that he could be picked out easily without noting his rider's colours. Then came scarlet with white sleeves and cap, the rider of a horse called Murder, who was fancied next after the favourite. A few more fences, at which none fell, and these two horses both passed the favourite and Rory's fancy ; but not by much. A fifth horse came up, white jacket and cap and green sleeves, and drew level with Ratcatcher, but could not pass him. The favourite dropped back a little. Two horses seemed to be dropping out of the race, but yet one more came to join the bunch of five that were all so close together that a fair-sized garden would have held them. They came to a double, which is to say a fence too big to fly, thrown up from two ditches. The chestnut touched the top with Murder beside him; and there something went wrong, and the chestnut made a bad landing, and stumbled and four horses landed almost on top of him. Three fell besides the chestnut, and among the men on the ground Rory could see the one in the yellow jacket with blue sleeves and cap. At once he was up and running to his horse. He might win yet, thought Rory. But the jockey ran past his horse with his hands out as though he were dazed. The chestnut horse was galloping on with the rest, two horses were standing, breathing after their fall, and one was lying still. The jockey turned round, still with his hands stretched out, and blundered into a rein; then he pulled himself together and remounted, and the yellow jacket with the bright blue sleeves and cap was in the race again. The two last horses checked their pace at the double, so as to steer their way through the men and horses with which the landing was littered; and Rory saw with delight that, by the time those sunny colours were in the saddle again, there was only one horse in front of him. It was white jacket and cap and green sleeves that was leading now, and very soon Rory saw the gap decreasing; while the two last horses, that were very near, had neither of them overtaken yellow jacket, blue sleeves and cap.

"Come on Ratcatcher," shouted Rory.

And, as though his words had been heard, the gap between first and second decreased still more; but it was still a gap of three hundred yards. There was only another mile and a half to go. Could he do it? And, as though in answer to Rory's thoughts, a man beside him said to another, "Ratcatcher's not the horse to do it."

"Ah, sure, never," said the other. "He can't stay and he hasn't the pace for it."

Yet still the gap was decreasing. And Rory's colours were drawing away from the two that had come up close.

"Sure, his fall has done him good," said another man.

And, after all, there was only one horse, of those that were left in the race, that had had a rest while the other three were galloping very nearly two furlongs.

The leader, a horse at 20 to 1, called Slieveronan, seemed to have made his effort earlier in the race, when he caught up the favourite; but he seemed to be tiring now, and still the gap decreased. When no more than a hundred yards separated the first and second, there were fifty yards between the second and third. With half a mile to go the lead was down to fifty; and then the jockey in the yellow jacket with blue sleeves and cap seemed to think that he had asked enough of his horse, for he was taking his fences slower, and gaining only little upon the leader. But now the other two began to come up. And so they went for a while, with the third and fourth closing in on the second, and the second gaining only slightly upon the first; till there was only another quarter of a mile to go. And now the leader was fast tiring, and dropping back nearer and nearer the second without the rider of the second horse having to make much effort on his account any longer; but he was beginning to ride harder to prevent the other two from passing him, for they were nearly alongside now. Three hundred yards from the winning-post all were level; and there was shouting in the crowd and confusion, and men calling for different horses to come on, and contradicting each other. It was the horse that made the effort; the jockey in yellow and blue was swaying, and men saw as he came to the crowd how dazed he was. Would he stay in the saddle, someone asked. But his seat was all right, though his face looked pale and vacant. He was leading by twenty yards now, and still the good horse was drawing away from the rest. The jockey steadied himself, or was steadied by the shouting of the crowd, and the knowledge that the winning post was near and that he was winning. Rory threw a swift glance to where his Bookie stood. He was still there, under his black board. A hundred pounds! It seemed a glittering prize. And then the yellow jacket and blue sleeves and cap passed the winning-post, firm in the saddle, thirty yards ahead of the second. There was shouting and more confusion. At that instant some of the splendour seemed to slide from a hundred pounds. It is sad, but perfectly true, that the glory of the sum seemed less to Rory than when it had been remoter.

There was mud along one side of the blue cap, as the jockey in the yellow jacket and blue sleeves rode to the weighing-tent, splendid above the dark coats of the crowd. And from the weighing-tent the owner came out to meet him. The jockey smiled at him, as though he had forgotten him and suddenly had remembered who he was.

"Where is your horse?" shouted the owner.

"Here," said the jockey, pointing downwards and touching the withers with his finger.

"Where is MY horse ?" shouted the owner then.

And the jockey looked at the horse again, and fainted.

AFTER THE RACE

James Joyce

Although James Joyce is probably Ireland's most celebrated novelist, his long years of struggle with the Irish literary establishment over the publication not only of *Ulysses*, his most famous work, but also of *The Dubliners* from which the following story is taken, caused him never to set foot in Ireland again after he left Dublin in 1912.

"After the Race" is a description of a party held after a motor race and brilliantly evokes the fascination and glamor of gambling in good company.

THE CARS came scudding in towards Dublin, running evenly like pellets in the groove of the Naas Road. At the crest of the hill at Inchicore sight-seers had gathered in clumps to watch the cars careering homeward and through this channel of poverty and inaction the Continent sped its wealth and industry. Now and again the clumps of people raised the cheer of the gratefully oppressed. Their sympathy, however, was for the blue cars – the cars of their friends, the French.

The French, moreover, were virtual victors. Their team had finished solidly; they had been placed second and third and the driver of the winning German car was reported a Belgian. Each blue car, therefore, received a double measure of welcome as it topped the crest of the hill and each cheer of welcome was acknowledged with smiles and nods by those in the car. In one of these trimly built cars was a party of four young men whose spirits seemed to be at present well above the level of successful Gallicism : in fact, these four young men were almost hilarious. They were Charles Ségouin, the owner of the car ; André Rivière, a young electrician of Canadian birth; a huge Hungarian named Villona and a neatly groomed young man named Doyle. Ségouin was in good humour because he had unexpectedly received some orders in advance (he was about to start a motor establishment in Paris) and Rivière was in good humour because he was to be appointed manager of the establishment ; these two young men (who were cousins) were also in good humour because of the success of the French cars. Villona was in good humour because he had had a very satisfactory luncheon ; and besides he was an optimist by nature. The fourth member of the party, however, was too excited to be genuinely happy.

He was about twenty-six years of age, with a soft, light brown moustache and rather innocent-looking grey eyes. His father, who had begun life as an advanced Nationalist, had modified his views early. He had made his money as a butcher in Kingstown and by opening shops in Dublin and in the suburbs he had made his money many times over. He had also been fortunate enough to secure some of the police contracts and in the end he had become rich enough to be alluded to in the Dublin newspapers as a merchant prince. He had sent his son to England to be educated in a big Catholic college and had afterwards sent him to Dublin University to study law. Jimmy did not study very earnestly and took to bad courses for a while. He had money and he was popular ; and he divided his time curiously between musical and motoring circles. Then he had been sent for a term to Cambridge to see a little life. His father, remonstrative, but covertly proud of the excess, had paid his bills and brought him home. It was at Cambridge that he had met Ségouin. They were not much more than acquaintances as yet but Jimmy found great pleasure in the society of one who had seen so much of the world and was reputed to own some of the biggest hotels in France. Such a person (as his father agreed) was well worth knowing, even if he had not been the charming companion he was. Villona was entertaining also – a brilliant pianist – but, unfortunately, very poor.

The car ran on merrily with its cargo of hilarious youth. The two cousins sat on the front seat; Jimmy and his Hungarian friend sat behind. Decidedly Villona was in excellent spirits ; he kept up a deep bass hum of melody for miles of the road. The Frenchmen flung their laughter and light words over their shoulders and often Jimmy had to strain forward to catch the quick phrase. This was not altogether pleasant for him, as he had nearly always to make a deft guess at the meaning and shout back a suitable answer in the face of a high wind. Besides Villona's humming would confuse anybody ; the noise of the car, too.

Rapid motion through space elates one; so does notoriety; so does the possession of money. These were three good reasons for Jimmy's excitement. He had been seen by many of his friends that day in the company of these Continentals. At the control Ségouin had presented him to one of the French competitors and, in answer to his confused murmur of compliment, the swarthy face of the driver had disclosed a line of shining white teeth. It was pleasant after that honour to return to the profane world of spectators amid nudges and significant looks. Then as to money – he really had a great sum under his control. Ségouin, perhaps, would not think it a great sum but Jimmy who, in spite of temporary errors, was at heart the inheritor of solid instincts knew well with what difficulty it had been got together. This knowledge had previously kept his bills within the limits of reasonable recklessness and, if he had been so conscious of the labour latent in money when there had been question merely of some freak of the higher intelligence, how much more so now when he was about to stake the greater part of his substance! It was a serious thing for him.

Of course, the investment was a good one and Ségouin had managed to give the impression that it was by a favour of friendship the mite of Irish money was to be included in the capital of the concern. Jimmy had a respect for his father's shrewdness in business matters and in this case it had been his father who had first suggested the investment; money to be made in the motor business, pots of money. Moreover Ségouin had the unmistakable air of wealth. Jimmy set out to translate into days' work that lordly car in which he sat. How smoothly it ran. In what style they had come careering along the country roads! The journey laid a magical finger on the genuine pulse of life and gallantly the machinery of human nerves strove to answer the bounding courses of the swift blue animal.

They drove down Dame Street. The street was busy with unusual traffic, loud with the horns of motorists and the gongs of impatient tramdrivers. Near the Bank Ségouin drew up and Jimmy and his friend alighted. A little knot of people collected on the footpath to pay homage to the snorting motor. The party was to dine together that evening in Ségouin's hotel and, meanwhile, Jimmy and his friend, who was staying with him, were to go home to dress. The car steered out slowly for Grafton Street while the two young men pushed their way through the knot of gazers. They walked northward with a curious feeling of disappointment in the exercise, while the city hung its pale globes of light above them in a haze of summer evening.

In Jimmy's house this dinner had been pronounced an occasion. A certain pride mingled with his parents' trepidation, a certain eagerness, also, to play fast and loose for the names of great foreign cities have at least this virtue. Jimmy, too, looked very well when he was dressed and, as he stood in the hall giving a last equation to the bows of his dress tie, his father may have felt even commercially satisfied at having secured for his son qualities often unpurchaseable. His father, therefore, was unusually friendly with Villona and his manner expressed a real respect for foreign accomplishments; but this subtlety of his host was probably lost upon the Hungarian, who was beginning to have a sharp desire for his dinner.

The dinner was excellent, exquisite. Ségouin, Jimmy decided, had a very refined taste. The party was increased by a young Englishman named Routh whom Jimmy had seen with Ségouin at Cambridge. The young men supped in a snug room lit by electric candle lamps. They talked volubly and with little reserve. Jimmy, whose imagination was kindling, conceived the lively youth of the Frenchmen twined elegantly upon the firm framework of the Englishman's manner. A graceful image of his, he thought, and a just one. He admired the dexterity with which their host directed the conversation. The five young men had various tastes and their tongues had been loosened. Villona, with immense respect, began to discover to the mildly surprised Englishman the beauties of the English madrigal, deploring the loss of old instruments. Rivière, not wholly ingenuously, undertook to explain to Jimmy the triumph of the French mechanicians. The resonant voice of the Hungarian was about to prevail in ridicule of the spurious lutes of the romantic painters when Ségouin shepherded his party into politics. Here was congenial ground for all. Jimmy, under generous influences, felt the buried zeal of his father wake to life within him: he aroused the torpid Routh at last. The room grew doubly hot and Ségouin's task grew harder each moment: there was even danger of personal spite. The alert host at an opportunity lifted his glass to Humanity and, when the toast had been drunk, he threw open a window significantly.

That night the city wore the mask of a capital. The five young men strolled along Stephen's Green in a faint cloud of aromatic smoke. They talked loudly and gaily and their cloaks dangled from their shoulders. The people made way for them. At the corner of Grafton Street a short fat man was putting two handsome ladies on a car in charge of another fat man. The car drove off and the short fat man caught sight of the party.

"André."

"It's Farley!"

A torrent of talk followed. Farley was an American. No one knew very well what the talk was about. Villona and Rivière were the noisiest, but all the men were excited. They got up on a car, squeezing themselves together amid much laughter. They drove by the crowd, blended now into soft colours, to a music of merry bells. They took the train at Westland Row and in a few seconds, as it seemed to Jimmy, they were walking out of Kingstown Station. The ticket-collector saluted Jimmy; he was an old man:

"Fine night, sir!"

It was a serene summer night; the harbour lay like a darkened mirror at their feet. They proceeded towards it with linked arms, singing *Cadet Roussel* in chorus, stamping their feet at every:

"Ho! Ho! Hohé, vraiment!"

They got into a rowboat at the slip and made out for the American's yacht. There was to be supper, music, cards. Villona said with conviction:

"It is delightful!"

There was a yacht piano in the cabin. Villona played a waltz for Farley and Rivière, Farley acting as cavalier and Rivière as lady. Then an impromptu square dance, the men devising original figures. What merriment! Jimmy took his part with a will; this was seeing life, at least. Then Farley got out of breath and cried *"Stop!"* A man brought in a light supper, and the young men sat down to it for form's sake. They drank, however: it was Bohemian. They drank Ireland, England, France, Hungary, the United States of America. Jimmy made a speech, a long speech, Villona saying: *"Hear! hear!"* whenever there was a pause. There was a great clapping of hands when he sat down. It must have been a good speech. Farley clapped him on the back and laughed loudly. What jovial fellows! What good company they were!

Cards! cards! The table was cleared. Villona returned quietly to his piano and played voluntaries for them. The other men played game after game, flinging themselves boldly into the adventure. They drank the health of the Queen of Hearts and of the Queen of Diamonds. Jimmy felt obscurely the lack of an audience: the wit was flashing. Play ran very high and paper began to pass. Jimmy did not know exactly who was winning but he knew that he was losing. But it was his own fault for he frequently mistook his cards and the other men had to calculate his I.O.U.'s for him. They were devils of fellows but he wished they would stop: it was getting late. Someone gave the toast of the yacht *The Belle of Newport* and then someone proposed one great game for a finish.

The piano had stopped; Villona must have gone up on deck. It was a terrible game. They stopped just before the end of it to drink for luck. Jimmy understood that the game lay between Routh and Ségouin. What excitement! Jimmy was excited too; he would lose, of course. How much had he written away? The men rose to their feet to play the last tricks, talking and gesticulating. Routh won. The cabin shook with the young men's cheering and the cards were bundled together. They began then to gather in what they had won. Farley and Jimmy were the heaviest losers.

He knew that he would regret in the morning but at present he was glad of the rest, glad of the dark stupor that would cover up his folly. He leaned his elbows on the table and rested his head between his hands, counting the beats of his temples. The cabin door opened and he saw the Hungarian standing in a shaft of grey light:

"Daybreak, gentlemen!"

BEATING THE SYSTEM

MONTE

Arnold Bennett

Arnold Bennett was very much a novelist of his time, portraying in *Anna of the Five Towns* and *The Card* the rising lower middle class of England's industrial heartland. Unashamedly brash and vulgar in his life style, his work has often been criticised for demonstrating the same traits. Certainly they are not present in "Monte."

The story, has a distinctly autobiographical flavour and provides a useful lesson for the amateur gambler who is convinced he has an unbeatable system.

MONTE CARLO – the initiated call it merely "Monte" – has often been described, in fiction and out of it, but the frank confession of a ruined gambler is a rare thing; partly because the ruined gambler can't often write well enough to express himself accurately, partly because he isn't in the mood for literary composition, and partly because he is sometimes dead. So, since I am not dead, and since it is only by means of literary composition that I can hope to restore my shattered fortunes, I will give you the frank confession of a ruined gambler. Before I went to Monte Carlo I had all the usual ideas of the average sensible man about gambling in general, and about Monte Carlo in particular. "Where does all the exterior brilliance of Monte Carlo come from?" I asked sagely. And I said further: "The Casino administration does not disguise the fact that it makes a profit of about 50,000 francs a day. Where does that profit come from?" And I answered my own question with wonderful wisdom: "Out of the pockets of the foolish gamblers." I specially despised the gambler who gambles "on a system"; I despised him as a creature of supersition. For the "system" gambler will argue that if I toss a penny up six times and it falls "tail" every time, there is a strong probability that it will fall "head" the seventh time. "Now," I said, "can any rational creature be so foolish as to suppose that the six previous and done-with spins can possibly effect the seventh spin? What connection is there between them?" And I replied: "No rational creature can be so foolish. And there is no connection." In this spirit, superior, omniscient, I went to Monte Carlo.

Of course I went to study human nature and find material. The sole advantage of being a novelist is that when you are discovered in a place where, as a serious person, you would prefer not to be discovered, you can always aver that you are studying human nature and seeking material. I was much impressed by the fact of my being in Monte Carlo. I said to myself: "I am actually in Monte Carlo!" I was proud. And when I got into the gorgeous gaming saloons, amid that throng at once glittering and shabby, I said: "I am actually in the gaming saloons!" And the thought at the back of my mind was: "Henceforth I shall be able to say that I have been in the gaming saloons at Monte Carlo." After studying human nature at large, I began to study it at a roulette table. I had gambled before – notably with impassive Arab chiefs in that singular oasis of the Sahara desert, Biskra – but only a little, and always at *petits chevaux*. But I understood roulette, and I knew several "systems." I found the human nature very interesting; also the roulette. The sight of real gold, silver, and notes flung about in heaps warmed my imagination. At this point I felt a solitary five-franc piece in my pocket. And then the red turned up three times running, and I remembered a simple "system" that began after a sequence of three.

I don't know how it was, but long before I had formally decided to gamble I knew by instinct that I should stake that five-franc piece. I fought against the idea, but I couldn't take my hand empty out of my pocket. Then at last (the whole experience occupying perhaps ten seconds) I drew forth the five-franc piece and bashfully put it on black. I thought that all the fifty or sixty persons crowded round the table were staring at me and thinking to themselves: "There's a beginner!" However, black won, and the croupier pushed another five-franc piece alongside of mine, and I picked them both up very smartly, remembering all the tales I had ever heard of thieves leaning over you at Monte Carlo and snatching your ill-gotten gains. I then thought: "This is a bit of all right. Just for fun I'll continue the system." I did so. In an hour I had made fifty francs, without breaking into gold. Once a croupier made a slip and was raking in red stakes when red had won, and people hesitated (because croupiers never make mistakes, you know, and you have to be careful how you quarrel with the table at Monte Carlo), and I was the first to give vent to a protest, and the croupier looked at me and smiled and apologized, and the winners looked at me gratefully, and I began to think myself the deuce and all of a Monte Carlo habitué.

Having made fifty francs, I decided that I would prove my self-control by ceasing to play. So I did prove it, and went to have tea in the Casino café. In those moments fifty francs seemed to me to be a really enormous sum. I was as happy as though I had shot a reviewer without being found out. I gradually began to perceive, too, that though no rational creature could suppose that a spin could be effected by previous spins, nevertheless, it undoubtedly was so effected. I began to scorn a little the average sensible man who scorned the gambler. "There is more in roulette than is dreamed of in your philosophy, my conceited friend," I murmured. I was like a woman – I couldn't argue, but I knew infallibly. Then it suddenly occurred to me that if I had gambled with louis instead of five-franc pieces I should have made 200 francs – 200 francs in rather over an hour! Oh, luxury! Oh, being-in-the-swim! Oh, smartness! Oh, gilded and delicious sin!

Five days afterwards I went to Monte Carlo again, to lunch with some brother authors. In the meantime, though I had been chained to my desk by unalterable engagements, I had thought constantly upon the art and craft of gambling. One of these authors knew Monte Carlo, and all that therein is, as I know Fleet Street. And to my equal astonishment and pleasure he said, when I explained my system to him: "Couldn't have a better!" And he proceeded to remark positively that the man who had a decent system and the nerve to stick to it through all crises, would infallibly win from the tables – not a lot, but an average of several louis per sitting of two hours. "Gambling," he said, "is a matter of character. You have the right character," he added. You may guess whether I did not glow with joyous pride. "The tables make their money from the plunging fools," I said, privately, "and I am not a fool." A man was pointed out to me who extracted a regular income from the tables. "But why don't the authorities forbid him the rooms?" I demanded. "Because he's such a good advertisement. Can't you see?" I saw.

We went to the Casino late after lunch. I cut myself adrift from the rest of the party and began instantly to play. In forty-five minutes, with my "system," I had made forty-five francs. And then the rest of the party reappeared and talked about tea, and trains, and dinner. "Tea!" I murmured disgusted (yet I have a profound passion for tea), "when I am netting a franc a minute!" However, I yielded, and we went and had tea at the Restaurant de Paris across the way. And over the white-and-silver of the tea table, in the falling twilight, with the incomparable mountain landscape in front of us, and the most *chic* and decadent Parisianism around us, we talked roulette. Then the Russian Grand Duke, who had won several thousand pounds in a few minutes a week or two before, came veritably and ducally in, and sat at the next table. There was no mistaking his likeness to the Tsar. It is most extraordinary how the propinquity of a Grand Duke, experienced for the first time, affects even the proverbial phlegm of a British novelist. I seemed to be moving in a perfect atmosphere of Grand Dukes! And I, too, had won! The art of literature seemed a very little thing.

After I had made fifty and forty-five francs at two sittings, I developed suddenly, without visiting the tables again, into a complete and thorough gambler. I picked up all the technical terms like picking up marbles – the greater martingale, the lesser martingale, "en plein," "à cheval," "the horses of seventeen," "last square," and so on, and so on – and I had my own original theories about the alleged superiority of red-or-black to odd-or-even in betting on the even chances. In short, for many hours I lived roulette. I ate roulette for dinner, drank it in my Vichy, and smoked it in my cigar. At first I pretended that I was only pretending to be interested in gambling as a means of earning a livelihood (call it honest or dishonest, as you please). Then the average sensible man in me began to have rather a bad time, really. I frankly acknowledged to myself that I was veritably keen on the thing. I said: "Of course, ordinary people believe that the tables must win, but we who are initiated know better. All you want in order to win is a prudent system and great force of character." And I decided that it would be idle, that it would be falsely modest, that it would be inane, to deny that I had exceptional force of character. And beautiful schemes formed themselves in my mind: how I would gain a certain sum, and then increase my "units" from five-franc pieces to louis, and so quadruple the winnings, and how I would get a friend to practice the same system, and so double them again, and how generally we would have a quietly merry time at the expense of the tables during the next month.

And I was so calm, cool, collected, impassive. There was no hurry. I would not go to Monte Carlo the next day, but perhaps the day after. However, the next day proved to be very wet, and I was simply obliged to go to Monte Carlo. I didn't wish to go, but what could one do? Before starting, I reflected: "Well, there's just a *chance* – such things have been known," and I took a substantial part of my financial resources out of my pocketbook, and locked that reserve up in a drawer. After this, who will dare to say that I was not cool and sagacious ? The journey to Monte Carlo seemed very long. Just as I was entering the ornate portals I met some friends who had seen me there the previous day. The thought flashed through my mind : "These people will think I have got caught in the meshes of the vice just like ordinary idiots, whereas of course my case is not ordinary at all." So I quickly explained to them that it was very wet (as if they couldn't see), and that my other friends had left me, and that I had come to Monte Carlo merely to kill time. They appeared to regard this explanation as unnecessary.

I had a fancy for the table where I had previously played and won. I went to it, and by extraordinary good fortune secured a chair – a difficult thing to get in the afternoons. Behold me seated next door to a croupier, side by side with regular frequenters, regular practicers of systems, and doubtless envied by the outer ring of players and spectators! I was annoyed to find that every other occupant of a chair had a little printed card in black and red on which he marked the winning numbers. I had neglected to provide myself with this contrivance, and felt conspicuous ; I felt that I was not correct. However, I changed some gold for silver with the croupier, and laid the noble pieces in little piles in front of me, and looked as knowing and as initiated as I could. And at the first opening offered by the play I began the operation of my system, backing red, after black had won three times. Black won the fourth time, and I had lost five francs. . . . Black won the sixth time and I had lost thirty-five francs. Black won the seventh time, and I had lost seventy-five francs. "Steady, cool customer !" I addressed myself. I put down four louis (and kindly remember that in these hard times four louis is four louis – three English pounds and four English shillings), and, incredible to relate, black won the eighth time, and I had lost a hundred and fifty-five francs. The time occupied was a mere nine minutes. It was at this point that the "nerve" and the "force of character" were required, for it was an essential part of my system to "cut the loss" at the eighth turn. I said : "Hadn't I better put down eight louis and win all back again, *just this once*? Red's absolutely certain to win next time." But my confounded force of character came in, and forced me to cut the loss, and stick strictly to the system. And at the ninth spin red did win. If I had only put down that eight louis I should have been all right. I was extremely annoyed, especially when I realized that, even with decent luck, it would take me the best part of three hours to regain that hundred and fifty-five francs.

I was shaken. I was like a pugilist who had been knocked down in a prize fight, and hasn't quite made up his mind whether, on the whole, he won't be more comfortable, in the long run, where he is. I was like a soldier under a heavy fire, arguing with himself rapidly whether he prefers to be a Balaclava hero with death or the workhouse, or just a plain, ordinary, prudent Tommy. I was struck amidships. Then an American person behind my chair, just a casual foolish plunger, of the class out of which the Casino makes its profits, put a thousand franc note on the odd numbers, and thirty-three turned up. "A thousand for a thousand," said the croupier mechanically and nonchalantly, and handed to the foolish plunger the equivalent of eighty pounds sterling. And about two minutes afterwards the same foolish plunger made a hundred and sixty pounds at another single stroke. It was odious; I tell you positively it was odious. I collected the shattered bits of my character out of my boots, and recommended my system; made a bit; felt better; and then zero turned up twice – most unsettling, even when zero means only that your stake is "held over." Then two old and fussy ladies came and gambled very seriously over my head, and deranged my hair with the end of the rake in raking up their miserable winnings. . . . At five o'clock I had lost a hundred and ninety-five francs. I don't mind working hard, at great nervous tension, in a vitiated atmosphere, if I can reckon on netting a franc a minute; but I have a sort of objection to three laborious sittings such as I endured that week when the grand result is a dead loss of four pounds : I somehow failed to see the point. I departed in disgust, and ordered tea at the Café de Paris, not the Restaurant de Paris (I was in no mood for Grand Dukes). And while I imbibed the tea, a heated altercation went on inside me between the average sensible man and the man who knew that money could be made out of the tables and the gambling was a question of nerves, etc. It was a pretty show, that altercation. In about ten rounds the average sensible man had knocked his opponent right out of the ring. I breathed a long breath, and seemed to wake up out of a nightmare. Did I regret the episode ? I regretted the ruin, not the episode. For had I not all the time been studying human nature and getting material ? Besides that, as I grow older I grow too wise. Says Montaigne : *"Wisdome hath hir excesses, and no leise need of moderation, then follie."* (The italics are Montaigne's) . . . And there's a good deal in my system after all.

THE GREAT SERMON HANDICAP

P.G. Wodehouse

Beginning as a writer of traditional school stories for the boy's magazines of Edwardian England, P.G. Wodehouse gradually developed into a humorous novelist with an international following. Characters like Bertie Wooster and Jeeves have become household names across the world – and it has even been suggested that the Germans took Wodehouse's portrayal of the English ruling classes so seriously that they were positively encouraged to embark upon the Second World War.

In "The Great Sermon Handicap," Bertie Wooster is not above using a little inside information to help him win his bet, but once again things can always go wrong. . . .

YOU CAN ALWAYS rely on Jeeves. Just as I was wiping the brow and gasping like a stranded goldfish, in he drifted, merry and bright, with the good old tissue-restorers on a tray.

"Jeeves," I said, "It's beastly hot."

"The weather *is* oppressive, sir."

"Not all the soda, Jeeves."

"No, sir."

"London in August," I said, quaffing deeply of the flowing b., "rather tends to give me the pip. All my pals are away, most of the theatres are shut, and they're taking up Piccadilly in large spadefuls. The world is empty and smells of burning asphalt. Shift-ho, I think, Jeeves, what?"

"Just as you say, sir. There is a letter on the tray, sir."

"By Jove, Jeeves, that was practically poetry. Rhymed, did you notice?" I opened the letter. "I say, this is rather extraordinary."

"Sir?"

"You know Twing Hall?"

"Yes, sir."

"Well, Mr Little is there."

"Indeed, sir?"

"Absolutely in the flesh. He's had to take another of those tutoring jobs."

I don't know if you remember, but immediately after that fearful mix-up at Goodwood, young Bingo Little, a broken man, had touched me for a tenner and whizzed silently off into the unknown. I had been all over the place ever since, asking mutual friends if they had heard anything of him, but nobody had. And all the time he had been at Twing Hall. Rummy. And I'll tell you why it was rummy. Twing Hall belongs to old Lord Wickhammersley, a great pal of my guv'nor's when he was alive, and I have a standing invitation to pop down there when I like. I generally put in a week or two some time in the summer, and I was thinking of going there before I read the letter.

"And, what's more, Jeeves, my cousin Claude and my cousin Eustace – you remember them?"

"Very vividly, sir."

"Well, they're down there, too, reading for some exam or other with the vicar. I used to read with him myself at one time. He's known far and wide as a pretty hot coach for those of fairly feeble intellect. Well, when I tell you he got *me* through Smalls, you'll gather that he's a bit of a hummer. I call this most extraordinary."

I read the letter again. It was from Eustace. Claude and Eustace are twins, and more or less generally admitted to be the curse of the human race.

The Vicarage,
Twing, Glos.

DEAR BERTIE,

Do you want to make a bit of money? I hear you had a bad Goodwood, so you probably do. Well, come down here quick and get in on the biggest sporting event of the season. I'll explain when I see you, but you can take it from me it's all right.

Claude and I are with a reading-party at old Heppenstall's. There are nine of us, not counting your pal Bingo Little, who is tutoring the kid up at the Hall.

Don't miss this golden opportunity, which may never occur again. Come and join us.

Yours, EUSTACE

I handed this to Jeeves. He studied it thoughtfully.

"What do you make of it ? A rummy communication, what ?"

"Very high-spirited young gentlemen, sir, Mr Claude and Mr Eustace. Up to some game, I should be disposed to imagine."

"Yes. But what game, do you think ?"

"It is impossible to say, sir. Did you observe that the letter continues over the page ?"

"Eh, what ?" I grabbed the thing. This was what was on the other side of the last page :

SERMON HANDICAP

RUNNERS AND BETTING

PROBABLE STARTERS

Rev. Joseph Tucker (Badgwick), scratch.

Rev. Leonard Starkie (Stapleton), scratch.

Rev. Alexander Jones (Upper Bingley), receives three minutes.

Rev. W. Dix (Little Clickton-in-the-Wold), receives five minutes.

Rev. Francis Heppenstall (Twing), receives eight minutes.

Rev. Cuthbert Dibble (Boustead Parva), receives nine minutes.

Rev. Orlo Hough (Boustead Magna), receives nine minutes.

Rev. J. J. Roberts (Fale-by-the-Water), receives ten minutes.

Rev. G. Hayward (Lower Bingley), receives twelve minutes.

Rev. James Bates (Gandle-by-the-Hill), receives fifteen minutes.

The above have arrived.

Prices: 5–2, Tucker, Starkie; 3–1, Jones; 9–2, Dix; 6–1, Heppenstall, Dibble, Hough; 100–8 any other.

It baffled me.

"Do you understand it, Jeeves ?"

"No, sir."

"Well, I think we ought to have a look into it, anyway, what?"

"Undoubtedly, sir."

"Right-o, then. Pack our spare dickey and a tooth-brush in a neat brown-paper parcel, send a wire to Lord Wickhammersley to say we're coming, and buy two tickets on the five-ten at Paddington to-morrow."

The twins seemed pleased to see me.

"Good old Bertie !" said Claude.

"Stout fellow !" said Eustace. "The Rev. told us you had arrived. I thought that letter of mine would fetch you."

"You can always bank on Bertie," said Claude. "A sportsman to the finger-tips. Well, has Bingo told you about it?"

"Not a word. He's been—"

"We've been talking," said Bingo, hastily, "of other matters."

Claude pinched the last slice of thin bread-and-butter, and Eustace poured himself out a cup of tea.

"It's like this, Bertie," said Eustace, settling down cosily. "As I told you in my letter, there are nine of us marooned in this desert spot, reading with old Heppenstall. Well, of course, nothing is jollier than sweating up the Classics when it's a hundred in the shade, but there does come a time when you begin to feel the need of a little relaxation; and, by Jove, there are absolutely no facilities for relaxation in this place whatever. And then Steggles got this idea. Steggles is one of our reading-party, and, between ourselves, rather a worm as a general thing. Still, you have to give him credit for getting this idea."

"What idea?"

"Well, you know how many parsons there are round about here. There are about a dozen hamlets within a radius of six miles, and each hamlet has a church and each church has a parson and each parson preaches a sermon every Sunday. To-morrow week – Sunday the twenty-third – we're running off the great Sermon Handicap. Steggles is making the book. Each parson is to be clocked by a reliable steward of the course, and the one that preaches the longest sermon wins. Did you study the race-card I sent you?"

"I couldn't understand what it was all about."

"Why, you chump, it gives the handicaps and the current odds on each starter. I've got another one here, in case you've lost yours. Take a careful look at it. It gives you the thing in a nutshell. Jeeves, old son, do you want a sporting flutter?"

"Sir?" said Jeeves, who had just meandered in with my breakfast.

Claude explained the scheme. Amazing the way Jeeves grasped it right off. But he merely smiled in a paternal sort of way.

"Thank you, sir. I think not."

"Well, you're with us, Bertie, aren't you?" said Claude, sneaking a roll and a slice of bacon. "Have you studied that card? Well, tell me, does anything strike you about it?"

Of course it did. It had struck me the moment I looked at it.

"Why, it's a sitter for old Heppenstall," I said. "He's got the event sewed up in a parcel. There isn't a parson in the land who could give him eight minutes. Your pal Steggles must be an ass, giving him a handicap like that. Why, in the days when I was with him, old Heppenstall never used to preach under half an hour, and there was one sermon of his on Brotherly Love which lasted forty-five minutes if it lasted a second. Has he lost his vim lately, or what is it ?''

"Not a bit of it," said Eustace. "Tell him what happened, Claude."

"Why," said Claude, "the first Sunday we were here, we all went to Twing church, and old Heppenstall preached a sermon that was well under twenty minutes. This is what happened. Steggles didn't notice it, and the Rev. didn't notice it himself, but Eustace and I both spotted that he had dropped a chunk of at least half-a-dozen pages out of his sermon-case as he was walking up to the pulpit. He sort of flickered when he got to the gap in the manuscript, but carried on all right, and Steggles went away with the impression that twenty minutes or a bit under was his usual form. The next Sunday we heard Tucker and Starkie, and they both went well over the thirty-five minutes, so Steggles arranged the handicapping as you see on the card. You must come into this, Bertie. You see, the trouble is that I haven't a bean, and Eustace hasn't a bean, and Bingo Little hasn't a bean, so you'll have to finance the syndicate. Don't weaken! It's just putting money in all our pockets. Well, we'll have to be getting back now. Think the thing over, and 'phone me later in the day. And, if you let us down, Bertie, may a cousin's curse – Come on, Claude old thing."

The more I studied the scheme, the better it looked.

"How about it, Jeeves ?" I said.

Jeeves smiled gently, and drifted out.

"Jeeves has no sporting blood," said Bingo.

"Well, I have. I'm coming into this. Claude's quite right. It's like finding money by the wayside."

"Good man!" said Bingo. "Now I can see daylight. Say I have a tenner on Heppenstall, and cop; that'll give me a bit in hand to back Pink Pill with in the two o'clock at Gatwick the week after next: cop on that, put the pile on Musk-Rat for the one-thirty at Lewes, and there I am with a nice little sum to take to Alexandra Park on September the tenth, when I've got a tip straight from the stable."

It sounded like a bit out of 'Smiles's Self-Help'.

"And then," said young Bingo, "I'll be in a position to go to my uncle and beard him in his lair somewhat. He's quite a bit of a snob, you know, and when he hears that I'm going to marry the daughter of an earl—"

"I say, old man," I couldn't help saying, "aren't you looking ahead rather far ?"

"Oh, that's all right. It's true nothing's actually settled yet, but she practically told me the other day she was fond of me."

"What!"

"Well she said that the sort of man she liked was the self-reliant, manly man with strength, good looks, character, ambition, and initiative."

"Leave me, laddie," I said. "Leave me to my fried egg."

Directly I'd got up I went to the 'phone, snatched Eustace away from his morning's work, and instructed him to put a tenner on the Twing flier at current odds for each of the syndicate; and after lunch Eustace rang me up to say that he had done business at a snappy seven-to-one, the odds having lengthened owing to a rumour in knowledgeable circles that the Rev. was subject to hay-fever and was taking big chances strolling in the paddock behind the Vicarage in the early mornings. And it was dashed lucky, I thought next day, that we had managed to get the money on in time, for on the Sunday morning old Heppenstall fairly took the bit between his teeth, and gave us thirty-six solid minutes on Certain Popular Superstitions. I was sitting next to Steggles in the pew, and I saw him blench visibly. He was a little, rat-faced fellow, with shifty eyes and a suspicious nature. The first thing he did when we emerged into the open air was to announce, formally, that anyone who fancied the Rev. could now be accommodated at fifteen-to-eight on, and he added, in a rather hasty manner, that if he had his way, this sort of in-and-out running would be brought to the attention of the Jockey Club, but that he supposed that there was nothing to be done about it. This ruinous price checked the punters at once, and there was little money in sight. And so matters stood till just after lunch on Tuesday afternoon, when, as I was strolling up and down in front of the house with a cigarette, Claude and Eustace came bursting up the drive on bicycles, dripping with momentous news.

"Bertie," said Claude, deeply agitated, "unless we take immediate action and do a bit of quick thinking, we're in the cart."

"What's the matter?"

"G. Hayward's the matter," said Eustace, morosely. "The Lower Bingley starter."

"We never even considered him," said Claude. "Somehow or other, he got overlooked. It's always the way. Steggles overlooked him. We all overlooked him. But Eustace and I happened by the merest fluke to be riding through Lower Bingley this morning, and there was a wedding on at the church, and it suddenly struck us that it wouldn't be a bad move to get a line on G. Hayward's form, in case he might be a dark horse."

"And it was jolly lucky we did," said Eustace. "He delivered an address of twenty-six minutes by Claude's stop-watch. At a village wedding, mark you! What'll he do when he really extends himself!"

"There's only one thing to be done, Bertie," said Claude. "You must spring some more funds, so that we can hedge on Hayward and save ourselves."

"But –"

"Well, it's the only way out."

"But I say, you know, I hate the idea of all that money we put on Heppenstall being chucked away."

"What else can you suggest? You don't suppose the Rev. can give this absolute marvel a handicap and win, do you?"

"I've got it!" I said.

"What?"

"I see a way by which we can make it safe for our nominee. I'll pop over this afternoon, and ask him as a personal favour to preach that sermon of his on Brotherly Love on Sunday."

Claude and Eustace looked at each other, like those chappies in the poem, with a wild surmise.

"It's a scheme," said Claude.

"A jolly brainy scheme," said Eustace. "I didn't think you had it in you, Bertie."

"But even so," said Claude, "fizzer as that sermon no doubt is, will it be good enough in the face of a four-minute handicap?"

"Rather!" I said. "When I told you it lasted forty-five minutes, I was probably understating it. I should call it – from my recollection of the thing – nearer fifty."

"Then carry on," said Claude.

I toddled over in the evening and fixed the thing up. Old Heppenstall was most decent about the whole affair. He seemed pleased and touched that I should have remembered the sermon all these years, and said he had once or twice had an idea of preaching it again, only it had seemed to him, on reflection, that it was perhaps a trifle long for a rustic congregation.

"And in these restless times, my dear Wooster," he said, "I fear that brevity in the pulpit is becoming more and more desiderated by even the bucolic church-goer, who one might have supposed would be less afflicted with the spirit of hurry and impatience than his metropolitan brother. I have had many arguments on the subject with my nephew, young Bates, who is taking my old friend Spettigue's cure over at Gandle-by-the-Hill.

His view is that a sermon nowadays should be a bright, brisk, straight-from-the-shoulder address, never lasting more than ten or twelve minutes."

"Long?" I said. "Why, my goodness! you don't call that Brotherly Love sermon of yours *long*, do you?"

"It takes fully fifty minutes to deliver."

"Surely not?"

"Your incredulity, my dear Wooster, is extremely flattering – far more flattering, of course, than I deserve. Nevertheless, the facts are as I have stated. You are sure that I would not be well advised to make certain excisions and eliminations? You do not think it would be a good thing to cut, to prune? I might, for example, delete the rather exhaustive excursus into the family life of the early Assyrians?"

"Don't touch a word of it, or you'll spoil the whole thing," I said earnestly.

"I am delighted to hear you say so, and I shall preach the sermon without fail next Sunday morning."

What I have always said, and what I always shall say, is that this ante-post betting is a mistake, an error, and a mug's game. You never can tell what's going to happen. If fellows would only stick to the good old S.P. there would be fewer young men go wrong. I'd hardly finished my breakfast on the Saturday morning, when Jeeves came to my bedside to say that Eustace wanted me on the telephone.

"Good Lord, Jeeves, what's the matter, do you think?"

I'm bound to say I was beginning to get a bit jumpy by this time.

"Mr Eustace did not confide in me, sir."

"Has he got the wind up?"

"Somewhat vertically, sir, to judge by his voice."

"Do you know what I think, Jeeves? Something's gone wrong with the favourite."

"Which is the favourite, sir?"

"Mr Heppenstall. He's gone to odds on. He was intending to preach a sermon on Brotherly Love which would have brought him home by lengths. I wonder if anything's happened to him."

"You could ascertain, sir, by speaking to Mr Eustace on the telephone. He is holding the wire."

"By Jove, yes!"

I shoved on a dressing-gown, and flew downstairs like a mighty, rushing wind. The moment I heard Eustace's voice I knew we were for it. It had a croak of agony in it.

"Bertie?"

"Here I am."

"Deuce of a time you've been. Bertie, we're sunk. The favourite's blown up."

"No!"

"Yes. Coughing in his stable all last night."

"What!"

"Absolutely! Hay-fever."

"Oh, my sainted aunt!"

"The doctor is with him now, and it's only a question of minutes before he's officially scratched. That means the curate will show up at the post instead, and he's no good at all. He is being offered at a hundred-to-six, but no takers. What shall we do?"

I had to grapple with the thing for a moment in silence.

"Eustace."

"Hallo?"

"What can you get on G. Hayward?"

"Only four-to-one now. I think there's been a leak, and Steggles has heard something. The odds shortened late last night in a significant manner."

"Well, four-to-one will clear us. Put another fiver all round on G. Hayward for the syndicate. That'll bring us out on the right side of the ledger."

"If he wins."

"What do you mean? I thought you considered him a cert., bar Heppenstall."

"I'm beginning to wonder," said Eustace, gloomily, "if there's such a thing as a cert. in this world. I'm told the Rev. Joseph Tucker did an extraordinarily fine trial gallop at a mothers' meeting over at Badgwick yesterday. However, it seems our only chance. So-long."

Not being one of the official stewards, I had my choice of churches next morning, and naturally I didn't hesitate. The only drawback to going to Lower Bingley was that it was ten miles away, which meant an early start, but I borrowed a bicycle from one of the grooms and tooled off. I had only Eustace's word for it that G. Hayward was such a stayer, and it might have been that he had showed too flattering form at that wedding where the twins had heard him preach; but any misgivings I may have had disappeared the moment he got into the pulpit. Eustace had been right.

The man was a trier. He was a tall, rangy-looking greybeard, and he went off from the start with a nice, easy action, pausing and clearing his throat at the end of each sentence, and it wasn't five minutes before I realised that here was the winner. His habit of stopping dead and looking round the church at intervals was worth minutes to us, and in the home stretch we gained no little advantage owing to his dropping his pince-nez and having to grope for them. At the twenty-minute mark he had merely settled down. Twenty-five minutes saw him going strong. And when he finally finished with a good burst, the clock showed thirty-five minutes fourteen seconds. With the handicap which he had been given, this seemed to me to make the event easy for him, and it was with much *bonhomie* and good-will to all men that I hopped on to the old bike and started back to the Hall for lunch.

Bingo was talking on the 'phone when I arrived.

"Fine! Spendid! Topping!" he was saying. "Eh? Oh, we needn't worry about him. Right-o, I'll tell Bertie." He hung up the receiver and caught sight of me. "Oh, hallo, Bertie; I was just talking to Eustace. It's all right, old man. The report from Lower Bingley has just got in. G. Hayward romps home."

"I knew he would. I've just come from there."

"Oh, were you there? I went to Badgwick. Tucker ran a splendid race, but the handicap was too much for him. Starkie had a sore throat and was nowhere. Roberts, of Fale-by-the-Water, ran third. Good old G. Hayward!" said Bingo, affectionately, and we strolled out on to the terrace.

"Are all the returns in then?" I asked.

"All except Gandle-by-the-Hill. But we needn't worry about Bates. He never had a chance. By the way, poor old Jeeves loses his tenner. Silly ass!"

"Jeeves? How do you mean?"

"He came to me this morning, just after you had left, and asked me to put a tenner on Bates for him. I told him he was a chump and begged him not to throw his money away, but he would do it."

"I beg your pardon, sir. This note arrived for you just after you had left the house this morning."

Jeeves had materialised from nowhere, and was standing at my elbow.

"Eh? What? Note?"

"The Reverend Mr Heppenstall's butler brought it over from the Vicarage, sir. It came too late to be delivered to you at the moment."

Young Bingo was talking to Jeeves like a father on the subject of betting against the form-book. The yell I gave made him bite his tongue in the middle of a sentence.

"What the dickens is the matter?" he asked, not a little peeved.

"We're dished! Listen to this!"

I read him the note:

The Vicarage,
Twing, Glos.

MY DEAR WOOSTER,

As you may have heard, circumstances over which I have no control will prevent my preaching the sermon on Brotherly Love for which you made such a flattering request. I am unwilling, however, that you shall be disappointed, so, if you will attend divine service at Gandle-by-the-Hill this morning, you will hear my sermon preached by young Bates, my nephew. I have lent him the manuscript at his urgent desire, for, between ourselves, there are wheels within wheels. My nephew is one of the candidates for the headmastership of a well-known public school, and the choice has narrowed down between him and one rival.

Late yesterday evening James received private information that the head of the Board of Governors of the school proposed to sit under him this Sunday in order to judge of the merits of his preaching, a most important item in swaying the Board's choice. I acceded to his plea that I lend him my sermon on Brotherly Love, of which, like you, he apparently retains a vivid recollection. It would have been too late for him to compose a sermon of suitable length in place of the brief address which – mistakenly, in my opinion – he had designed to deliver to his rustic flock, and I wished to help the boy.

Trusting that his preaching of the sermon will supply you with as pleasant memories as you say you have of mine, I remain,

Cordially yours,
F. HEPPENSTALL

P.S. The hay-fever has rendered my eyes unpleasantly weak for the time being, so I am dictating this letter to my butler, Brookfield, who will convey it to you.

I don't know when I've experienced a more massive silence than the one that followed my reading of this cheery epistle. Young Bingo gulped once or twice, and practically every known emotion came and went on his face. Jeeves coughed one soft, low, gentle cough like a sheep with a blade of grass stuck in its throat, and then stood gazing serenely at the landscape. Finally young Bingo spoke.

"Great Scot!" he whispered, hoarsely. "An S.P. job!"

"I believe that is the technical term, sir," said Jeeves.

"So you had inside information, dash it!" said young Bingo.

"Why, yes, sir," said Jeeves. "Brookfield happened to mention the contents of the note to me when he brought it. We are old friends. . . ."

There was silence.

"I think I'll go for a walk," said Bingo.

"But, my dear old thing," I said, "It's just lunchtime. The gong will be going any minute now."

"I don't want any lunch!" said Bingo.

HOW TO WIN WHILE LOSING

William Saroyan

"I spend most of my time loafing, walking to the ocean or around town, shooting rotation pool, playing poker, betting on the horses and so on," claims William Saroyan, one of America's most popular contemporary writers. Certainly gambling is a part of his life and as a result of recognizing it as such, he succeeds far better than most in putting it into perspective. In "How to Win While Losing," William Saroyan shows how he has contrived on occasions to turn even apparently disastrous losses to his advantage.

ONCE YOU HAVE messed with gambling, winning or losing, once you have gone into a gambling house, your goose is cooked, you are no longer good for anything else, except more of the same order of derangement, of total dismissal of time and sequence, for that is basically what gambling is. For the true gambler, that is. For the kind of gambler I was, and probably still am, I certainly would be that kind of gambler if I went back to gambling at all, as I probably shall. Money ceases to be money. A thousand means nothing, ten thousand means nothing, whether it is dollars, francs, lire, beans, or points. The only thing that means anything is the right or the wrong of it, and myself in relation to right and wrong. The theory is that if I am right I can do no wrong, and I have all too frequently demonstrated the validity of the theory. But I have even more frequently had it brought home to me that if I am wrong, I can do no right, either. And by that time there is some arithmetic to do, which I tend to do with the sobriety I knew as a newsboy, counting the coins in my hand, and then counting my papers, and then counting the coins again, and then the papers again, because a nickel was missing. The arithmetic might reveal, over the years of gambling, beginning on Third Street in San Francisco, that a dollar was missing, five dollars were missing, ten, twenty, fifty, a hundred, a thousand dollars, two thousand, three, five, ten, twenty thousand dollars were missing.

Now, of course, if you lose money at gambling, you haven't got the money any more.

As a losing Presidential candidate once said, "Under our great democratic system, the losing candidate does not win." Everybody understood what he meant, though, and rather admired him for not crying. He meant that the losing candidate offers his congratulations to the winning candidate, but somewhere in the midst of the thought, his loss troubled him, confused him, astonished him, proved to be not yet totally acceptable. He was still in the midst of disbelief. How could it be possible that he had lost, especially in that he had come so near to winning ? And so, in his befuddlement, and with an unmistakable courage, perhaps even bravery, and certainly with a good deal of charm, his language became garbled. In an instant, though, he corrected the garbling, speaking off the cuff and quickly, awfully tired, as gamblers who have stopped gambling always are, too, and hoping that the pathos of his position, and of what he had said, might not have been noticed, as losing gamblers hope the real extent of their losses will not become known.

I am not mentioning the names of Presidential candidates, or Presidents, winners or losers, because when they write their lies I don't expect them to use my name. I don't know them and they don't know me. They gamble and I gamble. They win and they lose, and I win and I lose.

But in the end I stop, and I do the necessary arithmetic. If it tells me I have won, I try to find out how much. If it tells me I have lost, I try to decide how I am going to get the lost money back.

Well, you never do. You never get anything back. You always get something, but it isn't back. Getting something back is part of the fantasy of the gambler, and for all I know of Presidential candidates who have lost, who run again, who lose again, but in having lost twice get something, surely something very valuable, too. And finally they don't run again. They decide not to, or they are not permitted to, but again they get something. They certainly get older, as I have gotten older getting various things but not getting back anything, not getting back the money, the time, the abandoned sequence, or anything else I may have lost. I have gotten other things, some of them better than the things lost.

Now, as a poor illustration of this, but not as an apology for folly, for foolishness, for aberration, for illness, for anything we want to call it, I may say that every time I have lost enough money to be deeply annoyed by the enormity of it, which has always been picayune, even when it has been fifty thousand dollars, I have gotten something I could not otherwise have gotten. My money losses are picayune, because there are billions of dollars. If a man has a million or two he remains entirely the same as anybody else in the basic involvement with time, sequence, and the human experience. Money itself is picayune. Even so, every time I have lost, and have been annoyed about the difference between right and wrong, with the edge of the wrong moving to me, I have made up my mind to somehow right the wrong, to balance the imbalance, to earn more than the sum lost.

What's more, I have done so, and it has always been by means of writing.

But the point I am trying to make is that I believe all such writing is writing I would *not* have done had I not lost at gambling.

Hence, while I have not always won back the money lost, I *have* gotten a number of things from *having* lost.

I have sat down and written steadily for a month, and of course *that* is something. The writing has been published, and of course *that* is something, too. I have sometimes been paid more for the writing than I lost at gambling, and *that* is also something.

But most important of all, my annoyance has *conditioned* what I have written. Consequently, I have a new book, a new novel, or a new play, with a style I could not have otherwise put into it. The annoyance about the loss of money, of time and sequence, gave the work its style, and now and then that style has been rare enough to please me.

A lame explanation ? *More* than lame – cripple. But maybe it's the truth, too. How should I know ? In the meantime, the facts, as they're called. Las

Vegas 1942. Five thousand dollars lost. *The Human Comedy* written. Two hundred and fifty thousand dollars earned. Las Vegas again, 1949. Fifty thousand dollars lost. *Tracy's Tiger, Rock Wagram*, and *The Laughing Matter* written. No dollars and no cents earned, but I *have* the books, they are there, they are going, they will soon be gone perhaps, but until they are, they are being read and readers are getting something out of them.

SCIENCE v. LUCK

Mark Twain

Mark Twain (alias Samuel Clemens) is probably not only America's but the world's best known humorist, a reputation gained during the extensive lecture tours undertaken when he was in dire financial straits following the collapse of his publishing house. After a spell as a journeyman printer and then as an apprentice riverboat pilot on the Mississippi, the young Mark Twain soon graduated to journalism and took up writing full time after being sent on a world tour to write travel sketches for his newspaper.

"Science v. Luck" is a typical Mark Twain tale in which he takes an apparently absurd proposition and proves it up to the hilt. It is probably the nearest a gambler will ever get to consistently beating the system.

AT THAT TIME, in Kentucky (said the Hon. Mr K—), the law was very strict against what it termed "games of chance." About a dozen of the boys were detected playing "seven up" or "old sledge" for money, and the grand jury found a true bill against them. Jim Sturgis was retained to defend them when the case came up, of course. The more he studied over the matter, and looked into the evidence, the plainer it was that he must lose a case at last – there was no getting around that painful fact. Those boys had certainly been betting money on a game of chance. Even public sympathy was roused in behalf of Sturgis. People said it was a pity to see him mar his successful career with a big prominent case like this which must go against him.

But after several restless nights an inspired idea flashed upon Sturgis, and he sprang out of bed delighted. He thought he saw his way through. The next day he whispered around a little among his clients and a few friends, and then when the case came up in court he acknowledged the seven-up and the betting, and, as his sole defense, had the astounding effrontery to put in the plea that old sledge was not a game of chance! There was the broadest sort of a smile all over the faces of that sophisticated audience. The judge smiled with the rest. But Sturgis maintained a countenance whose earnestness was even severe. The opposite counsel tried to ridicule him out of his position, and did not succeed. The judge jested in a ponderous judicial way about the thing, but did not move him. The matter was becoming grave. The judge lost a little of his patience, and said the joke had gone far enough. Jim Sturgis said he knew of no joke in the matter – his clients could not be punished for indulging in what some people chose to consider a game of chance until it was *proven* that it was a game of chance. Judge and counsel said that would be an easy matter, and forthwith called Deacons Job, Peters, Burke, and Johnson, and Dominies Wirt and Miggies, to testify, and they unanimously and with strong feeling put down the legal quibble of Sturgis by pronouncing that old sledge *was* a game of chance.

"What do you call it *now*?" said the judge.

"I call it a game of science!" retorted Sturgis; "And I'll prove it, too!"

They saw his little game.

He brought in a cloud of witnesses, and produced an overwhelming mass of testimony, to show that old sledge was not a game of chance but a game of science.

Instead of being the simplest case in the world, it had somehow turned out to be an excessively knotty one. The judge scratched his head over it awhile, and said there was no way of coming to a determination, because just as many men could be brought into court who would testify on one side as could be found to testify on the other. But he said he was willing to do the fair thing by all parties, and would act upon any suggestion Mr Sturgis would make for the solution of the difficulty.

Mr Sturgis was on his feet in a second.

"Impanel a jury of six of each, Luck *versus* Science. Give them candles and a couple of decks of cards. Send them into the jury-room, and just abide by the result!''

There was no disputing the fairness of the proposition. The four deacons and the two dominies were sworn in as the ''chance'' jurymen, and six inveterate old seven-up professors were chosen to represent the ''science'' side of the issue. They retired to the jury-room.

In about two hours Deacon Peters sent into court to borrow three dollars from a friend. [Sensation.] In about two hours more Dominie Miggles sent into court to borrow a ''stake'' from a friend. [Sensation.] During the next three or four hours the other dominie and the other deacons sent into court for small loans. And still the packed audience waited, for it was a prodigious occasion in Bull's Corners, and one in which every father of a family was necessarily interested.

The rest of the story can be told briefly. About daylight the jury came in, and Deacon Job, the foreman, read the following:

We, the jury in the case of the Commonwealth of Kentucky *vs*. John Wheeler *et al*., have carefully considered the points of the case, and tested the merits of the several theories advanced, and do hereby unanimously decide that the game commonly known as old sledge or seven-up is eminently a game of science and not of chance. In demonstration whereof it is hereby and herein stated, iterated, reiterated, set forth, and made manifest that, during the entire night, the ''chance'' men never won a game or turned a jack, although both feats were common and frequent to the opposition; and furthermore, in support of this our verdict, we call attention to the significant fact that the ''chance'' men are all busted, and the ''science'' men have got the money. It is the deliberate opinion of this jury, that the ''chance'' theory concerning seven-up is a pernicious doctrine, and calculated to inflict untold suffering and pecuniary loss upon any community that takes stock in it.

''That is the way that seven-up came to be set apart and particularized in the statute-books of Kentucky as being a game not of chance but of science, and therefore not punishable under the law,'' said Mr K—. ''That verdict is of record, and holds good to this day.''

RIEN NE VA PLUS

Alexander Woollcott

Alexander Woollcott was a journalist and drama critic on *The New York Times*, *The Herald* and *The Sun* before becoming a pioneer broadcaster with CBS and one of the most popular columnists on *The New Yorker*.

Interested in anything and everything, Alexander Woollcott was particularly fascinated by gambling and in the following story he tells how human ingenuity contrived on at least one occasion to triumph over the roulette wheel.

WE WERE SITTING under the midsummer stars at Monte Carlo, eating a soufflé and talking about suicide, when a passing newsmonger stopped at our table all aglow with the tidings that that young American with the white forelock had just been found crumpled on the beach, a bullet-hole in his heart. Earlier in the evening – it was shortly before we came out of the Casino in quest of dinner – we had all seen him wiped out by a final disastrous turn of the wheel. And now he lay dead on the shore.

I shall have to admit that the news gave a fillip to the occasion. It came towards the end of a long, luscious dinner on the terrace opposite the Casino. We were a casually assembled carful, who had driven over from Antibes in the late afternoon, planning to play a little roulette as an appetizer and then to dine interminably.

When we had arrived in the *Salles Privées* a few hours before, there was only standing room around our table at first. In this rapt fringe, I encountered Sam Fletcher, a dawdling journalist who lived on occasional assignments from the Paris offices of American newspapers. He pointed out the notables to me. There was Mary Garden, for instance, playing intently, losing and winning, losing and winning, with that economy of emotional expenditure which one usually reserves for setting-up exercises. Then there was an English dowager who looked as though she were held together by adhesive tape. She was betting parsimoniously, but Fletcher whispered to me that she lived in Monte Carlo on an ample allowance provided by her son-in-law, with the sole stipulation that she never embarrass the family by coming home. A moribund remittance woman. Next to her sat a pallid old gentleman whose hands, as they caressed his stack of counters, were conspicuously encased in braided gloves of gray silk. It seems that in his youth, he had been a wastrel, and, on her deathbed, his mother had squeezed from him a solemn promise never to touch card or chip again as long as he lived.

As for young White Lock, there was, until his final bet, nothing else noticeable about him except that he was the only man then at the table wearing a dinner coat. We heard later that at first he had lost heavily and had had to make several trips to the *caisse* to replenish his supply of plaques. By the time I came along he had settled to a more cautious play but finally, as if from boredom, he took all his plaques and counters and stacked them on the red. To this pile he added, just as the wheel began to turn, the contents of his wallet – emptying out a small cascade of thousand-franc notes, with a single hundred-franc note among them. But this one he retrieved at the last moment as if to be sure of carfare home. There was that breathless spinning moment, then the fateful *"Rien ne va plus"*, issuing in the same dead voice with which the intoning of the mass falls on infidel ears. Then the decision. *"Noir."* Around that table you could hear the word for black being *exhaled* in every language the world has known since Babel.

The young man gave a little laugh as the *croupier* called the turn. He sat quite still as his last gauge was raked into the bank. With all eyes on him, he shoved his chair back from the table, reached for his wallet, took out the aforesaid hundred-francs note and pushed it, with white, fastidious fingers, toward the center of the patterned baize. *"Pour le personnel,"* he said, with a kind of wry grandeur which hushed the usual twitter of thanks from the *croupiers*. "And that," he added, "is that." So saying, he got to his feet, yawned a little, and sauntered out of the room. I remember thinking, at the time, that he was behaving rather like any desperate young man in any Zoë Akins play. But it was a good performance. And now, it seems, he lay dead by the water's edge.

It was Fletcher himself who brought the news. It came, I say, just as we were eating soufflé and talking of suicide. This, of course, was no obliging coincidence. One always tells tall tales of self-slaughter at Monte Carlo. It is part of the legend of the principality – as strong in its force of suggestion, I suppose, as the legend of Lourdes is strong in its hint to hysterics that the

71

time has come to cast away their crutches. Fletcher told us that the sound of the shot had brought a watchman running. The youth lay on his back, his chin tilted to the stars, one outstretched hand limply holding the revolver, a dark stain on the pleated whiteness of his breast. Before Fletcher could wire his report to Paris, he would have to await certain – well – formalities. In a conspiratorial whisper, he explained there had been so many such suicides of late that a new rule was but recently put into effect. Whenever any client of the Casino was found self-slain with empty pockets, it was customary for the Casino to rush a bankroll to the spot before notifying the police, so that the victim would seem to have ended it all from *Weltschmerz*. Even now, Fletcher said, this trick must be in progress, and in the meantime he ought to be seeking such obituary data as might be gleaned in the registry office.

We were still lingering over our coffee when he came hurrying back to us, all bristling with the end of the story. Notified in due course, the *gendarmerie* had repaired to the beach in quest of the body. But there was none. Not at the indicated spot, nor anywhere else on the shore. After further search, the minor chieftain from the Casino, who had himself tucked ten thousand francs into the pocket of the now missing suicide and was still lurking, much puzzled, in the middle-distance, returned at last to the *Salles Privées*, only to find them humming with a new chapter. It seems that that young American with the white forelock – the one somebody or other had inaccurately reported as killed – had reappeared apparently restored in spirits, and certainly restored in funds. He had bet tremendously, lingered for only three turns of the wheel, and departed with a hundred thousand francs. The attendants assumed he had merely been out to dinner. At least the careless fellow had spilled some tomato sauce on his shirt front.

THE DESPERATE GAMBLER

ESTHER WATERS

George Moore

The father of the Irish novelist George Moore was a racehorse owner of note, and it is perhaps not surprising that the book *Esther Waters*, which made his son's name is the story of a servant girl in Victorian England set against a racing background.

Esther Waters is one of the first of the so-called "realistic" novels in the English language and the following story of a man who is literally betting for his life is almost painful in its realism. The idea that because the gambler needs to win, he must win, is an example of the tragic self-delusion which so often takes hold of the compulsive gambler.

"SO YOU MARRIED a betting man! Miss Rice did say something about it, but I don't think I understood that he was a betting man; I thought he was a publican."

"So he was, sir. We lost our licence through the betting."

"You say he's being examined by the doctor. Is it a bad case?"

"I am afraid it is, sir."

They walked on in silence until they reached the gate.

"To me this place is infinitely pathetic. That little cough never silent for long. Did you hear that poor girl say with surprise that her cough is no better than it was last Christmas?"

"Yes, sir. Poor girl, I don't think she's long for this world."

"But tell me about your husband, Esther," he said, and his face filled with an expression of true sympathy. "I am a subscriber, and if your husband would like to become an indoor patient, I hope you'll let me know."

"Thank you, sir; you was always the kindest, but there's no reason why I should trouble you. Some friends of ours have already recommended him, and it only rests with himself to remain out or go in."

He pulled out his watch and said, "I am sorry to have met you in such sad circumstances, but I am glad to have seen you. It must be seven years or more since you left Miss Rice. You haven't changed much; you keep your good looks."

"Oh, sir."

He laughed at her embarrassment and walked across the road hailing a hansom just as he used to in old times when he came to see Miss Rice. The memory of those days came back upon her, and she felt she had seen him for the last time. But it was foolish, and wicked too, to think of such things – her husband dying. But she couldn't help it; he reminded her of so much of what was past and gone. A moment after she dashed these personal tears aside and walked open-hearted to meet William. What had the doctor said? She must know the truth. If she was to lose him she would lose everything. No, not everything; her boy would still remain to her, and she felt that, after all, her boy was most what was real to her in life. These were the thoughts that passed through her mind before William had time to answer her question.

"He said the left lung was gone, that I'd never be able to stand another winter in England. He said I must go to Egypt."

"Egypt," she repeated. "Is that very far from here?"

"What matter how far it is! If I can't live in England I must go where I can live."

"Don't be cross, dear. I know it's your health that makes you that irritable, but it's hard to bear at times."

"You won't care to go to Egypt with me."

"How can you think that, Bill? Have I ever refused you anything?"

"Quite right, old girl, I'm sorry. I know you'd do anything for me. I've always said so, haven't I? It's this cough that makes me sharp-tempered and fretful. I shall be different when I get to Egypt."

"When do we start?"

"If we get away by the end of October it will be all right. It will cost a lot of money; the journey is expensive, and we shall have to stop there six months. I couldn't think of coming home before the end of April."

Esther did not answer. They walked some yards in silence. Then he said:

"I've been very unlucky lately; there isn't much over a hundred pounds in the bank."

"How much shall we want?"

"Three or four hundred pounds at least. We won't take the boy with us, we couldn't afford that; but I should like to pay a couple of quarters in advance."

"That won't be much."

"Not if I have any luck. The luck must turn, and I have some splendid information about the Great Ebor and the Yorkshire Stakes. Stacks knows of a horse or two that's being kept for Sandown. Unfortunately there is not much doing in August. I must try to make up the money: it's a matter of life and death."

It was for his very life that her husband was now gambling on the race-course, and a sensation of great wickedness came up in her mind, but she stifled it. But William noticed the look of fear that appeared in her eyes, and he said:

"It's my last chance. I can't get the money any other way; and I don't want to die yet awhile. I haven't been as good to you as I'd like, and I want to do something for the boy, you know."

He had been told not to remain out after sundown, but he was resolved to leave no stone unturned in his search for information, and often he returned home as late as nine and ten o'clock at night coughing – Esther could hear him all up the street. He came in ready to drop with fatigue, his pockets filled with sporting papers, and these he studied, spreading them on the table under the lamp, while Esther sat striving to do some needlework. It often dropped out of her hands, and her eyes filled with tears. But she took care that he should not see these tears. Sometimes he read out the horses' names and asked her which she thought would win, which seemed to her a likely name. But she begged of him not to ask her; they had many quarrels on this subject, but in the end he understood that it was not fair to ask her. Sometimes Stack and Journeyman came in, and they argued about weights and distances, until midnight; old John came to see them and every day he had heard some new tip. It often rose to Esther's lips to tell William to back his fancy and have done with it: she could see that these discussions only fatigued him; that he was no nearer to the truth now than he was a fortnight ago. Meanwhile, the horse he had thought of backing had gone up in the betting. But he said that he must be very careful. They had only a hundred pounds left; he must be careful not to risk this money foolishly – it was his very life-blood. If he were to lose all this money, he wouldn't only sign his own death-warrant, but also hers. He might linger on a long while – there was no knowing, – but he would never be able to do any work, that was certain (unless he went out to Egypt); the doctor had said so, and then it would be she who would have to support him. And if God were merciful enough to take him off at once he would leave her in a worse plight than he had found her in, and the boy growing up! Oh, it was terrible! He buried his face in his hands, and seemed quite overcome. Then the cough would take him, and for a few minutes he could only think of himself. Esther gave him a little milk to drink, and he said:

"There's a hundred pounds left, Esther. It isn't much, but it's something. I don't believe that there's much use in my going to Egypt. I shall never get well. It is better that I should pitch myself into the river. That would be the least selfish way out of it."

"William, I will not have you talk in that way," Esther said, laying down her work and going over to him. "If you was to do such a thing I should never forgive you. I could never think the same of you."

"All right, old girl, don't be frightened. I've been thinking too much about them horses, and am a bit depressed. I daresay it will come out all right. I think that Mahomet is sure to win the Great Ebor, don't you?"

"I don't think there's no better judge than yourself. They all say if he don't fall lame that he's bound to win."

"Then Mahomet shall carry my money. I'll back him to-morrow."

Now that he had made up his mind what horse to back his spirits revived. He was able to dismiss the subject from his mind, and they talked of other things, of their son, and they laid projects for his welfare. But on the day of the race, from early morning, William could barely contain himself. Usually he took his winnings and losings very quietly. When he had been especially unlucky he swore a bit, but Esther had never seen any great excitement before a race was run. The issues of this race were extraordinary, and it was heart-breaking to see him suffer; he could not remain still a moment. A prey to all the terrors of hope, exhausted with anticipation, he rested himself against the sideboard and wiped drops of sweat from his forehead. A broiling sunlight infested their window-panes, the room grew oven-like, and he was obliged at last to go into the back parlour and lie down. He lay there in his shirt sleeves quite exhausted, hardly able to breathe; the arm once so strong and healthy was shrunken to a little nothing. He seemed quite bloodless, and looking at him Esther could hardly hope that any climate would restore him to health. He just asked her what the time was, and said, "The race is being run now." A few minutes after he said, "I think Mahomet has won. I fancied I saw him get first past the post." He spoke as if he were sure, and said nothing about the evening paper. If he were disappointed, Esther felt that it would kill him, and she knelt down by the bedside and prayed that God would allow the horse to win. It meant her husband's life, that was all she knew. Oh, that the horse might win! Presently he said, "There's no use praying, I feel sure it is all right. Go into the next room, stand on the balcony so that you may see the boy coming along."

With agonised soul the woman viewed the serenity of the evening sky and heard the cry. "Win-ner, win-ner" coming up the street. It came from the north, from the east, and now from the west. Ah, if it should prove bad news! But somehow she too felt that the news was good, and ran to meet the boy. She had a halfpenny ready in her hand; he fumbled, striving to detach a single paper from the quire under his arm. Seeing her impatience, he said, "Mahomet's won." Then the pavement seemed to slide beneath her feet, and she could hardly see, so full was her heart, so burdened with the happiness that she was bringing to the poor sick fellow who lay in his shirt sleeves on the bed in the back room. "It's all right," she said. "I thought so too; it seemed like it." His face flushed, life seemed to come back. He sat up and took the paper from her. "There," he said, "I've got my place-money, too. I hope Stack and Journeyman come in to-night. I'd like to have a chat about this. Come, give me a kiss, dear. I'm not going to die, after all. It isn't a pleasant thing to think that you must die, that there's no hope for you, that you must go under ground."

The next thing to do was to pick the winner of the Yorkshire Handicap. In this he was not successful, but he backed several winners at Sandown Park, and at the close of the week had made nearly enough to take him to Egypt.

The Doncaster week, however, proved disastrous. He lost most of his winnings, and had to look forward to retrieving his fortunes at Newmarket. "The worst of it is, if I don't make up the money by October, it will be no use. They say the November fogs will polish me off."

Between Doncaster and Newmarket he lost a bet, and this bet carried him back into despondency. He felt it was no use struggling against fate. Better remain in London and be taken away at the end of November or December; he couldn't last much longer than that. This would allow him to leave Esther at least fifty pounds to go on with. The boy would soon be able to earn money. It would be better so. No use wasting all this money for the sake of his health, which wasn't worth twopence three-farthings. It was like throwing sovereigns after farthings. He didn't want to do any betting; he was as hollow as a shell inside, he could feel it. Egypt could do nothing for him, and as he had to go, better sooner than later. Esther argued with him. What should she have to live for if he was taken from her? The doctors had said that Egypt might set him right. She didn't know much about such things, but she had always heard that it was extraordinary how people got cured out there.

"That's true," he said. "I've heard that people who couldn't live a week in England, who haven't the length of your finger of lung left, can go on all right out there. I might get something to do out there, and the boy might come out after us."

"That's the way I like to hear you talk. Who knows, at Newmarket we might have luck! Just one big bet, a winner at fifty to one, that's all we want."

"That's just what has been passing in my mind. I've got particular information about the Cesarewitch and Cambridgeshire. I could get the price you speak of – fifty to one against the two, Matchbox and Chasuble – the double event, you know. I'm inclined to go it. It's my last chance."

When Matchbox galloped home the winner of the Cesarewitch by five lengths, William was lying in his bed, seemingly at death's door. He had remained out late one evening, had caught cold, and his mouth was constantly filled with blood. He was much worse, and could hardly take notice of the good news. When he revived a little he said, "It has come too late." But when Chasuble was backed to win thousands at ten to one, and Journeyman and Stack assured him that the stable was quite confident of being able to pull it off, his spirits revived. He spoke of hedging. "If," he said to Esther, "I was to get out at eight or nine to one I should be able to leave you something, you know in case of accidents." But he would not entrust laying off his bet to either Stack or Journeyman; he spoke of a cab and seeing to it himself. If he did this the doctor assured him that it would not much matter whether Chasuble won or lost. "The best thing he could do," the doctor said, "would be to become an indoor patient at once. In the hospital he would be in an equable temperature, and he would receive an attention which he could not get at home."

William did not like going into the hospital; it would be a bad omen. If he did, he felt sure that Chasuble would not win.

"What has going or not going to the hospital to do with Chasuble's chance of winning the Cambridgeshire?" said the doctor. "This window is loose in its sash, a draught comes under the door and if you close out the draughts the atmosphere of the room becomes stuffy. You're thinking of going abroad; a fortnight's nice rest is just what you want to set you up for your journey."

So he allowed himself to be persuaded; he was taken to the hospital, and Esther remained at home waiting for the fateful afternoon. Now that the dying man was taken from her she had no work to distract her thought. The unanswerable question – would Chasuble win? – was always before her. She saw the slender greyhound creatures as she had seen them at Epsom, through a sea of heads and hats, and she asked herself if Chasuble was the brown horse that had galloped in first, or the chestnut that had trotted in last. She often thought she was going mad – her head seemed like it – a sensation of splitting like a piece of calico. She went to see her boy, a great tall fellow of fifteen, who had happily lost none of his affection for his mother, and great sweetness rose up within her as she looked at his long, straight, yellow-stockinged legs, and settled the collar of his cloak, and slipped her fingers into his leathern belt as they walked side by side. He was bare-headed, according to the fashion of his school, and she kissed the wild, dark curls with which his head was run over; they were much brighter in colour when he was a little boy – those days when she slaved seventeen hours a day for his dear life! But he paid her back tenfold for the hardship she had undergone, and she listened to the excellent report his masters gave of his progress, and walked through the quadrangles and the corridors with him, thinking of the sound of his voice as he told her the story of his classes and his studies. She must live for him; though for herself she had had enough of life. But, thank God, she had her darling boy, and whatever unhappiness there might be in store for her she would bear it for his sake. He knew that his father was ill, but she checked her tongue and told him no word of the tragedy that was hanging over them, for the noble instincts which were so intrinsically Esther's told her that it were a pity to soil at the outset a young life with a sordid story, and though it would have been a great relief to her to have shared her trouble with her boy, she forced back her tears and bore her cross alone, without once allowing its edge to touch him.

And every day that visitors were allowed she went to the hospital with the newspaper, containing the last betting. "Chasuble, ten to one taken," William read out. The mare had advanced three points, and William looked at Esther inquiringly, and with hope in his eyes.

"I think she'll win," he said, raising himself in his cane chair.

"I hope so, dear," she murmured, and she settled his cushions.

Two days after the mare was back again at thirteen to one taken and offered; she went back even as far as eighteen to one, and then returned for a while to twelve to one. This fluctuation meant that something was wrong, and William began to lose hope. But on the following day the mare was backed to win a good deal of money at Tattersall's, and once more she stood at ten to one. Seeing her back at the old price made William look so hopeful that a patient stopped as he passed down the corridor, and catching sight of the *Sportsman* on William's lap, he asked him if he was interested in racing. William told him that he was, and that if Chasuble won he would be able to go to Egypt.

"Them that has money can buy health as well as everything else. We'd all get well if we could get out there."

William told him how much he stood to win.

"That'll keep you going long enough to set you straight. You say the mare's backed at ten to one – two hundred to twenty. I wonder if I could get the money. I might sell up the 'ouse."

But before he had time to realise the necessary money the mare was driven back to eighteen to one, and he said:

"She won't win. I might as well leave the wife in the 'ouse. There's no luck for them that comes 'ere."

On the day of the race Esther walked through the streets like one daft, stupidly interested in the passers-by and the disputes that arose between the drivers of cabs and omnibuses. Now and then her thoughts collected, and it seemed to her impossible that the mare should win. If she did they would have £2,500, and would go to Egypt. But she could not imagine such a thing; it seemed so much more natural that the mare should lose, and that her husband should die, and that she should have to face the world once more. She offered up prayers that Chasuble might win, although it did not seem right to address God on the subject, but her heart so often felt like breaking that she had to do something. God would forgive her. But now that the day had come she did not feel as if He had granted her request. Yet it did not seem that her husband was going to die.

She stopped at the "Bell and Horns" to see what the time was, and was surprised to find it was half-an-hour later than she had expected. The race was being run, Chasuble's hoofs were deciding whether her husband was to live or die. It was on the wire by this time. The wires were distinct upon a blue and dove-coloured sky. Did that one go to Newmarket, or the other? Which?

The red building came in sight, and a patient walked slowly up the walk, his back turned to her; another had sat down to rest. Sixteen years ago patients were walking there, and the leaves were scattering then just as now. She began to wonder when the first boy would appear with the news. William was not in the grounds; he was upstairs behind those windows. Poor fellow, she could fancy him sitting there. Perhaps he was watching for her out of one of those windows. But there was no use her going up until she had the news; she must wait for the paper. She walked up and down listening for the cry. Every now and then expectation led her to mistake some ordinary cry for the terrible "Win-ner, all the win-ners," with which the whole town would echo in a few minutes. She hastened forward. No, it was not it. At last she heard the word shrieked behind her. She hastened after the boy, but failed to overtake him. Returning, she met another, gave him a halfpenny and took a paper. Then she remembered she must ask the boy to tell her who won. But heedless of her question he had run across the road to sell papers to some men who had come out of a public-house. She must not give William the paper and wait for him to read the news to her. If the news were bad the shock might kill him. She must learn first what the news was, so that her face and manner might prepare him for the worst if need be. So she offered the paper to the porter and asked him to tell her. "Bramble, King of Trumps, Young Hopeful," he read out.

"Are you sure that Chasuble hasn't won?"

"Of course I'm sure, there it is."

"I can't read," she said as she turned away.

The news had stunned her; the world seemed to lose reality; she was uncertain what to do, and several times repeated to herself, "There's nothing for it but to go up and tell him. I don't see what else I can do." The staircase was very steep; she climbed it slowly, and stopped at the first landing and looked out of the window. A poor hollow-chested creature, the wreck of a human being, struggled up behind her. He had to rest several times, and in the hollow building his cough sounded loud and hollow. "It isn't generally so loud as that," she thought, and wondered how she could tell William the news. "He wanted to see Jack grow up to be a man. He thought that we might all go to Egypt, and that he'd get quite well there, for there's plenty of sunshine there, but now he'll have to make up his mind to die in the November fogs." Her thoughts came strangely clear, and she was astonished at her indifference, until a sudden revulsion of feeling took her as she was going up the last flight. She couldn't tell him the news; it was too cruel. She let the patient pass her, and when alone on the landing she looked down into the depth. She thought she'd like to fall over; anything rather than to do what she knew she must do. But her cowardice only endured for a moment, and with a firm step she walked into the corridor. It seemed to cross the entire building, and was floored and wainscoted with the same brown varnished wood as the staircase. There were benches along the walls; and emaciated and worn-out men lay on the long cane chairs in the windowed recesses by which the passage was lighted. The wards, containing sometimes three, sometimes six or seven beds, opened on to this passage. The doors of the wards were all open, and as she passed along she started at the sight of a boy sitting up in bed. His head had been shaved, and only a slight bristle covered the crown. The head and face were a large white mass with two eyes.

At the end of the passage there was a window; and William sat there reading a book. He saw her before she saw him, and when she caught sight of him she stopped, holding the paper loose before her between finger and thumb, and as she approached she saw that her manner had already broken the news to him.

"I see that she didn't win," he said.

"No, dear, she didn't win. We wasn't lucky this time next time—"

"There is no next time, at least for me. I shall be far away from here when flat racing begins again. The November fogs will do for me, I feel that they will. I hope there'll be no lingering, that's all. Better to know the worst and make up your mind. So I have to go, have I? So there's no hope, and I shall be under ground before the next meeting. I shall never lay or take the odds again. It do seem strange. If only that mare had won. I knew damned well she wouldn't if I came here."

Then, catching sight of the pained look on his wife's face, he said, "I don't suppose it made no difference; it was to be, and what has to be has to be. I've got to go under ground. I felt it was to be all along. Egypt would have done me no good; I never believed in it – only a lot of false hope. You don't think what I say is true. Look 'ere, do you know what book this is? This is the Bible; that'll prove to you that I knew the game was up. I knew, I can't tell you how, but I knew the mare wouldn't win. You always seems to know. Even when I backed her I didn't feel about her like I did about the other one, and ever since I've been feeling more and more sure that is wasn't to be. Somehow it didn't seem likely, and to-day something told me that the game was up, so I asked for this book. . . . There's wonderful, beautiful things in it."

"There is, indeed, Bill; and I hope you won't get tired of it, but will go on reading it."

"It's extraordinary how consoling it is. Listen to this. Isn't it beautiful;

ain't them words heavenly?"

"They is, indeed. I knew you'd come to God at last."

"I'm afraid I've not led a good life. I wouldn't listen to you when you used to tell me of the lot of harm the betting used to bring on the poor people what used to come to our place. There's Sarah, I suppose she's out of prison by this. You've seen nothing of her, I suppose?"

"No, nothing."

"There was Ketley."

"No, Bill, don't let's think about it. If you're truly sorry, God will forgive."

"Do you think He will – and the others that we know nothing about? I wouldn't listen to you; I was headstrong, but I understand it all now. My eyes 'ave been opened. Them pious folk that got up the prosecution knew what they was about. I forgive them one and all."

William coughed a little. The conversation paused, and the cough was repeated down the corridor. Now it came from the men lying on the long cane chairs; now from the poor emaciated creature, hollow cheeks, brown eyes and beard, who had just come out of his ward and had sat down on a bench by the wall. Now it came from an old man six feet high, with snow-white hair. He sat near them, and worked assiduously at a piece of tapestry. "It'll be better when it's cut," he said to one of the nurses, who had stopped to compliment him on his work; "It'll be better when it's cut." Then the cough came from one of the wards, and Esther thought of the fearsome boy sitting bolt up, his huge tallow-like face staring through the silence of the room. A moment after the cough came from her husband's lips, and they looked at each other. Both wanted to speak, and neither knew what to say. At last William spoke.

"I was saying that I never had that feeling about Chasuble that you 'as about a winner. Did she run second? Just like my luck if she did. Let me see the paper."

Esther handed it to him.

"Bramble, a fifty to one chance, not one man in a hundred backed her; King of Trumps, there was some place money lost on him; Young Hopeful, a rank outsider. What a day for the bookies!"

"You mustn't think of them things no more," said Esther. "You've got the Book; it'll do you more good."

"If I'd only have thought of Bramble. I could have had a hundred to one against Matchbox and Bramble coupled."

"What's the use of thinking of things that's over? We should think of the future."

"If I'd only been able to hedge that bet I should have been able to leave you something to go on with, but now, when everything is paid for, you'll have hardly a five-pound note. You've been a good wife to me, and I've been a bad husband to you."

"Bill, you mustn't speak like that. You must try to make your peace with God. Think of Him. He'll think of us that you leave behind. I've always had faith in Him. He'll not desert me."

Her eyes were quite dry; the instinct of life seemed to have left her. They spoke some little while longer, until it was time for visitors to leave the hospital. It was not until she got into the Fulham Road that tears began to run down her cheeks; they poured faster and faster, like rain after long dry weather. The whole world disappeared in a mist of tears. And so overcome was she by her grief that she had to lean against the railings, and the passers-by turned and looked at her curiously.

A GAMBLER

Paul Bourget

Paul Bourget was a disciple of the French philosopher, Taine, and the sternly moralistic tone of much of his writing clearly reflects the latter's influence.

This short story is concerned with the fascination that gambling has for the novice and of the fatal results that can ensue. It is written with a characteristic messianic fervor and is reminiscent of the work of the Russian writers of the period.

ON LEAVING THE THEATRE I went to the club, and there I loitered by the baccarat table. I watched, perched up on one of those high chairs used by players who cannot get near the green cloth, or by curious idlers like myself. It was, in the language of the *cercle*, a good game. The banker, a handsome young man in evening dress, with a gardenia in his coat, had lost about three thousand louis. His man-about-town mask struggled against the betrayal of any emotion; but the words dropped dryly from his lips; and he would not have chewed so nervously at the stump of his extinguished cigar if his thought and imagination had not been all engrossed in the cold frenzy of gaming. Opposite him was a person with white hair, a professional gambler, who acted as croupier. He, on the contrary, took no pains to conceal his bad temper at the turn of his luck, which, hand after hand, diminished the pile of counters before him. But the greatest joviality lighted up the countenances of the punters, who, seated at the table, spread out their winnings and marked with a pencil on a piece of paper the alternation of the deal, with that superstition the most sceptical cannot avoid the moment they touch a card. Certainly there is a fascination in every struggle, a seven against an eight, or a king against an ace, that rivets our curiosity; for there we were round those players, some fifty or so of us, following the game most intently, and never noticing how the night was slipping by.

Some philosopher has still to explain that curious inertia of the small hours to which, in Paris, so many men are liable; no matter where, so long as it is away from their own quarters, they will rest immobile from work or pleasure. For my part I do not regret in the least having given over that particular night to the unhealthy charm of midnight watches, for, had I gone home properly at a respectable hour, I should not have seen my friend, the painter Miraut, in the supper-room taking his little bowl of soup all by himself; he would not have offered to drop me at my door, and then I should never have heard the gambling story he told me, which I wrote down next morning as well as I could, and which he has now given me permission to retell.

"What the devil were you doing at the club so late?" he asked me. "You did not have supper there?"

"Watching the play," I answered. "I left young Lautrec getting on nicely; he had lost to the tune of sixty thousand . . ."

The carriage rocked as I pronounced these words. I saw Miraut side-face, lighting his cigarette. I took in again his air of Francis the First – the Titian portrait in the Louvre – a profile whose beauty was but amplified and filled out by the fifty summers it had seen. Is it not strange that with his solid build, his broad shoulders, his expression of greedy, almost gluttonous sensuality, he should remain the most exquisite painter of flowers and of women? Add that the most musical of voices comes from his gladiator chest, that his hands – I remarked them afresh as he manoeuvred the match and the cigarette – have a delicacy almost feminine.

I know very well, from experience, that my weather-beaten friend has real warmth in his heart, and I was not much astonished at the melancholy confidence I involuntarily evoked by my remarks on the game of baccarat. Fortunately he had plenty of time to tell me the story.

As we approached the Seine the fog became denser, the carriage went only at a walk, and my companion let himself go, recalling for me a story deeply buried in his memory. Policemen passed hither and thither carrying torches; other torches were burning along the coping of the bridge over which we were passing, and running over the stonework in streams of flaming resin; fantastic silhouettes of other carriages that passed ours, in the filthy black fog pierced here and there with the moving lights in the street, no doubt heightened the impression of the past to which my friend abandoned himself, for little by little his voice became softer and lower, as if in spirit he was drifting far, far away from me. Now and then I interrupted him an instant, but no more than gently to excite his memory.

"I have never," he began, "played but twice, and – will you believe me? – I cannot to this day even bear to look at players. There are moments, you know, one's nerves are not always equally steady, when the very sight of a card forces me to leave the room. Ah! what it means to me, those two games! . . . a terrible recollection. . . ."

"Who has not similarly?" I interrupted. "I was present when our poor friend Paul Durien thought fit to quarrel over a doubtful point in that very club we have just quitted; and then that ridiculous duel . . . and we laid him in the earth four days after I had pressed his hand up there, before that very green table. . . . There is always tragedy more or less connected with cards; crime and suicide and dishonour. . . . But somehow nothing can prevent one going back to them; just as in Spain one goes again and again to bull-fights, for all the horses ripped up, the wounded picadors, the tortured and slaughtered bull."

"That may be," resumed Miraut, "provided one has not been a party to such a tragedy; which is precisely my case. Oh! and the circumstances were so simple! . . . When you have heard them you will understand that the most innocent proposal of bezique gives me a sickness of horror such as a man would experience in a rifle range if he had once killed someone by accident while cleaning a gun. . . . It was in the first year of my joining the club, in 1872; the year also of my first success at the Salon. . . ."

"Your Ophelia among the flowers? . . . How well I remember it! . . . I can still see that knot of pale roses against the fair hair, roses of a pallor so blond, so tender, and the roses that lay upon her heart, black roses like splashes of blood. . . . Who has that picture, by the way?"

"A New York banker," said the painter, heaving a sigh; "he paid forty thousand for it, and I sold it at the time for fifteen hundred. . . . Ah! I was not then the fortunate painter of whom your malicious *alter ego* Claude Larcher could say: 'Happy Miraut, to look all day at an American girl and get fifteen thousand francs for his trouble!' . . . Between you and me he might have found a fitter subject than an old friend for his pleasantries. . . . *Enfin*, God rest his soul. But if I mention figures," he continued, laying his hand upon my arm to check the impetuous defence I was ready to make of the memory of dear Claude, "do not think I wish to boast of my commercial value. No. Only those fifteen hundred francs have to do with what I am telling you. Imagine that I had never in my life before handled such a sum. I had had a very hard time of it. When I came to Paris it was with a little subsidy from my native township, a thousand francs a year, and for six years I had to do what I could with that alone . . . practically. . . ."

"I have known something of such hardship," I said, "but not for long. Did you ever go to Polydore's, Rue Monsieur le Prince, like us, where you can manage to get a *déjeuner* for eighteen sous? When next you see Jacques Molan and he begins to bore you with his society women, and the exquisite tone of his next novel, just you ask him about Polydore. It won't take long, and you will be rid of him in five minutes. . . ."

"We resolved the problem by communism," resumed the painter. "Some comrades and I took pot-luck together. The sweetheart of one of us, who had formerly been a cook – pardon, but it is a fact – managed two meals a day for us, at the rate of forty francs a month. Fifteen francs for a bedroom. No attendance. I used to make my own bed. So, sixty francs for essentials. I dressed like a beggar, and I never knew the luxury of an omnibus. The others lived in the same style, and we did not do so badly on the whole. There was Tardif the sculptor, Sudre the animal painter, Rivals the engraver, and then the most talented of the lot, the 'steward' – our housekeeper was known as the 'stewardess' – Ladrat. . . ."

"Ladrat? Ladrat?" said I, trying to recall. "I know that name."

"You read it in the papers," continued the painter, whose face was gradually darkening; "But I shall come to that. This Ladrat, who carried off all the prizes at the school, was already the victim of the terrible vice. He drank. What would you expect? In the loose life we led, half-workmen, and everlastingly mixed up with models and work-people, we were exposed to plenty of low temptations, and to that particular one most of all. Ladrat fell to it. I only tell you this that you may not judge me too harshly presently. It was this lamentable proclivity that spoilt his chance for the Prix de Rome. He soaked himself so thoroughly in drink that the composition he had sketched out with the hand of master was a pitiable fiasco when he completed it. In short, in 1872 he was the only one of the original company who was still in the gutter – and a dirty gutter it was. He had become what we call a *tapeur*, the man who wanders from one studio to another, and borrows five francs here, five francs there, with the most distinct determination never to repay. That style of life can go on for years."

"And I suppose he thanked you with a kick," I replied, "like that Legrimandet whom I knew, who never went to see Mareuil without asking him to remember the grotto – that was his formula – and without insulting him afterwards to save his dignity. One day, for example, he found him correcting the proofs of an article that was about to appear. He begged. André acceded. 'Monsieur,' he said, as the white coin slipped into his pocket, 'would you like to know how to determine whether a writer has talent? You have only to know if the journals take his copy. If they do it is all up with him, he is a mediocrity. . . . Good-bye. . . .' That is the sort of man?"

"No," said Miraut, "Ladrat was not a man of that kind. He was thankful, he burst into tears, swore he would work, and went off to the first café to soak himself with absinthe. Then he was ashamed of himself, and would not reappear for several days. Besides, he never borrowed very much – never more than five francs. So I was not a little surprised one afternoon coming in to find a long letter from him, asking me for no less a sum that two hundred francs. More than six months had elapsed since last I had seen him, and he rehearsed to me at length how, during those six months, he had struggled against his besetting vice, how he had not drunk, how he had tried to work, but that his strength had failed him, that his wife was ill – he still lived with the 'stewardess' – really one of those piteous letters of entreaty that make one's heart turn sick."

"When one takes it all in," I insinuated, "for in ten years of Paris one gets so many such letters, and out of the lot, perhaps two genuine ones. . . ."

"Better to risk being a dupe to all the others than to refuse those two," said the painter. "Besides, I had not the slightest doubt of Ladrat's sincerity. It happened that the same day I had received the fifteen hundred francs for the Ophelia. I have always been very scrupulous with regard to money. I had no debts, and I had in a drawer about as much again set aside for an evil hour. My studio was certain, my wardrobe was well stocked for that year at all events. I remember how in thought I drew up an inventory of my position, as I brushed my dress things to turn up at one of my first dinners, one of those dinners to which one goes as a lion, with the appetite of a vagrant, and the *amour-propre* of a schoolboy. One credits equally the genuineness of the wines and the sincerity of the eulogy. All the time I compared my own enviable position with that of the poor devil I had once lived with, and I had one of those generous impulses that come to youth as readily as its grace and lightheartedness. I took ten louis, put them in an envelope, addressed it, and called the concierge. If that man had been in his place my poor friend would have had the money that very evening, but the concierge was away on some errand. 'It will do to-morrow,' I said to myself, and I went off, leaving the envelope all ready on the table. My resolution was so firm on the subject that I experienced in advance all the complacency of conscience that a generous action vouchsafes. The sensation is perhaps born of petty vanity, but it is very human; there are many others more ignoble; witness the one that succeeded, for me, the same evening, and almost immediately.

"At the house where I dined I sat between two most elegant women, who rivalled one another in the fuss and flattery they bestowed upon me. In short, I went away towards eleven o'clock helpless in a vertigo of fatuity, feeling myself master of the whole world; I found myself at our club, which then occupied a house in the Place Vendôme, escorted by a man who had been dining at the same house and who had undertaken to chaperon me. I had not set foot there during the six weeks I had been a member and I did not know a soul. Two painters had proposed me, and the prospect of the annual exhibition was the only thing that had induced me to stand for election. We came into the big room. I was so childishly simple that I asked my mentor what game it was that attracted such a swarm of people about the table. He laughed, and in a few words explained to me the rules of baccarat. 'That doesn't tempt you?' he said. 'Why not?' I replied, a little vexed at my ignorance, 'except that I have no money about me.' He explained to me, much amused all the time, that I had only to go to the secretary and write my name to get three thousand francs, on the promise to repay within twenty-four hours. I understood afterwards that this person had simply tempted me for what the proverbial novice's luck might bring to himself. But I would have tempted myself without his help. I was in the state where one cries, like that other, to the ferryman in the storm, 'You carry Caesar and his fortune. . . .' Oh! a very small fortune, for as I sat down to the table, I whispered to my companion: 'I am going to sign for five louis, and, if I lose, I am off. . . .'"

"And you lost, but stayed on. There is an echo to that in my own memory," I replied, laughing.

"It was not quite as simple as that," answered Miraut. "My tempter, who sat beside me, told me to await my hand. I obeyed. The hand came to me. I threw down mine. I had risked my five louis. 'Double,' whispered my adviser. I doubled. I threw down eight. I doubled again, seven, and I had won. Then I passed six times running. At the seventh hand, still advised by my companion, I staked a louis only. I lost. But I had about three thousand francs before me.

"My companion, who had won about the same sum, rose up and said to me, 'If you are wise, you will come now.' But I did not listen to him. The fascination I felt was too strong for me to tear myself away so easily. I am not of those you call analysts of the mind, whom I call – what is the word I want? – hair-splitters, egoists – and I do not pass my life dissecting my thoughts and emotions. Pardon me then if I only explain myself to you crudely, and by the first images that come to my fancy. During the short time I had been winning, all my being was invaded by intoxicating pride; a sort of exalted consciousness of my personality stirred me, buoyed me up. I have experienced a similar emotion swimming in deep sea. The vast restless mass of water that threatens you and rocks you on its face, that you dominate with your own strength; yes, that is the exact symbol of what gambling was for me in its first phase, victory; for I won again in the same proportions as at first, and again and again. I risked heavy sums upon my own hands, and only trivial stakes on those of others; but every time I touched the cards my luck was so invariable that there was a dead silence around me until I threw down, and then a thrill of admiration.

"Perhaps without that admiration I could have had the courage to desist. Alas! I have always had the confidence of the very devil; it has led me into a hundred scrapes already, and no doubt, in spite of my grey hair, has others yet in store for me. I know it, mark you, I take it into account; but, not a bit of good, given a gallery, I cannot bear that anyone should say, 'He has thrown up.' It is sublime to be like that when the scene is, say, at the bridge of Arcole, but at a baccarat table, and before the hazard of cards, it is idiotic; nevertheless my pride was so childish that after having shown off under a run of good luck, I would not bend before the turn of bad which I felt was approaching. For I *did* feel it: there came a certain moment when I knew I was going to lose, and the faith in my fortune,

which previously had made me take up the cards with absolute confidence, was suddenly eclipsed. I was destined in that one sitting to
experience all the emotions gambling can give to its devotees; after the
intoxication of gain comes the sharp and exquisite intoxication of losing.
For, yes, such it is. You know the saying, 'At play, after the pleasure of loss
. . .' I can find no other words to explain to you that sort of vitiated ardour,
that mixture of hope and despair, of cowardice and obstinacy. One counts
on overcoming misfortune, knowing all the time that one will be beaten.
One loses the faculty of reasoning, one plays on hands that one sees are
absurd. And the counters dwindle, first the red, then the white, and fresh
vouchers have to be signed. After having had the habit during ten years of
looking hard at thirty-five sous for a cab, as I had had, one stakes five
hundred, a thousand francs, without hesitation. But I will sum it all up in
one word: I had gone into the club at eleven o'clock, at two I turned the
key of my door, having lost the entire three thousand francs to my credit;
and that, as I told you, was practically all I had."

"Ah, well," I said to him, "if you did not become a gambler after that
blow, it is because you were not born for it. It was enough to have ruined
you for life."

"You are right," replied Miraut; "when I awoke next morning from the
dejected sleep that follows such sensations, all the scenes of the previous
night came back to my memory, and I had two ideas only; first, to take my
revenge the same evening, and second, to stake differently in accordance
with the experience I had gained. Mentally I replayed certain hands that I
had lost but ought to have won. Suddenly my eyes fell on the envelope
addressed to Ladrat that was lying on the table. An involuntary calculation passed in my brain; surely the gift to Ladrat of the money he asked for
would be a senseless sacrifice. When I had paid the three thousand francs I
owed I should have scarcely anything left. In order to put something in my
pocket that would permit me yo return to the club in the evening – and I
felt that it was out of my power not to return – I should have to borrow
from a picture-dealer, to get rid of some of my studies. In that way I should
raise fifty louis, ten of which I was going to set aside for that good-for-
nothing, for that drunkard, that liar! For I wished to convince myself that
his letter was nothing but a tissue of falsehood. I took it up and re-read it.
Ah! its tone tore my heart afresh. But no. I did not want to hear that voice,
so I jumped up immediately and dashed off a letter of refusal – swiftly and
dryly I wrote it, in order to put the irreparable between my old comrade
and my pity. The letter gone, I felt a certain amount of shame and

remorse; but I deadened my feelings as well as I could, going about the business of raising the money which lay before me. 'Besides,' I said to myself, to calm my conscience absolutely, 'If I win I shall be able to send the sum to Ladrat to-morrow – and I am going to win.'"

"And did you?" I asked, as he stopped.

"Yes," he replied, in a voice that was quite different, "more than five hundred louis, but next day it was too late. Immediately on receiving my letter of refusal, Ladrat, who had not lied at all, was seized no doubt with the madness of despair. His mistress and he took the fatal resolution and suffocated themselves. They were found dead upon their bed, and it was I – I, mark you, who had the door forced. I had the two hundred francs with me. . . . Yes, it was too late!. . . That is how it is you remember having read the name of Ladrat in the papers. Do you understand now why the sight of a card fills me with horror?"

"But think," I said, "if you had sent him the money in the evening, that might have saved him for a month, or perhaps two; but sooner or later he would have gone down, his vice would have reasserted itself, and he would have finished in the same way."

"That is quite possible," replied the painter, "but, you see, in life one must not be the drop that makes the cup overflow."

A GAMBLER'S DEATH

William Thackeray

One of the great figures of nineteenth century English literature, Thackeray was nevertheless not an immediate success and he spent nearly twenty-five years of his life in journalistic drudgery before rising to prominence in 1846 with the publication of *Vanity Fair*. The scion of a wealthy Yorkshire family, on leaving Cambridge in 1820 he had inherited a not inconsiderable fortune but soon dissipated it through gambling, bad investments and general extravagance. Thereafter he had no option but to write practically nonstop in order to keep his wife and family.

Thackeray has retained his popularity to the present day because of the essentially affectionate view of human nature expressed in his writings. In this short story from *A Paris Sketchbook*, Thackeray delineates the rise and fall of a young gambler with great understanding and sympathy and his death possesses all the elements of great tragedy – as well as a terrible warning to would-be gamblers.

ANYBODY who was at C— school, some twelve years since, must recollect Jack Attwood: he was the most dashing lad in the place, with more money in his pocket than belonged to the whole fifth form in which we were companions.

When he was about fifteen, Jack suddenly retreated from C—, and presently we heard that he had a commission in a cavalry regiment, and was to have a great fortune from his father, when that old gentleman should die. Jack himself came to confirm these stories a few months after, and paid a visit to his old school chums. He had laid aside his little school-jacket, and inky corduroys, and now appeared in such a splendid military suit as won the respect of all of us. His hair was dripping with oil, his hands were covered with rings, he had a dusky down over his upper lip, which looked not unlike a mustachio, and a multiplicity of frogs and braiding on his surtout, which would have sufficed to lace a field-marshal. When old Swishtail, the usher, passed, in his seedy black coat and gaiters, Jack gave him such a look of contempt as set us all a-laughing: in fact, it was his turn to laugh now; for he used to roar very stoutly some months before, when Swishtail was in the custom of belabouring him with his great cane.

Jack's talk was all about the regiment and the fine fellows in it: how he had ridden a steeple-chase with Captain Boldero, and licked him at the last hedge; and how he had very nearly fought a duel with Sir George Grig, about dancing with Lady Mary Slamken at a ball. "I soon made the baronet know what it was to deal with a man of the n—th," said Jack; – "dammee, sir, when I lugged out my barkers, and talked of fighting across the mess-room table, Grig turned as pale as a sheet, or as —"

"Or as you used to do, Attwood, when Swishtail hauled you up," piped out little Hicks, the foundation-boy.

It was beneath Jack's dignity to thrash anybody, now, but a grown-up baronet; so he let off little Hicks, and passed over the general titter which was raised at his expense. However, he entertained us with his histories about lords and ladies, and so-and-so "of ours," until we thought him one of the greatest men in his Majesty's service, and until the school-bell rung; when, with a heavy heart, we got our books together, and marched in to be whacked by old Swishtail. I promise you he revenged himself on us for Jack's contempt of him: I got, that day, at least twenty cuts to my share, which ought to have belonged to Cornet Attwood, of the n—th dragoons.

When we came to think more coolly over our quondam schoolfellow's swaggering talk and manner, we were not quite so impressed by his merits as at his first appearance among us. We recollected how he used, in former times, to tell us great stories, which were so monstrously improbable that the smallest boy in the school would scout at them; how often we caught him tripping in facts, and how unblushingly he admitted his little errors in the score of veracity. He and I, though never great friends, had been close companions: I was Jack's form-fellow (we fought with amazing emulation for the *last* place in the class); but still I was rather hurt at the coolness of my old comrade, who had forgotten all our former intimacy, in his steeple-chases with Captain Boldero, and his duel with Sir George Grig.

Nothing more was heard of Attwood for some years; a tailor one day came down to C—, who had made clothes for Jack in his school-days, and furnished him with regimentals: he produced a long bill for one hundred and twenty pounds and upwards, and asked where news might be had of his customer. Jack was in India, with his regiment, shooting tigers and jackalls, no doubt. Occasionally, from that distant country, some magnificent rumour would reach us of his proceedings. Once I heard that he had been called to a court-martial for unbecoming conduct; another time, that he kept twenty horses, and won the gold plate at the Calcutta races. Presently, however, as the recollections of the fifth form wore away, Jack's image disappeared likewise, and I ceased to ask or to think about my college chum.

A year since, as I was smoking my cigar in the "Estaminet du Grand Balcon," an excellent smoking-shop, where the tobacco is unexceptionable, and the Hollands of singular merit, a dark-looking, thick-set man, in a greasy well-cut coat, with a shabby hat, cocked on one side of his dirty face, took the place opposite to me, at the little marble table, and called for brandy. I did not much admire the impudence or the appearance of my friend, nor the fixed stare with which he chose to examine me. At last, he thrust a great greasy hand across the table, and said, "Titmarsh, do you forget your old friend Attwood?"

I confess my recognition of him was not so joyful as on the day ten years

earlier, when he had come, bedizened with lace and gold rings, to see us at
C— school: a man in the tenth part of a century learns a deal of worldly
wisdom, and his hand, which goes naturally forward to seize the gloved
finger of a millionnaire, or a milor, draws instinctively back from a dirty
fist, encompassed by a ragged wristband and a tattered cuff. But Attwood
was in nowise so backward; and the iron squeeze with which he shook my
passive paw, proved that he was either very affectionate or very poor.
"You, my dear sir, who are reading this history, know very well the great
art of shaking hands, recollect how you shook Lord Dash's hand the other
day, and how you shook *off* poor Blank, when he came to borrow five
pounds of you."

However, the genial influence of the Hollands speedily dissipated anything like coolness between us: and, in the course of an hour's conversation, we became almost as intimate as when we were suffering together
under the ferule of old Swishtail. Jack told me that he had quitted the
army in disgust; and that his father, who was to leave him a fortune, had
died ten thousand pounds in debt: he did not touch upon his own
circumstances; but I could read them in his elbows, which were peeping
through his old frock. He talked a great deal, however, of runs of luck,
good and bad; and related to me an infallible plan for breaking all the
play-banks in Europe – a great number of old tricks; – and a vast quantity
of gin-punch was consumed on the occasion; so long, in fact, did our conversation continue, that, I confess it with shame, the sentiment, or something stronger, quite got the better of me, and I have, to this day, no sort of
notion how our palaver concluded. – Only, on the next morning, I did not
possess a certain five-pound note, which, on the previous evening, was in
my sketch-book (by far the prettiest drawing by the way in the collection);
but there, instead, was a strip of paper, thus inscribed: –

I.O.U. Five Pounds

JOHN ATTWOOD
Late of the n—th dragoons.

I suppose Attwood borrowed the money, from this remarkable and
ceremonious acknowledgment on his part: had I been sober, I would just
as soon have lent him the nose on my face; for, in my then circumstances,
the note was of much more consequence to me.

As I lay, cursing my ill fortune, and thinking how on earth I should
manage to subsist for the next two months, Attwood burst into my little
garret – his face strangely flushed – singing and shouting as if it had been

the night before. "Titmarsh," cried he, "you are my preserver! – my best friend! Look here, and here, and here!" And at every word Mr Attwood produced a handful of gold, or a glittering heap of five-franc pieces, or a bundle of greasy, dusky bank-notes, more beautiful than either silver or gold; – he had won thirteen thousand francs after leaving me at midnight in my garret. He separated my poor little all, of six pieces, from this shining and imposing collection; and the passion of envy entered my soul: I felt far more anxious now than before, although starvation was then staring me in the face; I hated Attwood for *cheating* me out of all this wealth. Poor fellow! it had been better for him had he never seen a shilling of it.

However, a grand breakfast at the Café Anglais dissipated my chagrin; and I will do my friend the justice to say, that he nobly shared some portion of his good fortune with me. As far as the creature comforts were concerned, I feasted as well as he, and never was particular as to settling my share of the reckoning.

Jack now changed his lodgings; had cards, with Captain Attwood engraved on them, and drove about a prancing cab-horse, as tall as the Giraffe at the Jardin des Plantes; he had as many frogs on his coat as in the old days, and frequented all the flash restaurateurs and boarding-houses of the capital. Madame de Saint Laurent, and Madame la Baronne de Vaudry, and Madame la Comtesse de Don Jonville, ladies of the highest rank, who keep a *société choisie*, and condescend to give dinners, at five francs a-head, vied with each other in their attentions to Jack. His was the wing of the fowl, and the largest portion of the Charlotte-Russe; his was the place at the ecarté table, where the Countess would ease him nightly of a few pieces, declaring that he was the most charming cavalier, la fleur d'Albion. Jack's society, it may be seen, was not very select; nor, in truth, were his inclinations: he was a careless, dare-devil, Macheath kind of fellow, who might be seen daily with a wife on each arm.

It may be supposed, that, with the life he led, his five hundred pounds of winnings would not last him long; nor did they: but, for some time, his luck never deserted him: and his cash, instead of growing lower, seemed always to maintain a certain level; – he played every night.

Of course, such a humble fellow as I, could not hope for a continued acquaintance and intimacy with Attwood. He grew overbearing and cool, I thought; at any rate I did not admire my situation, as his follower and dependant, and left his grand dinner, for a certain ordinary, where I could partake of five capital dishes for ninepence. Occasionally, however,

Attwood favoured me with a visit, or gave me a drive behind his great cab-horse. He had formed a whole host of friends besides. There was Fips, the barrister; heaven knows what he was doing at Paris; and Gortz, the West Indian, who was there on the same business, and Flapper, a medical student, – all these three I met one night at Flapper's rooms, where Jack was invited, and a great "spread" was laid in honour of him.

Jack arrived rather late – he looked pale and agitated; and, though he ate no supper, he drank raw brandy in such a manner as made Flapper's eyes wink: the poor fellow had but three bottles, and Jack bid fair to swallow them all. However, the West Indian generously remedied the evil, and producing a napoleon, we speedily got the change for it in the shape of four bottles of champagne.

Our supper was uproariously harmonious; Fips sung the good "Old English gentleman;" Jack, the "British grenadiers;" and your humble servant, when called upon, sang that beautiful ditty, "When the bloom is on the rye," in a manner that drew tears from every eye, except Flapper's, who was asleep, and Jack's, who was singing the "Bay of Biscay, O," at the same time. Gortz and Fips were all the time lunging at each other with a pair of single-sticks, the barrister having a very strong notion that he was Richard the Third.

At last Fips hit the West Indian such a blow across his sconce, that the other grew furious; he seized a champagne bottle, which was, providentially, empty, and hurled it across the room at Fips: had that celebrated barrister not bowed his head at the moment, the Queen's Bench would have lost one of its most eloquent practitioners.

Fips stood as straight as he could; his cheek was pale with wrath. "M-m-ister Go-gortz," he said, "I always heard you were a blackguard; now I can pr-pr-peperove it. Flapper, your pistols! every ge-ge-genlmn knows what I mean."

Young Mr Flapper had a small pair of pocket-pistols, which the tipsy barrister had suddenly remembered, and with which he proposed to sacrifice the West Indian. Gortz was nothing loath, but was quite as valorous as the lawyer.

Attwood who in spite of his notations, seemed the soberest man of the party, had much enjoyed the scene, until this sudden demand for the weapons. "Pshaw!" said he, eagerly, "don't give these men the means of murdering each other; sit down, and let us have another song."

But they would not be still; and Flapper forthwith produced his pistol-case, and opened it, in order that the duel might take place on the spot. –

There were no pistols there! "I beg your pardon," said Attwood, looking much confused; "I – I took the pistols home with me, to clean them!"

I don't know what there was in his tone, or in the words, but we were sobered all of a sudden. Attwood was conscious of the singular effect produced by him, for he blushed, and endeavoured to speak of other things, but we could not bring our spirits back to the mark again, and soon separated for the night. As we issued into the street, Jack took me aside, and whispered "Have you a napoleon, Titmarsh, in your purse?" Alas! I was not so rich. My reply was, that I was coming to Jack, only in the morning, to borrow a similar sum.

He did not make any reply, but turned away homeward: I never heard him speak another word.

Two mornings after (for none of our party met on the day succeeding the supper), I was awakened by my porter, who brought a pressing letter from Mr Gortz.

DEAR T.,

I wish you would come over here to breakfast. There's a row about Attwood.

Yours truly,
SOLOMON GORTZ.

I immediately set forward to Gortz's; he lived in the Rue du Heldes, a few doors from Attwood's new lodging. If the reader is curious to know the house in which the catastrophe of this history took place, he has but to march some twenty doors down from the Boulevard des Italiens, when he will see a fine door, with a naked Cupid shooting at him from the hall, and a Venus beckoning him up the stairs.

On arriving at the West Indian's, at about midday (it was a Sunday morning), I found that gentleman in his dressing-gown, discussing, in the company of Mr Fips, a large plate of *bifteck aux pommes*.

"Here's a pretty row!" said Gortz, quoting from his letter; – "Attwood's off – have a bit of beefsteak?"

"What do you mean?" exclaimed I, adopting the familiar phraseology of my acquaintances: – "Attwood off? – has he cut his stick?"

"Not bad," said the feeling and elegant Fips – "not such a bad guess, my boy; but he has not exactly *cut his stick*."

"What then?"

"*Why, his throat.*" The man's mouth was full of bleeding beef as he uttered this gentlemanly witticism.

I wish I could say that I was myself in the least affected by the news. I did not joke about it like my friend Fips; this was more for propriety's sake than for feeling's: but for my old school acquaintance, the friend of my early days, the merry associate of the last few months, I own, with shame, that I had not a tear or a pang. In some German tale, there is an account of a creature, most beautiful and bewitching, whom all men admire and follow; but this charming and fantastic spirit only leads them, one by one, into ruin, and then leaves them. The novelist, who describes her beauty, says that his heroine is a fairy, and *has no heart*. I think the intimacy which is begotten over the wine bottle, is a spirit of this nature; I never knew a good feeling come from it, or an honest friendship made by it; it only entices men, and ruins them; it is only a phantom of friendship and feeling, called up by the delirious blood, and the wicked spells of the wine.

But to drop this strain of moralizing (in which the writer is not too anxious to proceed, for he cuts in it a most pitiful figure), we passed sundry criticisms upon poor Attwood's character, expressed our horror at his death, which sentiment was fully proved by Mr Fips, who declared that the notion of it made him feel quite faint, and was obliged to drink a large glass of brandy; and, finally, we agreed that we would go and see the poor fellow's corpse, and witness, if necessary, his burial.

Flapper, who had joined us, was the first to propose this visit: he said he did not mind the fifteen francs which Jack owed him for billiards, but that he was anxious to *get back his pistol*. Accordingly, we sallied forth, and speedily arrived at the hotel which Attwood inhabited still.

He had occupied, for a time, very fine apartments in this house; and it was only on arriving there that day, that we found he had been gradually driven from his magnificent suite of rooms, *au premier*, to a little chamber in the fifth story: – we mounted, and found him.

It was a little shabby room, with a few articles of ricketty furniture, and a bed in an alcove; the light from the one window was falling full upon the bed and the body.

Jack was dressed in a fine lawn shirt; he had kept it, poor fellow, *to die in*; for, in all his drawers and cupboards, there was not a single article of clothing; he had pawned everything by which he could raise a penny – desk, books, dressing-case, and clothes; and not a single half-penny was found in his possession.

He was lying as I have drawn him, one hand on his breast, the other falling towards the ground. There was an expression of perfect calm on the face, and no mark of blood to stain the side towards the light. On the other side, however, there was a great pool of black blood, and in it the pistol; it looked more like a toy than a weapon to take away the life of this vigorous young man. In his forehead, at the side, was a small black wound; Jack's life had passed through it; it was little bigger than a mole.

"Regardez un peu," said the landlady, *"Messieurs, il m'a gâté trois matelas, et il me doit quarante quatre francs."*

This was all his epitaph: he had spoiled three mattresses, and owed the landlady four-and-forty francs. In the whole world there was not a soul to love him or lament him. We, his friends, were looking at his body more as an object of curiosity, watching it with a kind of interest with which one follows the fifth act of a tragedy, and leaving it with the same feeling with which one leaves the theatre when the play is over and the curtain is down.

Beside Jack's bed, on his little "table de nuit," lay the remains of his last meal, and an open letter, which we read. It was from one of his suspicious acquaintances of former days, and ran thus: –

Où es tu, cher Jack? *why you not come and see me* – tu me dois de l'argent entends tu? – un chapeau, une cachemire, *a box of the Play.* Viens demain soir je t'attendrai, *at eight o'clock,* Passage des Panoramas. *My Sir is at his country.* Adieu à demain.

FIFINE.
Samedi.

I shuddered as I walked through this very Passage des Panoramas, in the evening. The girl was there, pacing to and fro, and looking in the countenance of every passer by, to recognise Attwood. "ADIEU A DEMAIN!'" – there was a dreadful meaning in the words, which the writer of them little knew. "Adieu à demain!" – the morrow was come, and the soul of the poor suicide was now in the presence of God. I dare not think of his fate; for, except in the fact of his poverty and desperation, was he worse than any of us, his companions, who had shared his debauches, and marched with him up to the very brink of the grave?

There is but one more circumstance to relate regarding poor Jack – his burial; it was of a piece with his death.

He was nailed into a paltry coffin, and buried, at the expense of the arrondissement, in a nook of the burial place, beyond the Barrière de l'Etoile. They buried him at six o'clock, of a bitter winter's morning, and it was with difficulty that an English clergyman could be found to read a service over his grave. The three men who have figured in this history, acted as Jack's mourners; and as the ceremony was to take place so early in the morning, these men sate up the night through, *and were almost drunk* as they followed his coffin to its resting place.

MORAL

"When we turned out in our great coats," said one of them afterwards, "reeking of cigars and brandy-and-water, d—e, sir, we quite frightened the old buck of a parson; he did not much like our company." After the ceremony was concluded, these gentlemen were very happy to get home to a warm and comfortable breakfast, and finished the day royally at Frascati's.

THE GAMBLER (1)

Fedor Dostoevsky

One of the great names of Russian literature, Dostoevsky pioneered the art of bringing psychological insight to bear on the novel, something which saw its fullest expression in his *Crime and Punishment*. Unfortunately, Dostoevsky's realism and his humanism soon brought him into conflict with the Czarist authorities, and he was arrested as a subversive and sentenced to four years in a Siberian prison camp.

A compulsive gambler all his life, Dostoevsky writes with deep personal understanding of the gambler's emotions in this extract from a novel called *The Gambler*. The hero is urged to play roulette, not for himself but for Polina with whom he is madly in love.

"LISTEN AND REMEMBER: take these seven hundred florins and go and play. Win me as much as you can at roulette; I must have money now, come what may."

Saying this, she called Nadenka and went into the Casino, where she joined the rest of the party. I turned into the first path to the left, wondering and reflecting. I felt as though I had had a blow on the head after the command to go and play roulette. Strange to say, I had plenty to think about, but I was completely absorbed in analysing the essential nature of my feeling towards Polina. It was true I had been more at ease during that fortnight's absence than I was now on the day of my return, though on the journey I had been as melancholy and restless as a madman, and at moments had even seen her in my dreams. Once, waking up in the train (in Switzerland), I began talking aloud, I believe, with Polina, which amused all the passengers in the carriage with me. And once more now I asked myself the question: "Do I love her?" and again I could not answer it, or, rather, I answered for the hundredth time that I hated her. Yes, she was hateful to me. There were moments (on every occasion at the end of our talks) when I would have given my life to strangle her! I swear if it had been possible on the spot to plunge a sharp knife in her bosom, I believe I should have snatched it up with relish. And yet I swear by all that's sacred that if at the Schlangenberg, at the fashionable peak, she really had said to me, "Throw yourself down," I should have thrown myself down at once, also with positive relish. I knew that. In one way or another it must be settled. All this she understood wonderfully well, and the idea that I knew, positively and distinctly, how utterly beyond my reach she was, how utterly impossible my mad dreams were of fulfilment – that thought, I am convinced, afforded her extraordinary satisfaction; if not, how could she, cautious and intelligent as she was, have been on such intimate and open terms with me? I believe she had hitherto looked on me as that empress of ancient times looked on the slave before whom she did not mind undressing because she did not regard him as a human being. Yes, often she did not regard me as a human being!

I had her commission, however, to win at roulette, at all costs. I had no time to consider why must I play, and why such haste, and what new scheme was hatching in that ever-calculating brain. Moreover, it was evident that during that fortnight new facts had arisen of which I had no idea yet. I must discover all that and get to the bottom of it and as quickly as possible. But there was no time now; I must go to roulette. . . .

I confess it was disagreeable to me. Though I had made up my mind that I would play, I had not proposed to play for other people. It rather threw me out of my reckoning, and I went into the gambling saloon with very disagreeable feelings. From the first glance I disliked everything in it. I cannot endure the flunkeyishness of the newspapers of the whole world, and especially our Russian papers, in which, almost every spring, the journalists write articles upon two things : first, on the extraordinary magnificence and luxury of the gambling saloons on the Rhine, and secondly, on the heaps of gold which are said to lie on the tables. They are not paid for it ; it is simply done from disinterested obsequiousness. There was no sort of magnificence in these trashy rooms, and not only were there no piles of gold lying on the table, but there was hardly any gold at all. No doubt some time, in the course of the season, some eccentric person, either an Englishman or an Asiatic of some sort, a Turk, perhaps (as it was that summer), would suddenly turn up and lose or win immense sums ; all the others play for paltry guldens, and on an average there is very little money lying on the tables.

As soon as I went into the gambling saloon (for the first time in my life), I could not for some time make up my mind to play. There was a crush besides. If I had been alone, even then, I believe, I should soon have gone away and not have begun playing. I confess my heart was beating and I was not cool. I knew for certain, and had made up my mind long before, that I should not leave Roulettenburg unchanged, that some radical and fundamental change would take place in my destiny ; so it must be and so it would be. Ridiculous as it may be that I should expect so much for myself from roulette, yet I consider even more ridiculous the conventional opinion accepted by all that it is stupid and absurd to expect anything from gambling. And why should gambling be worse than any other means of making money – for instance, commerce ? It is true that only one out of a hundred wins, but what is that to me ?

In any case I determined to look about me first and not to begin anything in earnest that evening. If anything did happen that evening it would happen by chance and be something slight, and I staked my money accordingly. Besides, I had to study the game ; for, in spite of the thousand descriptions of roulette which I had read so eagerly, I understood absolutely nothing of its working, until I saw it myself.

In the first place it all struck me as so dirty, somehow, morally horrid and dirty. I am not speaking at all of the greedy, uneasy faces which by dozens, even by hundreds, crowd round the gambling tables. I see absolutely nothing dirty in the wish to win as quickly and as much as possible. I always thought very stupid the answer of that fat and prosperous moralist, who replied to someone's excuse "that he played for a very small stake," "So much the worse, it is such petty covetousness." As though covetousness were not exactly the same, whether on a big scale or a petty one. It is a matter of proportion. What is paltry to Rothschild is wealth to me, and as for profits and winnings, people, not only at roulette, but everywhere, do nothing but try to gain or squeeze something out of one another. Whether profits or gains are nasty is a different question. But I am not solving that question here. Since I was myself possessed by an intense desire of winning, I felt as I went into the hall all this covetousness, and all this covetous filth if you like, in a sense congenial and convenient. It is most charming when people do not stand on ceremony with one another, but act openly and above-board. And, indeed, why deceive oneself? Gambling is a most foolish and imprudent pursuit! What was particularly ugly at first sight, in all the rabble round the roulette table, was the respect they paid to that pursuit, the solemnity and even reverence with which they all crowded round the tables. That is why a sharp distinction is drawn here between the kind of game that is *mauvais genre* and the kind that is permissible to well-bred people. There are two sorts of gambling: one the gentlemanly sort: the other the plebeian, mercenary sort, the game played by all sorts of riff-raff. The distinction is sternly observed here, and how contemptible this distinction really is! A gentleman may stake, for instance, five or ten louis d'or, rarely more; he may, however, stake as much as a thousand francs if he is very rich; but only for the sake of the play, simply for amusement, that is, simply to look on at the process of winning or of losing, but must on no account display an interest in winning. If he wins, he may laugh aloud, for instance; may make a remark to one of the bystanders; he may even put down another stake, and may even double it, but solely from curiosity, for the sake of watching and calculating the chances, and not from the plebeian desire to win. In fact, he must look on all gambling, roulette, *trente et quarante*, as nothing else than a pastime got up entirely for his amusement. He must not even suspect the greed for gain and the shifty dodges on which the bank depends. It would be extremely good form, too, if he should imagine that all the other gamblers, all the rabble, trembling over a gulden, were rich men and gentlemen like himself and were playing simply for their diversion and amusement. This complete ignorance of reality and innocent view of people would be, of course, extremely aristocratic. I have seen many mammas push forward their daughters, innocent and elegant Misses of fifteen and sixteen, and, giving them some gold coins, teach them how to play. The young lady wins or loses, invariably smiles and walks away, very well satisfied. Our General went up to the table with solid dignity; a flunkey rushed to hand him a chair, but he ignored the flunkey; he, very slowly and deliberately, took out his purse, very slowly and deliberately took three hundred francs in gold from his purse, staked them on the black, and won. He did not pick up his winnings, but left them on the table. Black turned up again; he didn't pick up his winnings that time either; and when, the third time, red turned up, he lost at once twelve hundred francs. He walked away with a smile and kept up his dignity. I a positive he was raging inwardly, and if the stake had been two or three times as much he would not have kept up his dignity but would have betrayed his feelings. A Frenchman did, however, before my eyes, win and lose as much as thirty thousand francs with perfect gaiety and no sign of emotion. A real gentleman should not show excitement even if he loses his whole fortune. Money ought to be so much below his gentlemanly dignity as to be scarcely worth noticing. Of course, it would have been extremely aristocratic not to notice the sordidness of all the rabble and all the sur-roundings. Sometimes, however, the opposite pose is no less aristocratic – to notice – that is, to look about one, even, perhaps, to stare through a lorgnette at the rabble; though always taking the rabble and the sordid-ness as nothing else but a diversion of a sort, as though it were a perform-ance got up for the amusement of gentlemen. One may be jostled in that crowd, but one must look about one with complete conviction that one is one-self a spectator and that one is in no sense part of it. Though, again, to look very attentively is not quite the thing; that, again, would not be gentlemanly because, in any case, the spectacle does not deserve much, or close, attention. And, in fact, few spectacles do deserve a gentleman's close attention. And yet it seemed to me that all this was deserving of very close attention, especially for one who had come not only to observe it, but sincerely and genuinely reckoned himself as one of the rabble. As for my hidden moral convictions, there is no place for them, of course, in my present reasonings. Let that be enough for the present. I speak to relieve my conscience. But I notice one thing: that of late it has become horribly repugnant to me to test my thoughts and actions by any moral standard whatever. I was guided by something different . . .

The rabble certainly did play very sordidly. I am ready to believe indeed, that a great deal of the most ordinary thieving goes on at the gaming table. The croupiers who sit at each end of the table look at the stakes and reckon the winnings; they have a great deal to do. They are rabble, too! For the most part they are French. However, I was watching and observing, not with the object of describing roulette. I kept a sharp look-out for my own sake, so that I might know how to behave in the future. I noticed, for instance, that nothing was more common than for someone to stretch out his hand and snatch what one had won. A dispute would begin, often an uproar, and a nice job one would have to find witnesses and to prove that it was one's stake!

At first it was all an inexplicable puzzle to me. All I could guess and distinguish was that the stakes were on the numbers, on odd and even, and on the colours. I made up my mind to risk a hundred guldens of Polina Alexandrovna's money. The thought that I was not playing for myself seemed to throw me out of my reckoning. It was an extremely unpleasant feeling, and I wanted to be rid of it as soon as possible. I kept feeling that by beginning for Polina I should break my own luck. Is it impossible to approach the gambling table without becoming infected with superstition? I began by taking out five friedrichs d'or (fifty gulden) and putting them on the even. The wheel went round and thirteen turned up – I had lost. With a sickly feeling I staked another five friedrich d'or on red, simply in order to settle the matter and go away. Red turned up. I staked all the ten friedrichs d'or – red turned up again. I staked all the money again on the same, and again red turned up. On receiving forty friedrichs d'or I staked twenty upon the twelve middle figures, not knowing what would come of it. I was paid three times my stake. In this way from ten friedrichs d'or I had all at once eighty. I was overcome by a strange, unusual feeling which was so unbearable that I made up my mind to go away. It seemed to me that I should not have been playing at all like that if I had been playing for myself. I staked the whole eighty friedrichs d'or, however, on even. This time four turned up; another eighty friedrichs d'or was poured out to me, and, gathering up the whole heap of a hundred and sixty friedrichs d'or, I set off to find Polina Alexandrovna.

They were all walking somewhere in the park and I only succeeded in seeing her after supper. This time the Frenchman was not of the party, and the General unbosomed himself. Among other things he thought fit to observe to me that he would not wish to see me at the gambling tables. It seemed to him that it would compromise him if I were to lose too much: "But even if you were to win a very large sum I should be compromised, too," he added significantly. "Of course, I have no right to dictate your actions, but you must admit yourself . . ." At this point he broke off, as his habit was. I answered, dryly, that I had very little money, and so I could not lose very conspicuously, even if I did play. Going upstairs to my room I succeeded in handing Polina her winnings, and told her that I would not play for her another time.

"Why not?" she asked, in a tremor.

"Because I want to play on my own account," I answered, looking at her with surprise; "and it hinders me."

"Then you will continue in your conviction that roulette is your only escape and salvation?" she asked ironically.

I answered very earnestly, that I did; that as for my confidence that I should win, it might be absurd; I was ready to admit it, but that I wanted to be let alone.

Polina Alexandrovna began insisting I should go halves with her in to-day's winnings, and was giving me eighty friedrichs d'or, suggesting that I should go on playing on those terms. I refused the half, positively and finally, and told her that I could not play for other people, not because I didn't want to, but because I should certainly lose.

"Yet I, too," she said, pondering, "stupid as it seems, am building all my hopes on roulette. And so you must go on playing, sharing with me, and – of course – you will."

At this point she walked away, without listening to further objections. . . .

. . . To-day has been an absurd, grotesque, ridiculous day. Now it is eleven o'clock at night. I am sitting in my little cupboard of a room, recalling it. It began with my having to go to roulette to play for Polina Alexandrovna. I took the hundred and sixty friedrichs d'or, but on two conditions: first, that I would not go halves – that is, if I won I would take nothing for myself; and secondly, that in the evening Polina should explain to me why she needed to win, and how much money. I can't, in any case, suppose that it is simply for the sake of money. Evidently the money is needed, and as quickly as possible, for some particular object. She promised to explain, and I set off. In the gambling hall the crowd was awful. How insolent and how greedy they all were! I forced my way into the middle and stood near the croupier; then I began timidly experimenting, staking two or three coins at a time. Meanwhile, I kept quiet and looked on; it seemed to me that calculation meant very little, and had by no means the importance attributed to it by some players. They sit with papers before them scrawled over in pencil, note the strokes, reckon, deduce the chances, calculate, finally stake and – lose exactly as we simple mortals who play without calculations. On the other hand, I drew one conclusion which I believe to be correct: that is, though there is no system, there really is a sort of order in the sequence of casual chances – and that, of course, is very strange. For instance, it happens that after the twelve middle numbers come the twelve later numbers; twice, for instance, it turns up on the twelve last numbers and passes to the twelve first numbers. After falling on the twelve first numbers, it passes again to numbers in the middle third, turns up three or four times in succession on numbers between thirteen and twenty-four, and again passes to numbers in the last third; then, after turning up two numbers between twenty-five and thirty-six, it passes to a number among the first twelve; turns up once again on a number among the first third, and again passes for three strokes in succession to the middle numbers, and in that way goes on for an hour and a half or two hours. One, three and two – one, three and two. It's very amusing. One day or one morning, for instance, red will be followed by black and back again almost without any order, shifting every minute, so that it never turns up red or black for more than two or three strokes in succession. Another day, or another evening, there will be nothing but red over and over again, turning up, for instance, more than twenty-two times in succession, and so for a whole day. A great deal of this was explained to me by Mr Astley, who spent the whole morning at the tables, but did not once put down a stake.

As for me, I lost every farthing very quickly. I staked straight off twenty friedrichs d'or on even and won, staked again and again won, and went on like that two or three times. I imagine I must have had about four hundred friedrichs d'or in my hands in about five minutes. At that point I ought to have gone away, but a strange sensation rose up in me, a sort of defiance of fate, a desire to challenge it, to put out my tongue at it. I laid down the largest stake allowed – four thousand gulden – and lost it. Then, getting hot, I pulled out all I had left, staked it on the same number, and lost again, after which I walked away from the table as though I were stunned. I could not even grasp what had happened to me, and did not tell Polina Alexandrovna of my losing till just before dinner. I spent the rest of the day sauntering in the park. . . .

. . . "Why did you give it to me to lose? I told you I could not play for other people – especially for you! I obey you, whatever you order me to do, but I can't answer for the result. I warned you that nothing would come of it. Are you very much upset about losing so much money? What do you want so much for?"

"Why these questions?"

"Why, you promised to explain to me . . . Listen: I am absolutely convinced that when I begin playing for myself (and I've got twelve friedrichs d'or) I shall win. Then you can borrow as much from me as you like."

She made a contemptuous grimace.

"Don't be angry with me for such a suggestion," I went on. "I am so deeply conscious that I am nothing beside you – that is, in your eyes – that you may even borrow money from me. Presents from me cannot insult you. Besides, I lost yours."

She looked at me quickly, and seeing that I was speaking irritably and sarcastically, interrupted the conversation again.

"There's nothing of interest to you in my circumstances. If you want to know, I'm simply in debt. I've borrowed money and I wanted to repay it. I had the strange and mad idea that I should be sure to win here at the gambling table. Why I had the idea I can't understand, but I believed in it. Who knows, perhaps I believed it because no other alternative was left me."

"Or because it was quite *necessary* you should win. It's exactly like a drowning man clutching at a straw. You will admit that if he were not drowning he would not look at a straw as a branch of a tree."

Polina was surprised.

"Why," she said, "you were reckoning on the same thing yourself! A fortnight ago you said a great deal to me about your being absolutely convinced that you could win here at roulette, and tried to persuade me not to look upon you as mad; or were you joking then? But I remember you spoke so seriously that it was impossible to take it as a joke."

"That's true," I answered thoughtfully. "I am convinced to this moment that I shall win. I confess you have led me now to wonder why my senseless and unseemly failure to-day has not left the slightest doubt in me. I am still fully convinced that as soon as I begin playing for myself I shall be certain to win."

"Why are you so positive?"

"If you will have it – I don't know. I only know that I *must* win, that it is the only resource left me. Well, that's why, perhaps, I fancy I am bound to win."

Sometimes the wildest idea, the most apparently impossible thought, takes possession of one's mind so strongly that one accepts it at last as something substantial ... more than that, if the idea is associated with a strong passionate desire, then sometimes one will accept it at last as something fated, inevitable, predestined – as something bound to be, and bound to happen. Perhaps there is something else in it, some combination of presentiments, some extraordinary effort of will, self-poisoning by one's own fancy – or something else – I don't know what, but on that evening (which I shall never in my life forget) something marvellous happened to me. Though it is quite justified by the laws of arithmetic, nevertheless it is a marvel to me to this day. And why, why had that conviction so long before taken such firm and deep root in my mind? I had certainly thought about it – I repeat – not as a chance among others which might or might not come to pass, but as something which was absolutely bound to happen!

It was a quarter-past ten. I went into the Casino with a confident expectation and at the same time with an excitement I had never experienced before. There were still a good many people in the gambling hall, though not half as many as in the morning.

Between ten and eleven there are still to be found in the gambling halls the genuine desperate gamblers for whom nothing exists at a spa but roulette, who have come for that alone, who scarcely notice what is going on around them and take no interest in anything during the whole season, but play from morning till night and would be ready perhaps to play all night till dawn, too, if it were possible. And they always disperse with annoyance when at twelve o'clock the roulette hall is closed. And when the senior croupier announces, just before midnight: *"Les trois derniers coups, messieurs,"* they are ready to stake on those last three strokes all they have in their pockets – and do, in fact, lose most at that time. I went up to the very table where Granny had sat that day. It was not crowded, and so I soon took my place at the table standing. Exactly before me was the word "Passe" scrawled on the green cloth.

"Passe" is the series of numbers from nineteen inclusive to thirty-six.

The first series of numbers from one to eighteen inclusive is called "Manque"; but what was that to me? I was not calculating, I had not even heard what had been the winning number last, and I did not ask about it when I began to play – as every player of any prudence would do. I pulled out all my twenty friedrichs d'or and staked them on "passe", the word which lay before me.

"Vingt deux," cried the croupier.

I had won and again staked all, including my winnings.

"Trente et un," cried the croupier.

I had won again. I had in all eighty friedrichs d'or. I staked the whole of that sum on the twelve middle numbers (my winnings would be three to one, but the chances were two to one against me.) The wheel rotated and stopped at twenty-four. I was passed three rolls each of fifty friedrichs d'or in paper and ten gold coins; I had now two hundred friedrichs d'or.

I was as though in delirium and I moved the whole heap of gold to red – and suddenly thought better of it. And for the only time that whole evening, all the time I was playing, I felt chilled with terror and a shudder made my arms and legs tremble. I felt with horror and instantly realised what losing would mean for me now! My whole life was at stake.

"Rouge," cried the croupier, and I drew a breath; fiery pins and needles were tingling all over my body. I was paid in bank-notes. It came to four thousand florins and eighty friedrichs d'or (I could still keep count at that stage).

Then, I remember, I staked two thousand florins on the twelve middle numbers, and lost: I staked my gold, the eighty friedrichs d'or, and lost. I was seized with fury: I snatched up the two thousand florins I had left and staked them on the first twelve numbers – haphazard, at random, without thinking! There was, however, an instant of suspense, like, perhaps, the feeling experienced by Madame Blanchard when she flew from a balloon in Paris to the earth.

"Quatre!" cried the croupier.

Now with my stake I had six thousand florins. I looked triumphant already. I was afraid of nothing – nothing, and staked four thousand florins on black. Nine people followed my example and staked on black. The croupiers exchanged glances and said something to one another. People were talking all round in suspense.

Black won. I don't remember my winnings after, nor what I staked on. I only remember as though in a dream that I won, I believe, sixteen thousand florins; suddenly three unlucky turns took twelve thousand from it; then I staked the last four thousand on "passe" (but I scarcely felt anything as I did so; I simply waited in a mechanical, senseless way) – and again I won; then I won four times running. I only remember that I gathered up money in thousands; I remember, too, that the middle twelve won most often and I kept to it. It turned up with a sort of regularity, certainly three or four times in succession, then it did not turn up twice running and then it followed three or four times in succession. Such astonishing regularity is sometimes met with in streaks, and that is what throws inveterate gamblers who calculate with a pencil in their hands out of their reckoning. And what horrible ironies of fate happen sometimes in such cases!

I believe not more than half an hour had passed since I came into the room, when suddenly the croupier informed me that I had won thirty thousand florins, and as the bank did not meet claims for a larger sum at one time the roulette would be closed till next morning. I snatched up all my gold, dropped it into my pockets, snatched up all my notes, and at once went into the other room where there was another roulette table; the whole crowd streamed after me; there at once a place was cleared for me and I fell to staking again haphazard without reckoning. I don't understand what saved me!

At times, however, a glimmer of prudence began to dawn upon my mind. I clung to certain numbers and combinations, but soon abandoned them and staked almost unconsciously. I must have been very absent-minded; I remember the croupiers several times corrected me. I made several gross mistakes. My temples were soaked with sweat and my hands were shaking. The Poles ran up, too, with offers of their services, but I listened to no one. My luck was unbroken! Suddenly there were sounds of loud talk and laughter, and everyone cried "Bravo, bravo!" some even clapped their hands. Here, too, I collected thirty thousand florins, and the bank closed till next day.

"Go away, go away," a voice whispered on my right.

It was a Frankfurt Jew; he was standing beside me all the time, and I believe sometimes helped me in my play.

"For goodness' sake go," another voice whispered in my left ear.

I took a hurried glance. It was a lady about thirty, very soberly and quietly dressed, with a tired, pale, sickly face which yet bore traces of having once been beautiful. At that moment I was stuffing my pockets with the notes, which I crumpled up anyhow, and gathering up the gold that lay on the table. Snatching up the last roll of notes, I succeeded in putting it into the pale lady's hands quite without attracting notice; I had an intense desire to do so at the time, and I remember her pale slim fingers pressed my hand warmly in token of gratitude. All that took place in one instant.

Having collected quickly all my winnings I went quickly to the trente et quarante.

Trente et quarante is frequented by the aristocratic public. Unlike roulette, it is a game of cards. Here the bank will pay up to a hundred thousand thalers at once. The largest stake is here also four thousand florins. I knew nothing of the game, and scarcely knew how to bet on it, except the red and the black, upon which one can bet in this game too. And I stuck to red and black. The whole Casino crowded round. I don't remember whether I once thought of Polina all this time. I was experiencing an overwhelming enjoyment in scooping up and taking away the notes which grew up in a heap before me.

It seemed as though fate were urging me on. This time, as luck would have it, a circumstance occurred which, however, is fairly frequent in the game. Chance favours red, for instance, ten or even fifteen times in succession. I had heard two days before that in the previous week red had turned up twenty-two times in succession; it was something which had never been remembered in roulette, and it was talked of with amazement. Everyone, of course, abandoned red at once, and after the tenth time, for instance, scarcely anyone dared to stake on it. But none of the experienced players staked on black either. The experienced gambler knows what is meant by this "freak of chance". It would mean that after red had won sixteen times, at the seventeenth time the luck would infallibly fall on black. Novices at play rush to this conclusion in crowds, double and treble their stakes, and lose terribly.

But, noticing that red had turned up seven times running, by strange perversity I staked on it. I am convinced that vanity was half responsible for it; I wanted to impress the spectators by taking a mad risk, and – oh, the strange sensation – I remember distinctly that, quite apart from the promptings of vanity, I was possessed by an intense craving for risk. Perhaps passing through so many sensations my soul was not satisfied but only irritated by them and craved still more sensation – and stronger and stronger ones – till utterly exhausted. And, truly I am not lying, if the regulations had allowed me to stake fifty thousand florins at once, I should certainly have staked them. People around shouted that it was madness – that red had won fourteen times already!

"*Monsieur a gagné déjà cent mille florins,*" I heard a voice say near me.

I suddenly came to myself. What? I had won during that evening a hundred thousand florins! And what more did I want? I fell on my banknotes, crumpled them up in my pockets without counting them, scooped up all my gold, all my rolls of notes, and ran out of the Casino. Everyone was laughing as I went through the room, looking at my bulging pockets and at the way I staggered under the weight of gold. I think it weighed over twenty pounds. Several hands were held out to me; I gave it away in handfuls as I snatched it up. Two Jews stopped me at the outer door.

"You are bold – you are very bold," they said to me, "but be sure to go away to-morrow as soon as possible, or else you will lose it all – you will lose it all . . ."

I didn't listen to them. The avenue was so dark that I could not see my hand before my face. It was half a mile to the hotel. I had never been afraid of thieves or robbers even as a small boy; I did not think of them now either. I don't remember what I thought of on the road; I had no thoughts. I was only aware of an immense enjoyment – success, victory, power – I don't know how to express it. Polina's image hovered before my mind too; I remembered her and was conscious I was going to her; I should be with her in a moment, should be telling her and showing her . . . But I hardly remembered what she had said to me earlier, and why I had gone, and all the sensations I had felt, not more than an hour and a half before, seemed to me something long past, transformed, grown old – something of which we should say no more because everything now would begin anew. Almost at the end of the avenue a sudden panic came upon me. What if I were robbed and murdered at this instant? At every step my panic grew greater. I almost ran. Suddenly, at the end of the avenue there was the glare of our hotel with its many windows lighted up – thank God, home!

I ran up to my storey and rapidly opened the door. Polina was there, sitting on the sofa with her arms crossed, with a lighted candle before her. She looked at me with amazement, and no doubt at that moment I must have looked rather strange. I stood before her and began flinging down all my piles of money on the table.

RECOLLECTIONS OF A SCORER

Leo Tolstoy

Thanks to the worldwide success of *War and Peace*, Leo Tolstoy is probably Russia's best known novelist, but he did not embark upon a literary career until he had spent some years as a rather dissolute student and then as a soldier in the Caucasus and the Crimea.

"Recollections of a Scorer" is reputed to be a largely autobiographical story of the Count's experiences in the Caucasus where he is known to have run up enormous gambling debts.

WELL, IT HAPPENED about three o'clock. The gentlemen were playing. There was the big stranger, as our men called him. The prince was there, – the two are always together. The whiskered bárin was there; also the little hussar, Oliver, who was an actor, and there was the *pan*. It was a pretty good crowd.

The big stranger and the prince were playing together. Now, here I was walking up and down around the billiard-table with my stick, keeping tally, – ten and forty-seven, twelve and forty-seven.

Everybody knows it's our business to score. You don't get a chance to get a bite of any thing, and you don't get to bed till two o'clock o' nights, but you're always being screamed at to bring the balls.

I was keeping tally; and I look, and see a new bárin comes in at the door. He gazed and gazed, and then sat down on the sofa. Very well!

"Now, who can that be?" thinks I to myself. "He must be somebody."

His dress was neat, – neat as a pin, – checkered tricot pants, stylish little short coat, plush vest, and gold chain and all sorts of trinkets dangling from it.

He was dressed neat; but there was something about the man neater still; slim, tall, his hair brushed forward in style, and his face fair and ruddy, – well, in a word, a fine young fellow.

You must know our business brings us into contact with all sorts of people. And there's many that ain't of much consequence, and there's a good deal of poor trash. So, though you're only a scorer, you get used to telling folks; that is, in a certain way you learn a thing or two.

I looked at the bárin. I see him sit down, modest and quiet, not knowing anybody; and the clothes on him are so bran-new, that thinks I, "Either he's a foreigner, – an Englishman maybe, – or some count just come. And though he's so young, he has an air of some distinction." Oliver sat down next him, so he moved along a little.

They began a game. The big man lost. He shouts to me. Says he, "You're always cheating. You don't count straight. Why don't you pay attention?"

He scolded away, then threw down his cue, and went out. Now, just look here! Evenings, he and the prince plays for fifty silver rubles a game; and here he only lost a bottle of Makon wine, and got mad. That's the kind of a character he is.

Another time he and the prince plays till two o'clock. They don't bank down any cash; and so I know neither of them's got any cash, but they are simply playing a bluff game.

"I'll go you twenty-five rubles," says he.

"All right."

Just yawning, and not even stopping to place the ball, – you see, he was not made of stone, – now just notice what he said. "We are playing for money," says he, "and not for chips."

But this man puzzled me worse than all the rest. Well, then, when the big man left, the prince says to the new Bárin, "Wouldn't you like," says he, "to play a game with me?"

"With pleasure," says he.

He sat there, and looked rather foolish, indeed he did. He may have been courageous in reality; but, at all events, he got up, went over to the billiard-table, and did not seem flustered as yet. He was not exactly flustered, but you couldn't help seeing that he was not quite at his ease.

Either his clothes were a little too new, or he was embarrassed because everybody was looking at him; at any rate, he seemed to have no energy. He sort of sidled up to the table, caught his pocket on the edge, began to chalk his cue, dropped his chalk.

Whenever he hit the ball, he always glanced around, and reddened. Not so the prince. He was used to it; he chalked and chalked his hand, tucked up his sleeve; he goes and sits down when he pockets the ball, even though he is such a little man.

They played two or three games; then I notice the prince puts up the cue, and says, "Would you mind telling me your name?"

"Nekhliudof," says he.

Says the prince, "Was your father commander in the corps of cadets?"

"Yes," says the other.

Then they began to talk in French, and I could not understand them. I suppose they were talking about family affairs.

"*Au revoir*," says the prince. "I am very glad to have made your acquaintance." He washed his hands, and went to get a lunch; but the other stood by the billiard-table with his cue, and was knocking the balls about.

It's our business, you know, when a new man comes along, to be rather sharp: it's the best way. I took the balls, and go to put them up. He reddened, and says, "Can't I play any longer?"

"Certainly you can," says I. "That's what billiards is for." But I don't pay any attention to him. I straighten the cues.

"Will you play with me?"

"Certainly, sir," says I.

I place the balls.

"Shall we play for odds?"

"What do you mean, – 'play for odds'?"

"Well," says I, "you give me a half-ruble, and I crawl under the table."

Of course, as he had never seen that sort of thing, it seemed strange to him: he laughs.

"Go ahead," says he.

"Very well," says I, "only you must give me odds."

"What!" says he, "are you a worse player than I am?"

"Most likely." says I. "We have few players who can be compared with you."

We began to play. He certainly had the idea that he was a crack shot. It was a caution to see him shoot; but the Pole sat there, and kept shouting out every time, –

"Ah, what a chance! ah, what a shot!"

But what a man he was! His ideas were good enough, but he didn't know how to carry them out. Well, as usual I lost the first game, crawled under the table, and grunted.

Thereupon Oliver and the Pole jumped down from their seats, and applauded, thumping with their cues.

"Splendid! Do it again," they cried, "once more."

Well enough to cry "once more," especially for the Pole. That fellow would have been glad enough to crawl under the billiard-table, or even under the Blue bridge, for a half-ruble! Yet he was the first to cry, "Splendid! but you haven't wiped off all the dust yet."

I, Petrushka the marker, was pretty well known to everybody.

Only, of course, I did not care to show my hand yet. I lost my second game.

"It does not become me at all to play with you, sir," says I.

He laughs. Then, as I was playing the third game, he stood forty-nine and I nothing. I laid the cue on the billiard-table, and said, "Bárin, shall we play off?"

"What do you mean by playing off?" says he. "How would you have it?"

"You make it three rubles or nothing," says I.

"Why," says he, "have I been playing with you for money?" The fool! He turned rather red.

Very good. He lost the game. He took out his pocket-book, – quite a new one, evidently just from the English shop, – opened it: I see he wanted to make a little splurge. It is stuffed full of bills, – nothing but hundred-ruble notes.

"No," says he, "there's no small stuff here."

He took three rubles from his purse. "There," says he, "there's your two rubles; the other pays for the games, and you keep the rest for vodka."

"Thank you, sir, most kindly." I see that he is a splendid fellow. For such a one I would crawl under any thing. For one thing, it's a pity that he won't play for money. For then, thinks I, I should know how to work him for twenty rubles, and maybe I could stretch it out to forty.

As soon as the Pole saw the young man's money, he says, "Wouldn't you like to try a little game with me? You play so admirably." Such sharpers prowl around.

"No," says the young man, "excuse me: I have not the time." And he went out. . . .

. . . In this way he used often to come to us. Once he came with the prince, and the whiskered man who was the prince's crony; the gentlemen always called him "Fedotka." He had prominent cheek-bones, and was homely enough, to be sure; but he used to dress neatly and ride in a carriage. What was the reason that the gentlemen were so fond of him? I really could not tell.

"Fedotka! Fedotka!" they'd call, and ask him to eat and to drink, and they'd spend their money paying up for him; but he was a thorough-going beat. If ever he lost, he would be sure not to pay; but if he won, you bet he wouldn't fail to collect his money. Often too he came to grief: yet there he was, walking arm in arm with the prince.

"You are lost without me," he would say to the prince. "I am, Fedot," says he; "but not a Fedot of that sort."

And what jokes he used to crack, to be sure! Well, as I said, they had already arrived that time, and one of them says, "Let's have the balls for three-handed pool."

"All right," says the other.

They began to play at three rubles a stake. Nekhliudof and the prince play, and chat about all sorts of things meantime.

"Ah!" says one of them, "you mind only what a neat little foot she has."

"Oh," says the other, "her foot is nothing; her beauty is her wealth of hair."

Of course they paid no attention to the game, only kept on talking to one another.

As to Fedotka, that fellow was alive to his work; he played his very best, but they didn't do themselves justice at all.

And so he won six rubles from each of them. God knows how many games he had won from the prince, yet I never knew them to pay each other any money; but Nekhliudof took out two greenbacks, and handed them over to him.

"No," says he, "I don't want to take your money. Let's square it: play 'quits or double,' – either double or nothing."

I set the balls. Fedotka began to play the first hand. Nekhliudof seemed to play only for fun: sometimes he would come very near winning a game, yet just fail of it. Says he, "It would be too easy a move, I won't have it so." But Fedotka did not forget what he was up to. Carelessly he proceeded with the game, and thus, as if it were unexpectedly, won.

"Let us play double stakes once more," says he.

"All right," says Nekhliudof.

Once more Fedotka won the game.

"Well," says he, "it began with a mere trifle. I don't wish to win much from you. Shall we make it once more or nothing?"

"Yes."

Say what you may, but fifty rubles is a pretty sum, and Nekhliudof himself began to propose, "Let us make it double or quit." So they played and played.

It kept going worse and worse for Nekhliudof. Two hundred and eighty rubles were written up against him. As to Fedotka, he had his own method: he would lose a simple game, but when the stake was doubled, he would win sure.

As for the prince, he sits by and looks on. He sees that the matter is growing serious.

"Enough!" says he, "hold on."

My! they keep increasing the stake.

At last it went so far that Nekhliudof was in for more than five hundred rubles. Fedotka laid down his cue, and said, –

"Aren't you satisfied for to-day? I'm tired," says he.

Yet I knew he was ready to play till dawn of day, provided there was money to be won. Stratagem, of course. And the other was all the more anxious to go on. "Come on! Come on!"

"No, –'pon my honor, I'm tired. Come," says Fedot; "let's go up-stairs; there you shall have your *revanche*."

Up-stairs with us meant the place where the gentlemen used to play cards. From that very day, Fedotka wound his net round him so that he began to come every day. He would play one or two games of billiards, and then proceed up-stairs, – every day up-stairs.

What they used to do there, God only knows; but it is a fact that from that time he began to be an entirely different kind of man, and seemed hand in glove with Fedotka. Formerly he used to be stylish, neat in his dress, with his hair slightly curled even; but now it would be only in the morning that he would be any thing like himself; but as soon as he had paid his visit up-stairs, he would not be at all like himself.

Once he came down from up-stairs with the prince, pale, his lips trembling, and talking excitedly.

"I cannot permit such a one as *he* is," says he, "to say that I am not" – How did he express himself? I cannot recollect, something like "not refined enough," or what, – "and that he won't play with me any more. I tell you I have paid him ten thousand, and I should think that he might be a little more considerate, before others, at least."

"Oh, bother!" says the prince, "is it worth while to lose one's temper with Fedotka?"

"No," says the other, "I will not let it go so."

"Why, old fellow, how can you think of such a thing as lowering yourself to have a row with Fedotka?"

"That is all very well; but there were strangers there, mind you."

"Well, what of that?" says the prince; "strangers? Well, if you wish, I will go and make him ask your pardon."

"No," says the other.

And then they began to chatter in French, and I could not understand what it was they were talking about.

And what would you think of it? That very evening he and Fedotka ate supper together, and they became friends again.

Well and good. At other times again he would come alone.

"Well," he would say, "do I play well?"

It's our business, you know, to try to make everybody contented, and so I would say, "Yes, indeed;" and yet how could it be called good play, when he would poke about with his cue without any sense whatever?

And from that very evening when he took in with Fedotka, he began to play for money all the time. Formerly he didn't care to play for stakes, either for a dinner or for champagne. Sometimes the prince would say, –

"Let's play for a bottle of champagne."

"No," he would say. "Let us rather have the wine by itself. Hollo there! bring a bottle!"

And now he began to play for money all the time; he used to spend his entire days in our establishment. He would either play with some one in the billiard-room, or he would go "up-stairs."

Well, thinks I to myself, every one else gets something from him, why don't I get some advantage out of it?

"Well, sir," says I one day, "it's a long time since you have had a game with me."

And so we began to play. Well, when I won ten half-rubles of him, I says, –

"Don't you want to make it double or quit, sir?"

He said nothing. Formerly, if you remember, he would call me a fool for such a boldness. And we went to playing "quit or double."

I won eighty rubles of him.

Well, what would you think? Since that first time he used to play with me every day. He would wait till there was no one about, for of course he would have been ashamed to play with a mere marker in presence of others. Once he had got rather warmed up by the play (he already owed me sixty rubles), and so he says, –

"Do you want to stake all you have won?"

"All right," says I.

I won. "One hundred and twenty to one hundred and twenty?"

"All right," says I.

Again I won. "Two hundred and forty against two hundred and forty?"

"Isn't that too much?" I ask.

He made no reply. We played the game. Once more it was mine. "Four hundred and eighty against four hundred and eighty?"

I says, "Well, sir, I don't want to wrong you. Let us make it a hundred rubles that you owe me, and call it square."

You ought to have heard how he yelled at this, and yet he was not a proud man at all. "Either play, or don't play!" says he.

Well, I see there's nothing to be done. "Three hundred and eighty, then, if you please," says I.

I really wanted to lose. I allowed him forty points in advance. He stood fifty-two to my thirty-six. He began to cut the yellow one, and missed eighteen points; and I was standing just at the turning-point. I made a stroke so as to knock the ball off of the billiard-table. No – so luck would have it. Do what I might, he even missed the doublet. I had won again.

"Listen," says he. "Peter," – he did not call me *Petrushka* then, – "I can't pay you the whole right away. In a couple of months I could pay three thousand even, if it were necessary."

And there he stood just as red, and his voice kind of trembled.

"Very good, sir," says I.

With this he laid down the cue. Then he began to walk up and down, up and down, the perspiration running down his face.

"Peter," says he, "let's try it again, double or quit."

And he almost burst into tears.

"What, sir, what! would you play against such luck?"

"Oh, let us play, I beg of you." And he brings the cue, and puts it in my hand.

I took the cue, and I threw the balls on the table so that they bounced over on to the floor; I could not help showing off a little, naturally. I say, "All right, sir."

But he was in such a hurry that he went and picked up the balls himself, and I thinks to myself, "Anyway, I'll never be able to get the seven hundred rubles from him, so I can lose them to him all the same." I began to play carelessly on purpose. But no – he won't have it so. "Why," says he, "you are playing badly on purpose."

But his hands trembled, and when the ball went towards a pocket, his fingers would spread out and his mouth would screw up to one side, as if he could by any means force the ball into the pocket. Even I couldn't stand it, and I say, "That won't do any good, sir."

Very well. As he won this game I says, "This will make it one hundred and eighty rubles you owe me, and fifty games; and now I must go and get my supper." So I laid down my cue, and went off.

I went and sat down all by myself, at a small table opposite the door; and I look in and see, and wonder what he will do. Well, what would you think? He began to walk up and down, up and down, probably thinking that no one's looking at him; and then he would give a pull at his hair, and then walk up and down again, and keep muttering to himself; and then he would pull his hair again.

After that he wasn't seen for a week. Once he came into the dining-room as gloomy as could be, but he didn't enter the billiard-room. The prince caught sight of him.

"Come," says he, "let's have a game."

"No," says the other, "I am not going to play any more."

"Nonsense! come along."

"No," says he, "I won't come, I tell you. For you it's all one whether I go or not, yet for me it's no good to come here."

And so he did not come for ten days more. And then, it being the holidays, he came dressed up in a dress suit: he'd evidently been into company. And he was here all day long; he kept playing, and he came the next day, and the third. . . .

And it began to go in the old style, and I thought it would be fine to have another trial with him.

"No," says he, "I'm not going to play with you; and as to the one hundred and eighty rubles that I owe you, if you'll come at the end of a month, you shall have it."

Very good. So I went to him at the end of a month.

"By God," says he, "I can't give it to you; but come back on Thursday."

Well, I went on Thursday. I found that he had a splendid suite of apartments.

"Well," says I, "is he at home?"

"He hasn't got up yet," I was told.

"Very good, I will wait."

For a body-servant he had one of his own serfs, such a gray-haired old man! That servant was perfectly single-minded, he didn't know any thing about beating about the bush. So we got into conversation.

"Well," says he, "what is the use of our living here, master and I? He's squandered all his property, and it's mighty little honor or good that we get out of this Petersburg of yours. As we started from the country, I thought it would be as it was with the last bárin (may his soul rest in peace!), we would go about with princes and counts and generals; he thought to himself, 'I'll find a countess for a sweet-heart, and she'll have a big dowry, and we'll live on a big scale.' But it's quite a different thing from what he expected; here we are, running about from one tavern to another as bad off as we could be! The Princess Rtishcheva, you know, is his own aunt, and Prince Borotintsef is his godfather. What do you think? He went to see them only once, that was at Christmas-time; he never shows his nose there. Yes, and even their people laugh about it to me. 'Why,' says they, 'your bárin is not a bit like his father!' And once I take it upon myself to say to him, –

"'Why wouldn't you go, sir, and visit your aunt? They are feeling bad because you haven't been for so long.'

"'It's stupid there, Demyánitch,' says he. Just to think, he found his only amusement here in the saloon! If he only would enter the service! yet, no: he has got entangled with cards and all the rest of it. When men get that way, there's no good in any thing; nothing comes to any good. . . . *E-ekh!* we are going to the dogs, and no mistake. . . . The late mistress (may her soul rest in peace!) left us a rich inheritance: no less than a thousand souls, and about three hundred thousand rubles worth of timber-lands. He has mortgaged it all, sold the timber, let the estate go to rack and ruin, and still no money on hand. When the master is away, of course, the overseer is more than the master. What does he care? He only cares to stuff his own pockets.

"A few days ago, a couple of peasants brought complaints from the whole estate. 'He has wasted the last of the property,' they say. What do you think? he pondered over the complaints, and gave the peasants ten rubles apiece. Says he, 'I'll be there very soon. I shall have some money, and I will settle all accounts when I come,' says he.

"But how can he settle accounts when we are getting into debt all the time? Money or no money, yet the winter here has cost eighty thousand rubles, and now there isn't a silver ruble in the house. And all owing to his kind-heartedness. You see, he's such a simple bárin that it would be hard to find his equal: that's the very reason that he's going to ruin, – going to ruin, all for nothing." And the old man almost wept.

Nekhliudof woke up about eleven, and called me in.

"They haven't sent me any money yet," says he. "But it isn't my fault. Shut the door," says he.

I shut the door.

"Here," says he, "take my watch or this diamond pin, and pawn it. They will give you more than one hundred and eighty rubles for it, and when I get my money I will redeem it," says he.

"No matter, sir," says I. "If you don't happen to have any money, it's no consequence; let me have the watch if you don't mind. I can wait for your convenience."

I can see that the watch is worth more than three hundred.

Very good. I pawned the watch for a hundred rubles, and carried him the ticket. "You will owe me eighty rubles," says I, "and you had better redeem the watch."

And so it happened that he still owed me eighty rubles.

After that he began to come to us again every day. I don't know how matters stood between him and the prince, but at all events he kept coming with him all the time, or else they would go and play cards up-stairs with Fedotka. And what queer accounts those three men kept between them! this one would lend money to the other, the other to the third, yet who it was that owed the money you never could find out.

And in this way he kept on coming our way for well-nigh two years; only it was to be plainly seen that he was a changed man, such a devil-may-care manner he assumed at times. He even went so far at times as to borrow a ruble of me to pay a hack-driver; and yet he would still play with the prince for a hundred rubles stake.

He grew gloomy, thin, sallow. As soon as he came he used to order a little glass of absinthe, take a bite of something, and drink some port wine, and then he would grow more lively.

He came one time before dinner; it happened to be carnival time, and he began to play with a hussar.

Says he, "Do you want to play for a stake?"

"Very well," says he. "What shall it be?"

"A bottle of Claude Vougeaux? What do you say?"

"All right."

Very good. The hussar won, and they went off for their dinner. They sat down at table, and then Nekhliudof says, "Simon, a bottle of Claude Vougeaux, and see that you warm it to the proper point."

Simon went out, brought in the dinner, but no wine.

"Well," says he, "Where's the wine?"

Simon hurried out, brought in the roast.

"Let us have the wine," says he.

Simon makes no reply.

"What's got into you? Here we've almost finished dinner, and no wine. Who wants to drink with dessert?"

Simon hurried out. "The landlord," says he, "wants to speak to you."

Nekhliudof turned scarlet. He sprang up from the table.

"What's the need of calling me?"

The landlord is standing at the door.

Says he, "I can't trust you any more, unless you settle my little bill."

"Well, didn't I tell you that I would pay the first of the month?"

"That will be all very well," says the landlord, "but I can't be all the time giving credit, and having no settlement. There are more than ten thousand rubles of debts outstanding now," says he.

"Well, that'll do, *monshoor*, you know that you can trust me! Send the bottle, and I assure you that I will pay you very soon."

And he hurried back.

"What was it? why did they call you out?" asked the hussar.

"Oh, some one wanted to ask me a question."

"Now it would be a good time," says the hussar, "to have a little warm wine to drink."

"Simon, hurry up_"

Simon came back, but still no wine, nothing. Too bad! He left the table, and came to me.

"For God's sake," says he, "Petrushka, let me have six rubles!"

He was pale as a sheet. "No, sir," says I: "by God, you owe me quite too much now."

"I will give forty rubles for six, in a week's time."

"If only I had it," says I, "I should not think of refusing you, but I haven't."

What do you think! He rushed away, his teeth set, his fist doubled up, and ran down the corridor like one mad, and all at once he gave himself a knock on the forehead.

"O my God!" says he, "what has it come to?"

But he did not return to the dining-room; he jumped into a carriage, and drove away. Didn't we have our laugh over it! The hussar asks, –

"Where is the gentleman who was dining with me?"

"He has gone," said some one.

"Where has he gone? What message did he leave?"

"He didn't leave any; he just took to his carriage, and went off."

"That's a fine way of entertaining a man!" says he.

Now, thinks I to myself, it'll be a long time before he comes again after this; that is, on account of this scandal. But no. On the next day he came about evening. He came into the billiard-room. He had a sort of a box in his hand. Took off his overcoat.

"Now let us have a game." says he.

He looked out from under his eyebrows, rather fierce like.

We played a game. "That's enough now," says he: "go and bring me a pen and paper; I must write a letter."

Not thinking any thing, not suspecting any thing, I bring some paper, and put it on the table in the little room.

"It's all ready, sir," says I.

"Very good." He sat down at the table. He kept on writing and writing, and muttering to himself all the time: then he jumps up, and, frowning, says, "Look and see if my carriage has come yet."

It was on a Friday, during carnival time, and so there weren't any of the customers on hand; they were all at some ball. I went to see about the carriage, and just as I was going out of the door, "Petrushka! Petrushka!"

he shouted, as if something suddenly frightened him.

I turn round. I see he's pale as a sheet, standing here and looking at me.

"Did you call me, sir?" says I.

He makes no reply.

"What do you want?" says I.

He says nothing. "Oh, yes!" says he. "Let's have another game."

Then says he, "Haven't I learned to play pretty well?"

He had just won the game. "Yes," says I.

"All right," says he; "go now, and see about my carriage." He himself walked up and down the room.

Without thinking anything, I went down to the door. I didn't see any carriage at all. I started to go up again.

Just as I am going up, I hear what sounds like the thud of a billiard-cue. I go into the billiard-room. I notice a peculiar smell.

I look around; and there he is lying on the floor in a pool of blood, with a pistol beside him. I was so scared that I could not speak a word.

He keeps twitching, twitching his leg; and stretched himself a little. Then he sort of snored, and stretched out his full length in such a strange way. And God knows why such a sin came about, – how it was that it occurred to him to ruin his own soul, – but as to what he left written on this paper, I don't understand it at all. Truly, you can never account for what is going on in the world.

"God gave me all that a man can desire, – wealth, name, intellect, noble aspirations. I wanted to enjoy myself, and I trod in the mire all that was best in me. I have done nothing dishonorable, I am not unfortunate, I have not committed any crime; but I have done worse: I have destroyed my feelings, my intellect, my youth. I became entangled in a filthy net, from which I could not escape, and to which I could not accustom myself. I feel that I am falling lower and lower every moment, and I cannot stop my fall.

"And what ruined me? Was there in me some strange passion which I might plead as an excuse? No!

"My recollections are pleasant. One fearful moment of forgetfulness, which can never be erased from my mind, led me to come to my senses. I shuddered when I saw what a measureless abyss separated me from what I desired to be, and might have been. In my imagination arose the hopes, the dreams, and the thoughts of my youth.

"Where are those lofty thoughts of life, of eternity, of God, which at times filled my soul with light and strength? Where that aimless power of love which kindled my heart with its comforting warmth? . . .

"But how good and happy I might have been, had I trodden that path which, at the very entrance of life, was pointed out to me by my fresh mind and true feelings! More than once did I try to go from the ruts in which my life ran, into that sacred path.

"I said to myself, Now I will use my whole strength of will; and yet I could not do it. When I happened to be alone, I felt awkward and timid. When I was with others, I no longer heard the inward voice; and I fell all the time lower and lower.

"At last I came to a terrible conviction that it was impossible for me to lift myself from this low plane. I ceased to think about it, and I wished to forget all; but hopeless repentance worried me still more and more. Then, for the first time, the thought of suicide occurred to me. . . .

"I once thought that the nearness of death would rouse my soul. I was mistaken. In a quarter of an hour I shall be no more, yet my view has not in the least changed. I see with the same eyes, I hear with the same ears, I think the same thoughts; there is the same strange incoherence, unsteadiness, and lightness in my thoughts.". . .

WITH INTENT TO DECEIVE

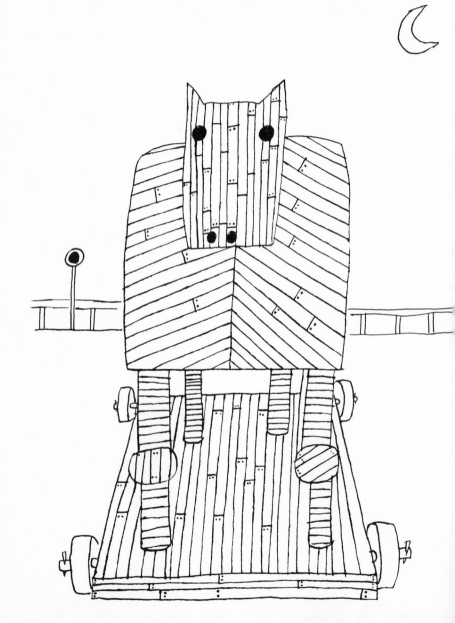

THE CELEBRATED JUMPING FROG
OF CALAVERAS COUNTY

Mark Twain

"The Celebrated Jumping Frog of Calaveras County" was first published in a New York newspaper in 1865 and made Mark Twain a nationally famous humorist overnight. Although it sounds a typically American tale, the jumping frog has a long and honorable history stretching back as far as Aeschylus in 405 B.C.

THERE WAS A FELLER here once by the name of *Jim* Smiley, in the winter of '49 – or maybe it was the spring of '50 – I don't recollect exactly, somehow, though what makes me think it was one or the other is because I remember the big flume wasn't finished when he first came to the camp; but anyway, he was the curiousest man about always betting on anything that turned up you ever see, if he could get anybody to bet on the other side; and if he couldn't, he'd change sides. Any way that suited the other man would suit him – any way just so's he got a bet, *he* was satisfied. But still he was lucky, uncommon lucky; he most always come out winner. He was always ready and laying for a chance; there couldn't be no solit'ry thing mentioned but that feller'd offer to bet on it, and take any side you please, as I was just telling you. If there was a horse race, you'd find him flush, or you'd find him busted at the end of it; if there was a dogfight, he'd bet on it; if there was a cat-fight, he'd bet on it; if there was a chicken-fight, he'd bet on it; why, if there was two birds setting on a fence, he would bet you which one would fly first; or if there was a camp meeting, he would be there reg'lar, to bet on Parson Walker, which he judged to be the best exhorter about here, and so he was, too, and a good man. If he even seen a straddlebug start to go anywheres, he would bet you how long it would take him to get wherever he was going to, and if you took him up, he would foller that straddlebug to Mexico but what he would find out where he was bound for and how long he was on the road. Lots of the boys here has seen that

Smiley, and can tell you about him. Why, it never made no difference to *him* – he would bet on *any*thing – the dangdest feller. Parson Walker's wife laid very sick once, for a good while, and it seemed as if they warn't going to save her; but one morning he come in, and Smiley asked how she was, and he said she was considerable better – thank the Lord for his inf'nit mercy – and coming on so smart that, with the blessing of Prov'dence, she'd get well yet; and Smiley, before he thought, says, "Well, I'll risk two-and-a-half that she don't, anyway."

Thish-yer Smiley had a mare— the boys called her the fifteen-minute nag, but that was only in fun, you know, because, of course, she was faster than that – and he used to win money on that horse, for all she was so slow and always had the asthma, or the distemper, or the consumption, or something of that kind. They used to give her two or three hundred yards start, and then pass her under way; but always at the fag end of the race she'd get excited and desperate-like, and come cavorting and straddling up, and scattering her legs around limber, sometimes in the air, and sometimes out to one side amongst the fences, and kicking up m-o-r-e dust, and raising m-o-r-e racket with her coughing and sneezing and blowing her nose – and always fetch up at the stand just about a neck ahead, as near as you could cipher it down.

And he had a little small bull pup, that to look at him you'd think he wan't worth a cent, but to set around and look ornery, and lay for a chance to steal something. But as soon as money was up on him, he was a different dog; his underjaw'd begin to stick out like the fo'castle of a steamboat, and his teeth would uncover, and shine savage like the furnaces. And a dog might tackle him, and bully-rag him, and bite him, and throw him over his shoulder two or three times, and Andrew Jackson – which was the name of the pup – Andrew Jackson would never let on but what *he* was satisfied, and hadn't expected nothing else – and the bets being doubled and doubled on the other side all the time, till the money was all up; and then all of a sudden he would grab that other dog jest by the j'int of his hind leg and freeze to it – not chaw, you understand, but only jest grip and hang on till they throwed up the sponge, if it was a year. Smiley always come out winner on that pup, till he harnessed a dog once that didn't have no hind legs, because they'd been sawed off by a circular saw, and when the thing had gone along far enough, and the money was all up, and he come to make a snatch for his pet holt, he saw in a minute how he'd been imposed on, and how the other dog had him in the door, so to speak, and he 'peared surprised, and then he looked sorter discouraged-like, and didn't try no more to win the fight, and so he got shucked out bad. He give Smiley a look, as much as to say his heart was broke, and it was *his* fault for putting up a dog that hadn't no hind legs for him to take holt of, which was his main dependence in a fight, and then he limped off a piece and laid down and died. It was a good pup, was that Andrew Jackson, and would have made a name for hisself if he'd lived, for the stuff was in him, and he had genius – I know it, because he hadn't had no opportunities to speak of, and it don't stand to reason that a dog could make such a fight as he could under them circumstances, if he hadn't no talent. It always makes me feel sorry when I think of that last fight of his'n, and the way it turned out.

Well, thish-yer Smiley had rat-tarriers, and chicken cocks, and tomcats, and all them kind of things, till you couldn't rest, and you couldn't fetch nothing for him to bet on but he'd match you. He ketched a frog one day, and took him home, and said he cal'klated to edercate him; and so he never done nothing for three months but set in his back yard and learn that frog to jump. And you bet you he *did* learn him, too. He'd give him a little punch behind, and the next minute you'd see that frog whirling in the air like a doughnut – see him turn one summerset, or may be a couple, if he got a good start, and come down flatfooted and all right, like a cat. He got up so in the matter of catching flies, and kept him in practice so constant, that he'd nail a fly every time as far as he could see him. Smiley said all a frog wanted was education, and he could do most anything – and I believe him. Why, I've seen him set Dan'l Webster down here on this floor – Dan'l Webster was the name of the frog – and sing out, "Flies, Dan'l, flies!" and quicker'n you could wink, he'd spring straight up, and snake a fly off'n the counter there, and flop down on the floor again as solid as a gob of mud, and fall to scratching the side of his head with his hind foot as indifferent as if he hadn't no idea he'd been doin' any more'n any frog might do. You never see a frog so modest and straightfor'ard as he was, for all he was so gifted. And when it come to fair and square jumping on a dead level, he could get over more ground at one straddle than any animal of his breed you ever see. Jumping on a dead level was his strong suit, you understand; and when it come to that, Smiley would ante up money on him as long as he had a red. Smiley was monstrous proud of his frog, and well he might be, for fellers that had traveled and been everywheres, all said he laid over any frog that ever *they* see.

Well, Smiley kept the beast in a little lattice box, and he used to fetch him downtown sometimes and lay for a bet. One day a feller – a stranger in the camp, he was – come across him with his box, and says:

"What might it be that you've got in the box?"

And Smiley says, sorter indifferent like, "It might be a parrot, or it might be a canary, maybe, but it an't – it's only just a frog."

And the feller took it, and looked at it careful, and turned it round this way and that, and says, "H'm – so 'tis. Well, what's *he* good for?"

"Well," Smiley says, easy and careless, "he's good enough for *one* thing, I should judge – he can outjump any frog in Calaveras county."

The feller took the box again, and took another long, particular look, and give it back to Smiley, and says, very deliberate, "Well, I don't see no p'ints about that frog that's any better'n any other frog."

"Maybe you don't," Smiley says. "Maybe you understand frogs, and maybe you don't understand 'em; maybe you've had experience, and maybe you an't only a amature, as it were. Anyways, I've got *my* opinion, and I'll risk forty dollars that he can outjump any frog in Calaveras county."

And the feller studied a minute, and then says, kinder sad like, "Well, I'm only a stranger here, and I an't got no frog; but if I had a frog, I'd bet you."

And then Smiley says, "That's all right – that's all right – if you'll hold my box a minute, I'll go and get you a frog." And so the feller took the box, and put up his forty dollars along with Smiley's, and set down to wait.

So he set there a good while thinking and thinking to hisself, and then he got the frog out and prized his mouth open and took a teaspoon and filled him full of quail shot – filled him pretty near up to his chin – and set him on the floor. Smiley he went to the swamp and slopped around in the mud for a long time, and finally he ketched a frog, and fetched him in, and give him to this feller, and says:

"Now, if you're ready, set him alongside of Dan'l, with his fore-paws just even with Dan'l, and I'll give the word." Then he says, "One – two – three – jump!" and him and the feller touched up the frogs from behind, and the new frog hopped off, but Dan'l give a heave, and hysted up his shoulders – so – like a Frenchman, but it wan't no use – he couldn't budge; he was planted as solid as an anvil, and he couldn't no more stir than if he was anchored out. Smiley was a good deal surprised, and he was disgusted too, but he didn't have no idea what the matter was, of course.

The feller took the money and started away; and when he was going out at the door, he sorter jerked his thumb over his shoulders – this way – at Dan'l, and says again, very deliberate, "Well, *I* don't see no p'ints about that frog that's any better'n any other frog."

Smiley he stood scratching his head and looking down at Dan'l a long time, and at last he says, "I do wonder what in the nation that frog throw'd off for – I wonder if there an't something the matter with him – he 'pears to look mighty baggy, somehow." And he ketched Dan'l by the nap of the neck, and lifted him up and says, "Why, blame my cats, if he don't weigh five pound!" and turned him upside down, and he belched out a double handful of shot. And then he see how it was, and he was the maddest man – he set the frog down and took out after that feller, but he never ketched him.

THE TERRACE, 1818

Helen Ashton

Novelist and literary biographer, Helen Ashton, was one of the first contemporary women writers to popularize historical fiction with her novels about William and Dorothy Wordsworth and the family of Jane Austen.

Belinda Grove is the story of a house and the chapter entitled "The Terrace 1818," is an evocative reconstruction of a tragic event involving card sharping and murder which occurred there during the Regency period.

IT WAS at Belinda Grove, in the autumn of 1818, that Lord Alciston, that notorious friend of the Prince Regent, was supposed to have met and murdered a naval captain in a duel.

My lord had taken the house at a time when its builder almost despaired of selling it, because of the value which he attached to its retired situation among the fields. He had furnished it with the taste and extravagance for which he was noted, and had established in it his mistress, Belinda Flower, a tall, ranting, full-bosomed Cyprian with a singularly beautiful and powerful voice, who had had some success in dramatic parts before my lord took her out of the green-room at Drury Lane and named Belinda Grove in her honour. She had other qualities of intelligence and cunning beside the beauty for which her protector had first chosen her; and she knew very well why he chose to bury her in such rural solitudes. She had his promise that she should return to London in due course, when the Grove had served its turn as a gambling-house in which he could pluck appointed victims at his leisure. She consoled herself for her exile as best she might, between his visits, lying in bed half the day, eating sweetmeats without regard for her figure, planning new gowns, and scolding her vinegar-faced lady's maid, Mrs Pretty, who had been a dresser at the Lane.

Lord Alciston had provided her with a small household of servants. Besides Mrs Pretty there were Mrs Pomfret, the cook; a couple of rosy country sluts who giggled together in the passages, did as little work as they could, and ogled the stable grooms; and the negro footman, Archelaus, who had been page to my lord's mother when such cattle were in fashion, and now languished in grizzled exile since my lord had taken a dislike, and Miss Flower a fancy, for his assiduous services. There was little for the lazy fellow to do except to open and shut doors for Miss Flower, stand at the back of her carriage when she went driving, loaf about the kitchen to steal sweets behind the cook's back, and get the basting-ladle about his ears when he stuck his black fingers into the creams and custards. The servants had an easy time when my lord was in town; but they were expected to make up for it when he was in residence.

On a certain November afternoon in 1818 he drove down in his yellow curricle, with the two tandem blacks, matched to a hair, and the Dalmatian carriage-dog running underneath. He brought with him a Corinthian crony from the bay-window at White's, Mr Francis Pye, whose face was familiar to the household at the villa. The guests who were strange to it were a young Mr Martlet, and his uncle, a naval captain, who posted down by chaise and arrived a little behind his lordship. Earlier in the day the yellow chariot had come with my lord's own man, Mr Litlington, of whom all the women servants were afraid, and his French cook, M Belchambre, who was reputed to make a better omelette than the Prince Regent's M Watier. They were accompanied by my lord's latest protégé, Sam Robins, the prize-fighter, formerly an apothecary's apprentice, who had been picked out from the young entry at Mendoza's school in the City Road. Lord Alciston prided himself on being a judge of the fancy and hoped great things from Robins, a well-built youth with a foxy head, broad shoulders, a slender waist and an air of quick-stepping confidence which was greatly admired by the women at Belinda Grove. They fluttered about him until Mr Litlington set them to their duties. Mrs

Pomfret bridled under the instructions of Belchambre, Mrs Pretty flounced off to answer Miss Flower's bell, and Sukey, the older and more flighty of the two house-maids, hurried upstairs and came down presently giggling, with a tale to tell. "The young gentleman's a handsome fellow, tall and yellow-haired and pleasant-spoken. He gave me half a guinea and tried to kiss me; but you can tell he's not had much practice. The uncle's a stiff old fellow, without a word to say to a girl; he's got as ugly a face as I've seen this twelvemonth. Mr Pye's just the same as usual. I met him on the stairs as I was coming down with my warming-pan. 'What's that for, child?' says he.

"'To air your bed with, sir,' says I, dropping my curtsey.

"'There are better ways of warming a bed than that,' says he, and gets his arm round me." She pulled a grimace at Polly's wide, startled eyes.

"Whatever did you do?" gasped the little maid, fresh that week from the country.

"I fended him off with the warming-pan, to be sure," Sukey boasted. "It's easy to manage Mr Pye. His bark is worse than his bite. If it had been my lord now, that would have been another matter. But he's got no eyes for anyone but Miss Flower."

"And pray why should he have eyes for anyone here?" demanded Mrs Pomfret awfully.

"Well, for my part, I prefer Mr Robins," giggled Sukey, edging up to the prize-fighter, who told her coolly, "Women are no use to me when I'm in training."

Thus ran the play belowstairs; above, in the bedroom with the bay window, Miss Flower was grumbling to my lord over the arrival of the strangers.

"Must you always bring such creatures, George, when you might be alone with me?"

"What do I keep this house for, except to pluck pigeons in at my leisure?" He smiled lazily at her, he thought her petulance amusing. She tossed her head, shrugged one fine shoulder, and allowed her body to droop towards him as if unconsciously; but he knew all her tricks.

"I thought you kept it to please me," she murmured. He put his arm round her waist as was expected of him, but showed a little impatience.

"Nonsense, my dear," he protested, pulling her on to his knee. "You'd be far happier in St John's Wood or Montpelier Row, where I could have more of your delightful company. I have other uses for this house, as you very well know, and you must help me for the present." He pinched her neck and then her ear, as she still kept her face averted.

"Come, kiss me and be reasonable, Belinda," he protested. "You must take a hand in to-night's affair. We shall have time for each other when we've trimmed those two fellows. Business first, pleasure afterwards."

She turned half round; he guessed that he had caught her attention. "This young Martlet is ripe for plucking," he told her, "and Franky and I are the boys to do it, with your help."

"Are you sure he's worth it? He looks like small game to me."

"That's where you're wrong, my girl." he pulled her closer and she did not resist him. "The boy's father is dead, and he has just come into a fine estate in Dorset. He knows nothing of cards and any fool can cheat him. Franky and I are on a hot scent, I tell you. The cards have been against me at White's since August and Franky has the Jews after him as usual. We can't afford to let that boy out of here till he's set us on our feet again."

"Then why did you let in that blockhead of a post-captain? He'll spoil your game. I can see it in his eye. He smells a rat somewhere. You should have left him out of it."

"Yes, plague take him; nobody asked him to come. He somehow managed to invite himself. My notion is, he means to look after his fool of a nephew. You'll have to divert him if you can, Belinda."

"He'd never look at me," said she, nibbling a finger anxiously. "The boy would be easy game, but not the uncle."

"We must try to make our profit out of both of them," declared my lord, yawning. "The Captain has been afloat since peace was declared and has only just touched his prize-money. Eight hundred pound is not much, but since he's here we may as well take what's left of it. I'll tell Litlington to keep his glass full at dinner."

"You'll not do it that way, George," observed the lady. "They've hard heads in the Navy."

"Well, if that don't serve we must try other methods. He may find the cards run against him. After all, this isn't Crockford's."*

"Oh, George," said she anxiously, "be careful how you play if you think he's suspicious."

"I'm always careful to lose at the beginning of the evening," said my lord, with a shrug for her fears.

They dined a little later in the newly furnished dining-room among all the elegancies with which Lord Alciston had tricked out his decoy-house – the Trafalgar chairs, the circular table supported by crouching, brass-footed lions, the spotted wallpaper against which the portraits hung by crimson cords, the mahogany sideboard with its urn-shaped knife-boxes at either end and its coffin-shaped cellaret beneath. As much state was kept up as in Grosvenor Square; the company were waited upon by Litlington in his decent black and Archelaus in a canary-coloured livery with his black hands concealed in white cotton gloves. Sukey and Polly tiptoed to the door and handed in the dishes, the oysters and French *entrées*, the pheasants from my lord's embarrassed estates in Worcestershire, the great rarity of a hothouse pineapple for dessert. Peeping through the crack, Polly got a candlelit picture of the five dining. Miss Flower was at the top of the table, in her red and gold finery, her bare shoulder to Mr Pye, who was eating steadily, choking in his folded neckcloth and flushed to the colour of his mulberry coat; her airs and graces were all for the noisy handsome boy beside her, or his uncle, frowning opposite over his wine. My lord had his back to the door; Polly could only see the shoulders of his high-collared yew-green coat and his chestnut curls haloed by candleshine; she peeped more freely once she knew that she was safe from his compelling, terrifying smile.

The gentlemen sat a great while over the wine from the cellars of Grosvenor Square; the servants had gone to their own dinner long before Miss Flower withdrew to the great drawing-room. It was the pride of her heart, with its Chinese flowered wallpaper, its yellow satin chairs and gilt mirrors, its marble hearth and malachite vases, and the Sphinx-headed sofa on which the men eventually found her reclining in a Grecian attitude, shielding her face from the fire with one affected hand. "I am hardly in voice to-night." she protested, when they came for their dish of tea, and young Mr Martlet, spying the gilt harp in the corner, begged for an Irish melody. My lord, however, cut short her ladylike protests with a glance from his heavy-lidded eyes; and the servants, tiptoe at the kitchen door, heard her mournful, melodious lament ringing for an hour through the house.

Lord Alciston and Mr Pye meanwhile had withdrawn to the fireside to talk of their own affairs, of Carlton House and Holland House, St James's and the Steyne, of Epsom and Newmarket, of prize-fights and cockpits and the public execution which they had attended at Newgate that morning. Captain Martlet showed his vexation when the singing was interrupted by Pye's loud voice, babbling, "No use your telling me to put my money on Robins, George. He's got a pretty style, I grant you, but sparring isn't fighting; and the best looker is often the worst stayer. I'll give you three to one that Sherry finishes him off inside ten rounds."

"Done with you – in thousands," said my lord, keeping his cool eye on the group round the harp-player. He judged that the domestic background had been sufficiently indicated, and presently he came forward with a negligent proposal for cards. Franky Pye and Belinda took the cue immediately; young Martlet accepted with enthusiasm; his uncle betrayed an obvious stiff reluctance, but Lord Alciston made it impossible for him to refuse and a bank at faro was arranged.

Nothing occurred over the green table before midnight which could arouse the suspicion of the most wary. Belinda staked and lost extravagantly with the money which my lord had given her for the purpose, Pye and the Captain played carefully with little gain or loss, the boy won enough from his host to make him confident; it was not until some hours had passed that he began to lose steadily, slowly and heavily. Captain Martlet had come expecting some such development, and he spurred himself to greater watchfulness. Except my lord, he was the most sober member of the party and a little attention betrayed to him the fact that his host was growing careless. Once and twice the sailor passed a doubtful opportunity; the third time he was quite certain that his eyes had not deceived him. The reckless, generous indignation which had hampered him throughout his life betrayed him once again to his undoing. Completely sober, he might have evaded the danger of the situation; as it was, he made quick movement, and there, before them all, was his brown, rough hand pinning down my lord's wrist. Belinda cried out, so did the startled boy; Mr Pye choked with amazement, Lord Alciston enquired with an oath what the Captain meant by stopping the deal. "I will apologise, my lord," said Martlet, "if the ace of spades is not under your hand."

There was a long pause, during which the sailor became uncomfortably conscious of a menacing silence about the players in that isolated, ill-reputed house. Lord Alciston did not trouble to deny or admit the justice of the accusation; neither did he make any movement to release his hand. He raised his fatigued eyelids as if it were an effort to look at his guest and said, in an indescribably offensive tone, "I don't like your Naval manners, Captain Martlet."

The Captain retorted, "I don't care for these accidental misdeals, sir." The boy made a nervous exclamation at that. Belinda said nothing; but her brilliant eyes went from one man to another, the gold collar on her naked bosom rose and fell, glittering uncertainly in the candlelight. Franky felt it his duty to try a little unsuccessful bluster: "Gentlemen, think what you're saying. George, you must have misunderstood Captain Martlet; sir, you can't have intended to accuse his lordship of – cheating." His voice cracked awkwardly upon the word; he realised too late that it would have been better left unspoken.

"That's just what I do mean," said the Captain, red-faced but obstinate. "That's what I believe we were brought down here for."

Franky mopped his brow anxiously; he was no longer so prompt in these emergencies as he had been in his youth. "There's only one way out of that," he muttered gloomily.

"Lord Alciston can please himself whether he fights or not," said the Captain, with a glum belated realisation of his own folly. "The card's there if he likes to turn it over." He withdrew his hand, but Lord Alciston kept his where it was, flat on the disputed card; the candlelight sparkled in an emerald which he wore on his signet finger.

"I suppose I shall have to meet the person, Franky," he said, in the tone in which he might have accepted an unwelcome invitation. "Act for me, will you, like a good fellow?" He leant back in his chair as if the matter had no further interest for him.

Franky stuttered a little over the arrangements. "No doubt your nephew will act for you, sir. His lordship has a pair of duelling pistols here, I believe." Captain Martlet bowed and looked as if the information hardly surprised him.

"Shall we say the lawn outside these windows, in an hour's time?" mumbled Franky, looking rather helplessly at the nephew. "The light will scarcely serve earlier."

The boy, who was quite without experience in such matters, glanced at his uncle for support.

"The earlier the better," said Captain Martlet. "I go on board my ship to-morrow at Chatham, and I wish to be in time for the coach."

"I trust that you will be able to do so," said Mr Pye gravely. "If you wish for a surgeon, there is none nearer than Islington, but Mr Robins has some experience in these matters."

"I daresay he'll do very well for anyone that needs him," observed the sailor, and then, "If that's all settled, I think I'll go to my room. Perhaps, Mr Pye, you'll be so good as to see that they send me up writing materials. I have a few matters to arrange. Dick, you'd better come with me. If this is your first affair of the kind, you'll be none the worse for a hint or two on how to behave." He made a stiff, awkward, but not undignified bow to the three who remained at the table, and marched out; the boy slunk after him, sobered and trembling. Their footsteps echoed across the marble pavement of the hall and died into the expectant quiet of the house.

My lord and his companions, left alone, looked at each other a little doubtfully; Alciston then lifted his hand, smiling slightly, and disclosed the ace of spades.

"You're out of practice with that trick, George," observed Belinda, with an unconvincing laugh.

"I'm in better practice with my duelling pistols," Lord Alciston admitted.

"I'm sure I hope so," said Franky, who seemed worried. "You must make sure of finishing the fellow off. It won't do to have this sort of tale getting about."

"Well," said my lord, "you can manage the loading, I suppose, as you did with the Scotchman last year. That cub won't see what you're doing if you're careful, and as I've been challenged I get first pick. If we can't manage that we must trust to my being quicker on the draw. We'll find some way of keeping the boy quiet afterwards." They exchanged no further glances; they understood each other perfectly.

"See to the wine, Belinda," Lord Alciston said.

The Captain meanwhile, in the uncertain shadows of a candlelit bedroom on the first floor, was cursing his nephew, who sat with hanging head, trying to realise what had happened.

"Perhaps this'll teach you to be a little more careful about playing with strangers. I told you the fellow was crooked and the other two in league with him. Cleverer men than you have been down here to listen to that woman's music and leave their money behind them." That first rage expended, he fell to blaming himself.

"To think of a man of my experience letting himself be trapped in a den like this. It makes me sick." He began to fling his few belongings together in his valise; he had only brought what the night needed; his sea-chest had gone to Rochester already.

"Not that I'm likely to need this dunnage again," he muttered grimly. "You can take it back home when you go, if ever you get out of this place with a whole skin, which isn't likely."

The boy was horrified and perplexed.

"But you can't tell which way a fair fight will go, Uncle." The sailor gave a short hard laugh.

"It won't be a fair fight, my lad, if they can help it. They daren't let this tale get about London; they must stop our mouths. Keep your eyes as wide open as you can – not that you'll be up to their tricks. Anyhow, I'm no match for a blackguard like Alciston. These fellows keep themselves in practice with the pistol, year in, year out. No, the *Candace* is like to sail with a new captain this voyage." And striding up and down, his preparations made, he growled, "This duelling is a barbarous, out-of-date business, and men like Pye and Alciston live by it. I should have remembered that and held my tongue. I had other work to do than to run my head into their net. They knew I couldn't get out of it, in uniform; they forced my hand, and I lost my temper, as I always do. I should have sat back and let you lose your money, you fool. Now listen to me, for we've little time to lose and perhaps you'll remember what I've got to say. About the Staunton estate, now. . . ." He had been his nephew's guardian until he came of age. He silenced the boy's tears and protestations by a stream of coarse but kindly invective mixed with shrewd practical advice, while the fire fell into ashes and the breadth of sky between the half-drawn curtains turned grey, like a dead man's face.

Polly and Sukey slept together in an attic under the cornice of the roof; it was lit by a curious circular window which pierced the centre of an ornamental pediment and overlooked the garden. Being country girls, they woke at six, and it was Sukey, huddling on her clothes and shuddering in the cold, who pinched Polly's arm in sudden excitement and dragged her to the window.

Something was happening in the garden. The Captain had come out and was striding up and down the terrace in front of the classical temple, as if he were on his own quarter-deck. He was bare-headed, but wrapped in an old, faded boat-cloak; he kept his hands in his armpits to warm them against the cold. His nephew turned and paced with him, always a step or two behind, like an anxious dog; they talked together in low voices. Almost immediately the prize-fighter came out in his tall white hat, blue-spotted neckerchief and many-caped coat, with a polished rosewood box under his arm. Sukey, the experienced, squeaked at that, "Lord, the gentlemen are going to fight."

"What, the Captain and his nephew?" gaped Polly.

"Of course not, you fool! Look, here come the others."

My lord had just stepped through the French windows, wrapped in his furred driving-cloak; Mr Pye, who was with him, left his side and went across the lawn, making a trail of deep footmarks in its frosted rime. He bowed to the Martlets as he approached the flight of steps which led up to the temple; the boy, nudged by his uncle, descended them awkwardly.

"Shall we step out our distances, sir?" said Pye formally. "Twenty paces is the usual thing."

The boy glanced at his uncle and got an impatient, "Go on, Dick." He went down with Pye to measure the ground, a matter of which he plainly knew nothing; he allowed the other man to select a pistol and load it. He watched the charge, wad, bullet being rammed home, he examined the priming, but he failed to notice, in his flurry, that no powder trickled through the touch-hole. He himself loaded the second pistol of the pair, which had, as it happened, a particular mark on the handle. My lord selected this weapon without hesitation and flung off cloak and coat with an air as he took his stand. Captain Martlet, dropping his mantle, turned up the collar of his uniform; he preferred to show no linen as a mark. He accepted the remaining pistol and weighed it in his hand, not expecting it to be of much service to him; he gave a final glance at the pale, classic, innocent-seeming house, behind whose noble outlines the sky was beginning to redden; he thought that probably it would be his last sight upon earth. He said to his nephew testily, "Stand out of the light, man." Mr Pye, raising his voice, intoned, "Gentlemen, I shall say *attention! fire!* and count *one, two, three.* You will fire after the word *two* and before the word *three.* Are you ready? Then, *attention! fire! one, two—*"

My lord fired instantly and accurately; the sailor's weapon missed fire and he dropped, choking and gasping; my lord's bullet was in his lungs.

"Scuppered, by George," said Pye, coming up with the prize-fighter. "Here, my boy, don't lay him flat. Hold him up and let Robins look at him. Not that it's much use," he added under his breath. The dying man made a frightful effort to speak; but the blood spattered from his mouth and choked him; he rolled from the boy's knee to the frosty shadow of the hedge. Young Martlet tried, but failed, to lift him up again.

"Let him alone," said Robins coolly. "He's dead by now." He knelt and straightened the sailor's limbs expertly, then picked a tuft of grass and cleaned his hands on it. Young Martlet, still on his knees, with his agonised face turned up to the indifferent men about him, stammered, "But his pistol didn't go off. He never fired at all."

"Some damned incompetent blunder of yours in the loading, I expect," said Lord Alciston, coming up and holding out his own weapon to Mr Pye, who had already picked up the dead man's pistol and returned it unobtrusively to the rosewood box.

"Some blackguardly foul play," stammered young Martlet, getting to his feet and glaring uncertainly from one to the other.

"You think so, do you, young puppy?" said Alciston, who was getting into his coat. "Here, Robins." He snapped his fingers as to a watch-dog, just in time. The prize-fighter, who had guessed the boy's intention as quickly as his master, stepped between the two and stopped Martlet's undisciplined rush with a blow on the point of the chin, which sent him sprawling on the grass.

"Thanks, Robins," said my lord, buttoning up his coat.

Mr Pye knelt by the young man's unconscious body and felt his wrist, then, more carefully, his heart; the boxer stood by uneasily.

"Gave him a bit more than you meant, didn't you?" commented Pye, looking up at him.

"How was I to know you wanted him treated tender?" grumbled Robins, examining his skinned knuckles. My lord buttoned his coat and asked indifferently, "Is the boy dead?"

"No, but he's in pretty bad shape," said Pye seriously. "Not Robins' fault, though. Look, he cracked his skull on that holly-root, coming down. The back of his head's bleeding."

"He's only knocked out," persisted Robins sulkily.

"George," said Belinda, deciding to cross the grass after all, "there'll be trouble about this. We shall have to think of a tale between us."

"Think of one yourself," said my lord, biting his nails. "Women are quicker at that kind of thing. The fellow told me I cheated at cards and we fought over it; that's regular enough, surely?"

"Better go over to Paris for a month or two, perhaps," said Belinda, "and take Robins with you. Duelling is going out of fashion nowadays, and we must smooth the business over. Say he went off early this morning, when the game was finished, before the servants were about. We don't know what kept him from joining his ship. I'll have this boy taken to the inn, with some story about a drunken fall, and keep an eye on him. If he dies of this, well and good; if he remembers enough to start a story, Franky must deal with him. It's only his word against all of us. . . ."

PROMOTING A COMPANY
or
SHRIMPS FOR THE MILLION

Samuel Bracebridge Hemyng

The author of *Sensational Tales of the Stock Exchange* was Samuel
Bracebridge Hemyng, surprisingly not a stockbroker himself
but a barrister of London's Middle Temple. Since it is
recorded that he was a student of law in 1843 and yet was not
called to the bar until nearly twenty years later, we can only
assume that Samuel Bracebridge Hemyng spent more time
writing than he did studying law. Indeed, he was the chief
contributor to *Boys of England*, "a magazine of Sport, Sensation, Fun and Instruction," an example of a class of literature
popularly known as "penny dreadfuls."

"Shrimps for the Million" is an acutely observed story
demonstrating that promoters of "concept" stocks were as
active a century ago as they are today. The parallel between
the stock exchange and the roulette wheel may seem to be
drawn rather melodramatically at the end of the story, but for
most stock market operators like Mr John Jeffries, it is only a
matter of time before the zero comes up.

IN THIS STORY, for obvious reasons, neither the real names of the parties
interested nor that of the company are correctly given, the object being to
show up a type of men who haunt the precincts of the city, and make it
their business to deceive the unwary. Not so long ago, every year proved
that a large section of the public was easily gulled, and that one of the
simplest ways of making money was to promote a company. Visions of
large profits were the spider's web, into which the flies fell, and so long as
people were not satisfied with a fair return for their money, they were
dazzled by undertakings which were never destined to be honoured by the
Stock Exchange with either an authorised quotation or a settling day. We

may premise, however, that the main incidents in the following burlesque of a sham company are strictly founded on fact, the chief victim being still alive, though shattered in mind and body.

Our space will not allow us to refer to the giants who settled large fortunes on their wives out of the proceeds of their bubble companies, and still prosper and flourish. We shall have something to say on this point, perhaps, in a subsequent volume.

Mr John Jeffries was a promoter of companies, and a member of some West End clubs, where baccarat is played for high stakes. Sometimes he took a run over to Monaco and punted at the tables. "Make your game, gentlemen," was a phrase he was well acquainted with. *Le jeu est fait, rien ne va plus.* He would watch the colours carefully, seize what he thought a favourable opportunity and put down his stake, and generally win. Taking his winnings, he would refrain from a laudable desire to break the bank, and next day Monaco would know him no more. He might be playing cards at the English club at Cannes, or strolling on the *Promenade des Anglais* at Nice. In fact he was a snapper-up of unconsidered trifles – all was fish that came to his net.

When he played cards he did not scruple to cheat, but he was so skilled that he seldom got found out. At poker he was a proficient, and he rarely failed to have three of a kind to beat two pair when it came to calling; he could bluff with a grave face, and was not afraid to raise the ante on a couple of trays. When he was once paying a flying visit to Ostend, he was very neatly bowled out. The game was unlimited loo, and he was playing at the club. A looker-on whispered to him, "I will stand in with you."

Jeffries shook his head.

"I say I will stand in with you, sir," repeated the stranger.

"No."

"I say I will!"

"Why should you?" asked Jeffries, in the same low tone.

"You are playing crooked, and I can prove it."

"All right. Keep quiet," said Jeffries, inwardly inclined to bite the fellow's head off.

"I said I should stand in," remarked the 'cute stranger with a smile; and during the rest of the play he kept account of Jeffries' gains.

When the latter rose from the table, they went outside and divided the spoil according to arrangement.

"Are you satisfied?" asked Jeffries, savagely, as the man pocketed the notes and gold.

"Quite; thank you. Ah! you're a wonder," was the reply.

"What?"

"A masterpiece. How did you do it? Captain Threestars was playing crooked too."

"Was he?"

"Yes. He had a card up his sleeve."

"Why didn't you stand in with him?"

"I spotted you first."

"Just like my luck."

"But how you could play against Captain Threestars puzzles me."

"My dear fellow," replied Jeffries, carelessly; "if he had a card up his sleeve, I always have two in my boots."

Yet at the age of forty he was no better off than he had been at twenty-five. All he possessed was a few hundreds in his drawing account at the City and Country Bank, the manager of which had such an opinion of his character and integrity, that he would neither discount for him or allow him to overdraw. In fact, he knew him too well to allow him such favour, but at the same time he did one thing for him, which managers of banks ought not to be permitted to do, by law. It often happened that Jeffries used to run his account so low, that without actually closing it, he would not have a balance of more than £5 to his credit. Nevertheless, he would give cheques with characteristic recklessness, and instead of returning them marked "N.S." or "not sufficient," the manager would return them endorsed "Refer to Drawer," which saved him from unpleasant consequences.

Many stories were told of him in the City.

At the Magatherium Club he was giving young Lord Headlong a dinner for a purpose. He never threw a dinner away. *Ecarté* was proposed; they adjourned to the card-room and played. His lordship lost £1,000.

"Hang it," he cried, "you always win."

"So much the better for me," replied Jeffries, folding up his lordship's cheque.

"I can't get in at all."

"So much the worse for you."

"Give me a chance."

"Certainly, if it gives me an equal one."

Jeffries did not care to give an opponent any advantage; he could not waste time in frivolity. Time with him was money, and he held that poverty was worse than a sin – it was a crime.

"We had a ripe Stilton at dinner," continued Lord Headlong. "Come to the dining-room, we will each have a plate, and put a maggot in the middle."

"Well?"

"The first maggot off wins."

"What is the stake?"

"Double or quits."

"Agreed," said Jeffries.

Entering the dining-room, Jeffries called a waiter.

"The Stilton," he exclaimed. "Two plates."

"Yes, sir."

And lowering his voice to a whisper, so as not to be heard by Lord Headlong, he added, "Hot mine."

The waiter nodded, and carried out his orders.

Lord Headlong selected a fine fat maggot; so did Jeffries. They held them in the bowls of two spoons, and dropped them on the plates as near the centre as possible. His lordship's made tracks for the side; Jeffries' jumped right off in two jumps.

"D— the brute," said Lord Headlong in disgust. "I never saw such a beastly lively maggot."

And with an ill grace he paid the second thousand.

But the most extraordinary thing of all was Jeffries lived for three years on a brickbat.

This was how he did it.

He invented what he called an aërated brick, for which he took out a patent. He had a sample brick made of white clay. It was perforated with holes, from which it was supposed to derive its hygienic and sanitary properties. He influenced men of position in it, and got up companies to bring it out, which collapsed one after the other, but he secured the promotion money. One day he met the well-known Mr X. coming out of his private room. Mr X. had often seen him hanging about the office, but, taking him for one of the Touting Brigade, had always refused to see him. He had under his arm a neat brown paper parcel, tied with pink tape.

"Can I speak with you privately?" asked Jeffries.

"What for?" asked X.

"To propose a plan. There is a fortune in this little parcel."

Mr X. led him inside.

"What does it contain?" he asked, "a steam-engine?"

"No. I have driven my carriage on it, but I haven't pushed it lately."

"Is it a new motive-power?"

"Again, no! I have lived on it for three years, and I want to interest an enterprising gentleman like yourself in it. Let me show it you."

He undid wrapper after wrapper and disclosed a brick.

"Aid me in getting up a company for it," he added.

"Where are your works?"

"We want none. The public will subscribe. They like bricks."

But he had come to the wrong shop this time. Mr X. gently pushed him out of the door, and threw his brick after him.

In addition to this, we may mention that he had a small house at Bexley Heath, where he resided with his wife and six children. A peculiar thing about rogues is that they generally have a wife and family to drag down when they fall. Sometimes the family ties are useful, they excite sympathy among his acquaintances: "for the sake of his wife and little ones, you know," is quite a familiar phrase. We have all heard it, and overlooked misdeeds. During his varied and chequered career, Jeffries had been the proprietor of a sauce, also a hair raiser. There was no hidden sarcasm in this, though he was saucy enough and had often raised people's hair by his wild-cat schemes. It sold well, and he disposed of the patent for a considerable sum, when at his lowest ebb he had started a barber's shop, where you could have your hair cut and get a bowl of soup for fourpence. His inventive genius did not stop here. Feeling that the bronchial sufferings of humanity ought to be relieved, he made up a cough mixture, which he advertised very extensively. Thousands had reason to bless it, though the principal ingredients were tincture of opium and syrup of squills. He sold this too, and started the Sea Water Supply Company, the bill for which however, he could not get through Parliament. He followed this with the Marriage Mart and Universal Matrimonial Agency, which came to an end through the conduct of the infuriated persons whom he introduced to one another. They contracted marriage; they did not like it, so they came down in a body, and wrecked his premises. Jeffries narrowly escaped with his life, one metamorphosed spinster of doubtful age threatening him with death.

He next interested himself in an Aerial Electric Locomotion Company, but though the company eventually went up in the air, the machines never did. His genius after that blossomed forth in the West-End Sedan Chair Company, it being his idea that fashionable ladies would like to be conveyed to parties and balls in Sedan chairs, as they were in the days of good Queen Anne. His models were highly approved, and the uniforms of his bearers pronounced perfect. Some old East Indians, who had not forgotten their palanquin journeys, took shares, but the public persistently preferred cabs and broughams, so the West-End Sedan Chair Company collapsed; but he had made a few thousands out of it. From all his undertakings, rotten and bad as they undoubtedly were, he cleared money, and might have done well if his evil genius had not at last induced him to go in for electric lights. Even then he would have made 120 per cent., but like a good many more victims, he held on for 300. It galvanised him. It shook him up; and he facetiously called the company The Electric Liver and Lights. Gas was to be nowhere. Pimlico, Fulham, and the districts where the hideous gasometers find a home were jubilant, for the inhabitants thought they would be done away with, but the gasometers still exist, and the Electric Liver and Lights is dead.

Though Jeffries was a schemer, we may mention that he was passionately attached to his wife and children, who were all very good-looking; the boys being handsome and manly, the girls beautiful. If he schemed it was for the sake of his family. Call him a mercenary villain, if you will; it was not for himself he laboured. He stood at nothing where money was concerned. His wife and he had known one another in their youth. He loved her; but they were parted. They met again, and were married. He worked hard, and never took a holiday. If he went abroad it was to make money. If he was harsh to men he was a child to a woman. His wife sings an old song, he turns away his head and cries; yet he would crush a man under his heel in business. On a Sunday he had taken his family to Windsor to see the beeches and the deer, and romped about like a boy in the old park. On Monday he was issuing prospectuses of an undertaking which would ruin hundreds.

He had once been bold enough to stand for Parliament. It was a metropolitan constituency for which he stood, but he retired in disgust before going to the poll. Innumerable deputations of women waited upon him, representing every real and fancied grievance: one lot objected to pictures representing nude studies being exhibited in the galleries; another wanted to regulate the social evil, representing that shop girls should be watched by the police, as comparatively respectable women had taken the place of the professional abandoned creatures of twenty years ago; in fact, he had no idea of the number of busybodies there are ready to ventilate grievances, evils, and abuses, until he endeavoured to become a public man.

His great friend who assisted him in all his enterprises was a man of about his own age, named Charles Bayldon, who had been a bookmaker, but was obliged to relinquish that lucrative profession because he one Monday neglected to settle with his creditors, and was posted at Tattersall's Subscription Room as a defaulter. He now described himself as an agent, and did a little business for customers, whom he met principally in taverns, though he was privileged to transact business in one of the two rooms which Jeffries rented in Bucklersbury. One morning in early spring Jeffries arrived at the Cannon Street Station at ten o'clock, and proceeded to his office, where he found Bayldon waiting for him, he having been summoned by letter to attend to new and important business. They shook hands, lighted their cigars, told the half-a-crown-a-week boy, who acted in the capacity of clerk, that they were visible to nobody, and retired into the inner room, which was marked "private."

"What's in the wind now?" asked Bayldon, expectantly.

"Money, my dear fellow," replied Jeffries, who was always optimistic in his views. "Money, and lots of it I hope."

"Another company?"

"Just so," said Jeffries, oracularly.

"I should have thought you had had enough of that line of business," remarked Bayldon, "after the Marriage Mart, the Sedan, the Aerated Brick, and the Electric Liver and Lights."

"This time I shall make a hit," interrupted Jeffries, "a palpable hit. The idea occurred to me all in a moment. I had been spending a few days at Southend, and walked over to Leigh. Now, what is Leigh famous for?"

"Mud," replied Bayldon, stroking his moustache with a ruminant air.

"No, my good man, it is where all the shrimps come from. I made the acquaintance of a fisherman named Trawler. He has got half a dozen smacks and nets to sell, with an old barn thrown in. We can buy the lot for a song, and have a going concern, lock, stock, and barrel."

"What for?"

"The London and Provincial Shrimp Breeding, Catching and Canning Company, Limited; works at Leigh, Essex," said Jeffries, earnestly. "You see, land for breeding purposes could easily be acquired. We shall soon have money in the bank."

"The mud bank, you mean."

"You know what I mean. We will buy a part of the foreshore of the river. Now, pay attention. Shrimps are scarce, shrimps are dear, and they are undoubtedly a favourite article of food with the masses. I ask you, what a Bank Holiday would be without shrimps? Would not Hampstead Heath become a howling waste, and Greenwich a desert without its teas and shrimps at ninepence a head? You can get your Souchong mildly tempered with Pekoe at two shillings per pound, but you cannot obtain the indispensable, the appetising, the all-absorbing shrimp for less than sixpence a quart, and the supply is deficient at that. The L. and P.S.B.C. and C.Company will cheapen and tend to still more popularise the shrimp. It will be a food for the people. The eye of the dyspeptic will glisten, for your fine fat fresh shrimp is as easy of digestion as an oyster; the innocent face of childhood will be wreathed with smiles, for what child ever despised his shrimp? the facial muscles of the horny handed son of toil will relax; the Blue Ribbon man will feel his heart expand, and the drinker will become gay, for all know what the shrimp is to a thirsty man; the comely matron will become more comely; in fact, we shall supply a long felt want. It will be a sweet boon to one and all, to rich and poor – the coroneted earl and the ill-fed, underpaid artisan. What the people want is cheap shrimps and plenty of them."

John Jeffries paused to get his breath.

"What do you think of it?" he asked, presently.

"Very good," replied Bayldon. "The possibilities of the company are infinite. We could add dabs, and might rise to oysters."

"Of course. I never thought of dabs or natives."

"And yet you are a dab at astonishing the natives," said Bayldon, perpetrating a mild joke.

"Don't be frivolous. Sit down and draw up the usual document. 'Articles of Agreement entered into between Charles Bayldon of the one part, acting on behalf of the London and Provincial Shrimp Breeding, Catching, and Canning Company, Limited, hereinafter called the Company, and Mr Timothy Trawler, for the purchase of —' You know how to go on."

"Yes, yes. I've got it by heart."

"Then write out the prospectus. I want to get the advertisements out as quick as possible. Offices of the company, here; bankers, City and Country. Put old File down as solicitor. My father-in-law and your brother will do as directors, with the baronet as chairman."

Taking pen, ink, and paper, Bayldon began to write facilely, for this kind of work was familiar to him, and while he is at work we will say a word about the directors. Mr Morley Morley, the father-in-law of Jeffries, was a tenant farmer, of no means, of the Uplands Farm, near Chelmsford, which sounded well in the prospectus. Mr Christopher Tatton Bayldon kept a grocer's shop at Highgate Rise, and had confined himself to his Christian names for some time past, owing to an irregularity in his accounts discovered by his creditors under his third bankruptcy, which had necessitated his withdrawal from public life for the space of six months on a judge's order. The baronet alluded to was Sir Augustus de Sarcenet Drake, who, for a couple of pounds a week, payable in advance, was always ready and willing to allow Jeffries to use his name in connection with his undertakings. He lodged in a small road, built on an estate called Bolingbroke Park, in a southern suburb, but he was invariably described as Sir Augustus de S. Drake, Bolingbroke Park, S.W., which looked very well in print.

"I've done the prospectus," said Bayldon, laying down his pen after a time.

"Very well; let us see how you've baited the hook," replied Jeffries, who had been busily figuring in a note book as to the estimated profits of the first twelve months, the amount of income over expenditure showing several thousand pounds net, and an approximate dividend of 50 per cent.

He looked as pleased as the young broker who went into the "House," and by a fluke made a sovereign in a minute and spent the rest of the day calculating, if he made a pound a minute every day, how much he would be worth at the end of the year.

Bayldon handed him a sheet of foolscap paper, on which was written –

The London and Provincial Shrimp Breeding, Catching, and Canning Company Limited. Capital, £30,000 in 30,000 shares of £1 each. Payable 5s. per share on application, and 15s on allotment.

Incorporated under the Companies' Acts 1862 to 1880, whereby the liability of shareholders is strictly limited to the amount of their shares.

DIRECTORS.
Sir Augustus de S. Drake, Bart., Bolingbroke Park, S.W.
Morley Morley, Esquire, The Uplands, Chelmsford, Essex.
Christopher Tatton, Esquire, The Rise, Highgate, London.
With power to add to their number.
Bankers: The City and Country, Bartholomew Lane, E.C.
Solicitor: W. Sharpe File, Clement's Inn.
Secretary pro tem: Charles Bayldon, Esquire.
Office: 175, Bucklersbury, London.

"That won't do," said Jeffries.

"What do you object to?" asked Bayldon.

"You ought to know better than to put yourself down as secretary."

"I forgot."

"Of course you did. Hang it all! we must start the company at the expense of the secretary."

"I only put myself in temporarily; we will advertise for a victim at once."

"Yes. We want one with about £2,000," said Jeffries.

Bayldon was a practical man, and saw the point at once. He was always sharp, short, and business-like. They said in the City that he was the hero of the longest and shortest correspondence on record.

His tailor had written to him every three months for seven years for his account. At last he replied: – "Sir, – Your letters to hand. If you annoy me any more I shall put the matter in the hands of my solicitor."

"The baronet is a good card," remarked Bayldon.

"I count on Sir Augustus to float the company, and the public to support it," answered Jeffries.

"He wants his fees in advance."

"Oh! I always humour Sir Augustus, though I once lost a good director by giving him his money before it was due; he withdrew; it frightened him; he thought the concern looked fishy."

"That's what they'll say of the Shrimp Breeding, Catching, and Canning Company."

"I spoiled a respectable man," sighed Jeffries, thinking of his lost director.

"Good L—! it wouldn't spoil me," laughed Bayldon.

"We can sell for cash and go on credit," continued Jeffries, recurring to his shrimps.

"You can acquire a retail business for a small sum. There is old Loader, who keeps a fish stall near the station, his stock usually consists of two lobsters and a pint of shrimps."

Jeffries laughed.

"It is a very old established business," added Bayldon, "and will go cheap to an immediate purchaser for prompt cash."

There was another laugh.

"By G—! old man, you're in it," Bayldon concluded, "and it will be good news for the baronet."

"Yes, he'll see a chance of paying his washerwoman," remarked Jeffries, "and his eyes will glisten."

"I've heard him say she's a tight 'un."

"I reckon she is about the only creditor he does pay."

"Laundresses and bakers are troublesome, and so are milkmen," exclaimed Bayldon, reflectively.

"Do you speak from experience?"

"Yes, I often drink champagne at home, though I greatly prefer milk."

"Why?"

"Because I can't get milk without money, and I've always plenty of champagne in the house; the wine merchant only sends in his bill once in six or twelve months."

"Well, how do you like my scheme?" asked Jeffries.

"It will be the greatest success you ever invented," returned Bayldon.

"I thought of bringing out a lead mine, but—"

"Bah! mines are no good; mines stink. Now listen to the prospectus."

"I am ready."

Bayldon began to read the particulars he had jotted down.

This was rather a lengthy affair, so we will only take the heads of it. The directors invited subscriptions for the shares of the above-named company, to enable them to purchase the fishing smacks, nets, premises, and plant generally of Timothy Trawler, Esq., fish merchant, of Leigh Essex, and to extend and develop the already existing large business done in catching and forwarding shrimps to the London and other markets; also to breed, pot, and can shrimps, a very lucrative trade in which could be done by a judicious outlay of capital. All companies engaged in the fishing trade were making enormous profits, and the company would have almost an exclusive field, which justifies the directors in anticipating a most satisfactory return to the shareholders.

The only contract entered into is one dated the 10th day of May between Mr Timothy Trawler of the one part, and Charles Bayldon of the other part, as trustee of the company, for the purchase of certain property, which, together with the articles of association, can be seen at the office of the solicitor.

Prospectuses and forms of application may be obtained from the bankers, solicitor, or from the secretary at the company's offices. In the event of no allotment being made to an applicant, the deposit will be returned in full. If a smaller number of shares are allotted than applied for, the surplus deposit will be credited towards the amount payable upon allotment.

Then followed a dissertation on shrimps, their market value, their fecundity, and their popularity. It was argued that a plentiful supply at sixpence the quart, retail measure, would enormously increase the consumption, and one came to the end of the prospectus with the firm conviction impressed on the mind that the social elevation of the masses was only to be effected by the means of cheap and abundant shrimps, for which the people of England had long been craving. They were to regenerate mankind, and build up the condition of succeeding generations of this great empire. One marvelled why the apostle of shrimp culture had never risen in our midst before, but the gap was to be stopped at last, and the country saved from speedy perdition. The adipose tissue and manly bearing of our shrimp-fed population in Essex was pointed to with pride, and it was clear that halcyon days were in store for us.

Jeffries made a few corrections, excisions, and additions, after which he expressed himself satisfied with the prospectus. The same day he went to Leigh with Bayldon, and bought the property that old Trawler wished to sell. In fact the boats were worn out, the nets full of holes, the boilers leaky, and the barn in a tumble-down condition. Trawler had had enough of shrimping, and wanted to go into the beer-house line, which offered a more congenial sphere to him. He was glad enough to get rid of his plant at any price, but Jeffries was equally pleased to obtain it, because it gave him something to work upon. Returning to London, he gave the manifold copy of the prospectus to the papers and awaited results. The baronet seeing his name in the paper, over his matutinal coffee, was one of the first to call. Having an income, as he would often observe jocosely, of nothing a year, paid quarterly, he recognised the fact that he was entitled to something, and did not deem it prudent to let capital, however small, lie idle. Money was at all times needed by him, for he had an unquenchable thirst, which was as expensive to him as a taste for orchids is to a duchess. Fully expecting him, Jeffries had a cheque ready on his desk, which, after shaking hands, he presented. It was for a month's pay as director at two guineas a week, and Sir Augustus pocketed it with a nod intended to convey his thanks.

"What's this new swindle?" he asked, irreverently.

"My dear sir, how can you talk like that?" replied Jeffries, greatly shocked, "It's the grandest idea of the present century."

"Humbug!" said Sir Augustus, "any one would think you were a Mahdi, going to bring about a millennium; but you can give me some shares if you think they will go to a premium."

"Sure to. We shall have them at three above par before the week's out. I'm having fifty got ready in your name."

"Can I borrow anything on them?" inquired the baronet, his eyes twinkling in a merry manner.

"Why not?"

"Say as collateral security for a bill of £170."

"Try it; they ought to be as good as a bank note to you," said Jeffries.

"Or a new pawn ticket," laughed Sir Augustus; "their value will only decrease with age. Oh, you can do it. I believe you'd take the pence out of a blind man's hat, or run away with a railway arch if you could carry it."

"How well he knows me," remarked Jeffries.

"Got any specimens? Pegwell Bays are my favourites," asked Sir Augustus.

"You must come down to the fishery," answered Jeffries. "This time we are on the right track, and have a sure fortune in hand."

Sir Augustus de Sarcenet Drake whistled.

"Upon my word, Jeffries," he remarked, "I sometimes fancy you tell 'em till you believe what you are saying. However, it does not make a pin's worth of difference to me. All I want is a cheque in advance. When do you hold your first board meeting?"

"You shall have due notice," was the rather dry answer.

"Where's Charley?"

"Bayldon? Oh, he's round the corner, I suppose. You generally know where to find him."

The baronet waved an adieu with his ungloved and not scrupulously clean hands – they said all his landed property was under his nails – leaving Jeffries to speculate as to the success of his new venture. Jeffries looked at his window on which was painted, "Mr John Jeffries, Financial Agent," and at a slip of paper placed underneath, on which was written the name of the new company. He could not help feeling that he was a clever fellow, but at the same time he wondered how it was he never made a fortune. It was true he lived. But how? From hand to mouth, as it were. Figuratively, the wolf was always barking at his door. He longed for rest; he wanted to get out of the busy, whirling maelstrom of City life. In reality, this man liked pastoral pursuits; he could have been contented in a cottage with a large garden growing fruit and flowers and vegetables, rearing poultry, and varying the monotony of such a life with a little fishing and shooting, always provided that he had his wife and children with him. But these things were not to be his. Similarly to Ixion he was bound to his wheel, and if he wanted to wear purple and fine linen he must spin to get it. While he was plotting and planning his clerk brought him a lady's card, which had engraved on it "Mrs Haydon, Brook Street, Grosvenor Square." He ordered his visitor to be admitted. She was a handsome, middle-aged woman, dressed in deep mourning. She had blue eyes and brown hair, and was of the Irish type. Mary Haydon had married an elderly man for his money. She had not loved him. In fact, she had never yet seen the man she could love. She was a pretty woman and a flirt. Now that her husband was dead she wanted association, feeling that she could not live alone. But she could not find what she wanted, but directly she saw Jeffries she felt that she could love him. It is so with many of us. We look round for years. At last we say, "This is the one I want." We know not why; we care not why. Yet it is so. Let each one ask his own heart. Jeffries was not a handsome man for a woman to fall in love with, but he was fascinating, and pleased women. He saw from her facial expression that she liked him, and he determined to take advantage of the weakness and get her money. All the time, however, he was strictly true and loyal to his wife and children. In her hand she held a newspaper, in which she had marked an advertisement of his. It set forth, among other things, that he was prepared to give advice to intending investors, and she explained her business at once by informing him that she was the widow of a physician who had left her fifteen thousand pounds, invested at three per cent., half of which she wanted to speculate with. She wished to see what she could do with seven thousand. At present this sum only brought her in an income of two hundred and ten pounds. What could she do for the best? She had heard that in the City, by taking shares in companies, she could treble or quadruple it. Was this true? Did not Electric Lights show a large profit?"

"They did not," replied Mr Jeffries, "but he had in his hands the very thing that would just suit her," and he presented her with a proof of the prospectus of the L. and P. S. B. C. and C. Company, upon the prospects of which he took advantage of the opportunity to dilate.

"I am willing," said Mrs Haydon, "to follow your advice, but I do hope you are not mistaken in your estimate of the probable profits of this concern, as I have young children, whose future I have to study."

"My dear madam, the prospectus speaks for itself. Everyone eats shrimps. We shall do an enormous business. You have come just in time," replied Jeffries, "for I expect that by to-morrow the shares will have been applied for twice over."

159

"I heard of a lady who invested in some oil shares, and after a time the wells dried up."

"Shrimps can never be exhausted, and people will eat them as long as England is a country."

So eloquent and enthusiastic did Jeffries become, that Mrs Haydon was persuaded to invest her surplus cash in the company. He called several times on her at her house. In the end she gave the promoter a cheque for seven thousand pounds he presenting her in return with a receipt for the amount, promising to have the shares ready for her in a day or two. His first care was to go to her bank and get the money in notes and gold. These he put in his side pocket. He felt as if he was treading on air. The idea of devoting the cash to the interests of the company did not occur to him for a moment. Feeling that it was a time when inspiration might be derived from the consumption of champagne, he strolled into a restaurant, where he met several friends, who congregated round him at once.

"Hullo, Jeff!" cried one.

"Here's old Jeff, in his best stride," said another. "Hurrah for Jeff!"

"He's looking more jolly than he did over Electric Liver and Lights!" remarked a third.

"What will you have?" said a fourth. "Perrier Jouet or Pommery Greno? Anything you like. What's it to be? Pommery or Moet?"

"Have you been to the 'House' – how are prices?" asked Jeffries, while the wine was being opened.

"The markets are firm. Your favourites, Chatham Prefs., are up 2. But I say, what is this new scheme of yours?"

He handed them each a prospectus.

"By Jove! that's a glorious idea! Supply a want, you know," exclaimed one of his friends.

"Shrimps are the thing; I always said so," remarked a second.

"They've been neglected too long," observed a third.

"Don't forget us when you make the allotment," said the fourth.

"No, no; Jeff never forgets his friends," replied the first speaker. "By G—! Jeff's a good fellow."

The object of this panegyric was about to raise his glass to his lips when a man in a threadbare coat and a shabby hat looked in at one of the doors.

Two years ago this man had been rich, but he was dazzled by the Aerated Patent Brick or the West-End Sedan – it does not matter which – and he lost his all. Since then he had haunted Jeffries, who always fled at the sight of him.

It was a case of the fly out of the mustard pot; he was off.

"Goodbye," he said, hurriedly, setting down his glass. "Pressing engagement – excuse me."

He rushed to a side door, and was soon out of sight.

"Villain!" yelled the ruined speculator, gnashing his teeth.

"Ha! ha!" laughed the friends; "one of Jeff's ghosts," and there was a chorus of "Ha! ha! ha!"

Jeffries walked away eastward until he got into unfrequented streets, and communed with himself. He was inclined to let the company take care of itself now that he had got Mrs Haydon's money. That the company never could and never would pay he knew perfectly well. Its explosion was only a question of time. If he could get abroad and change his name he would be able to start in some business, and send for his wife and children. To a man like himself this was an alluring prospect. He could not resist the temptation. What did it matter to him if he betrayed his friend Bayldon, and involved the name-lending baronet in disgrace? Such men as he only live for themselves. The very nature of their business makes them selfish. He would do it. Yes, he would throw care to the winds; and instead of going back to the office he went to a railway station, and booked himself to Paris. It was nothing new for him to leave his wife for days at a time without giving her any notice. She was used to such eccentricities on his part. Bayldon, however, was alarmed when his partner did not make his appearance on the following day. He guessed that something had happened. What it was he did not know until Mrs Haydon called again at the office in Bucklersbury, finding him there. She had done what she ought to have done before making the investment – that is, she had consulted her friends, who had advised her that she had done the wrong thing; so she wanted to sell her shares, and get her money back. But this was not so easy in practice as it looked in theory. Subscriptions did not come in very fast. The public fought shy of the company, and there was no market for the security. Then she told Bayldon how much money she had given to Jeffries, which opened his eyes.

"You will never see him again," he said, angrily, for he felt that he had been made a fool of, and left in the lurch.

"Why not? I – I do not understand you," replied Mrs Haydon.

"He has absconded."

"Then he is a swindler."

"Call him what you like. By this time he is in Paris, if he does not go to Monte Carlo direct. That's his loadstone."

Mrs Haydon wrung her hands tearfully.

"Oh! how cruelly I have been deceived, and my poor children robbed, but I, weak woman as I am, will follow him to the end of the world if necessary and get my money back."

Her pride was wounded and her jealousy aroused.

"If you can. It is sunk in a morass."

"You are in league with him, you are one of the gang of villains."

"I assure you, I have not had a shilling of the money," replied Bayldon, who put his hat on his head and rushed wildly from the office, not knowing what fresh trouble he would have to face if he remained there.

Mrs Haydon did not attempt to follow him. Jeffries was the man she wanted; she determined to hunt him down, and being a woman of considerable energy she set about it at once. Requiring assistance she engaged the services of a private detective, who ascertained that a gentleman answering the description of Jeffries had gone by the night mail to Paris on the preceding evening. Following up this slight clue, they started together for the French capital, where they found distinct traces of the absconder, but the bird had flown, they knew not whither. On a forlorn hope they went on to Monte Carlo, arriving there about ten o'clock on a beautiful moonlight night.

"You will want rest, madam," suggested her companion.

"No," she replied bravely, "my brain is on fire; to the tables."

They proceeded without making any alteration in their travelling attire to the gambling saloon. Here they saw Jeffries, who rose dejectedly from his seat and muttered, "All lost! all gone! Oh, my poor wife!"

"His wife! he talks of his wife," hissed Mrs Haydon.

Listlessly he strolled into the gardens, the sound of the music swelling on the night air; he had gambled and lost, that was evident enough. Mary Haydon pursued him, the detective was close behind. Jeffries paused under a tree, against the trunk of which he leant; his eyes were downcast, and he trembled violently, as if stricken with the ague; the rustle of a dress aroused him; he looked up, Mrs Haydon stood before him, their eyes met.

"My money!" shrieked she, "the money you robbed me of; I demand it back."

"Go to the croupier," replied Jeffries, recklessly.

"Have you lost it?"

"Every sovereign."

"Wretch!" cried the maddened woman, "you shall pay for this with your life."

She drew a pistol from her pocket, the polished barrel flashed before his eyes, and he saw that she intended to shoot him.

"Hold!" he exclaimed, "do not stain your hands with my blood."

"You think to escape me?"

"On the contrary, I will save you the trouble of killing me."

With a sudden movement, Jeffries snatched the pistol from her hand, put it to his head, pulled the trigger, and ere the report had died away fell down dead at her feet.

The servants of the Casino, accustomed to such scenes, and ever on the alert, came with an ambulance, and took the body away quickly, before the crowd could fix their morbid gaze upon the lifeless clay.

Mary Haydon was avenged!

But at what a price!

She had not meant to go so far, for to the last she had cherished a forlorn hope that she could make the unhappy man love her.

Certainly she felt the loss of her money – women always do feel this kind of thing more than men – but she would have set this off against his love.

Sinking on her knees with an agonised cry, she clasped her hands, and exclaimed, in a voice that quivered with emotion, "Good God! What have I done?"

Then she fell forward on her face in a dead faint.

And still the music floated on the breeze, and the croupier said, mechanically, "Make your game."

FOUR-LEGGED LOTTERY

Frank Hardy

The publication of Frank Hardy's first novel, *Power without Glory*, caused a major scandal in Australia when it was published in 1950. Not only was it a searing indictment of Australian society but many of the characters appeared to be thinly-disguised representations of leading politicians and other public figures.

In this extract from *Four-Legged Lottery*, the narrator, now in jail awaiting trial for embezzling his employer's funds to pay his gambling debts, recalls how Jim Roberts, the hero, first taught him the facts of life about racing in Australia. Jim, it should be explained, is also in prison under sentence of death for killing a welshing bookmaker. Frank Hardy cannot keep his political bias out of the story, but there is some remarkably good advice about using the law of probabilities rather than the law of averages which the amateur racegoer would do well to follow.

AFTER MY FIRST VISIT to the racecourse, the old and new fought out a battle within me. A sense of guilt soon began to afflict me. Fancy me, Paul Whittaker, squandering eight pounds on horses! What would Julia say? What would the bank authorities say? And fancy me leading a deceitful double life!

I resolved never to bet again! I didn't for many weeks! I continued to drink with Jim and his friends though. And I listened with growing interest to their racing talk, their forecasts on Fridays, their résumés on Mondays. They were having a winning run, they said, and Jim's bank account rose to four thousand five hundred pounds in proof of this.

One Monday, Tom Sparks fingered the lapels of a smart overcoat he wore and said: "Well, the bookies bought me a new coat. Thirty quid's worth. Nice bitta stuff. It's a budy!" Turning to me he contended: "You know, Paul, I always buy something solid when I have a win: a lot of furniture in my house is labelled. The big radiogram has a tag on it, won on such and such a horse from such and such a bookie, and so on."

His remark exercised my mind that evening, while I sat by our gas fire with Julia listening to her serials and quiz sessions on the radio.

Then Julia said: "Paul, we really should buy a radiogram. The Conways have just got a lovely one, with a cocktail cabinet and a three-speed motor."

I felt inclined to say that we rarely used the old one we had. But I was seeing visions of prosperity from gambling. There were a few things needed around our home. Julia would never be content until our finances improved. She needed new clothes and so did I. We needed a new car – and to be able to run it every day. The rates and mortgage payments were due. And we needed a higher income and more money in the bank.

The next Saturday, I lied to Julia again, and went to Moonee Valley racecourse with Jim and his friends. My tremendous excitement was not unmixed with secret shame.

I bet very cautiously. I backed the first three winners but resisted the temptation to raise my stake above one pound. On the day, I wagered on six winners, four in Melbourne and two in Sydney (by then special bookmakers were operating on Sydney races on all Melbourne racetracks). I won twenty pounds. Leaving the course, my main feeling was one of self-reproach – not because I had gambled but because I had failed to bet more heavily. I should have won a hundred, I told myself.

For some months, I went to the races as often as I could find an excuse to make to Julia. Yet I suffered pangs of conscience. My personality seemed to become wrenched. The revolt against my background, against the monotony of my work and life and against the essential failure of my marriage, seemed to crystallise. That revolt had lain dormant for some years, now it began to erupt in my growing friendship with Jim Roberts – and in the gambling habit. The change was slow. After almost every trip to the racecourse, I swore never to bet again. Once I was so remorseful that I went back to drinking with Trembath for a few days. . . .

My visits to the races remain vivid in my memory, but jumbled as in a kaleidoscope. Scraps of scenes I witnessed, of people I met, of remarks I heard, of facts I learned. A phantasmagoria of that strange, corrupt, fascinating world – Australian horse-racing. . . .

Gerald Roberts saying: "The game is run to make money for big-business interests. The racing clubs and horses should be nationalised."

Rich owners and breeders of thoroughbred horses dominate the Australian racing clubs. The game is run for them. Next come the leading trainers and jockeys, the bookmakers who nearly always win, the Government that always get its totalisator percentages and taxes, the caterers, and the few professional punters. The poor rank-and-file punter runs a bad last; he almost always loses; the game is conducted expressly to exploit him.

Of course, I soon accepted these self-evident facts, yet I continued betting. I was influenced by my belief in the infallibility of Jim Roberts – and I seemed to be mesmerised by the glamour, by the shouting of the bookmakers, by the afternoon of friendship, by the appeal of the gambler's leap into the dark, by the hope of quick profits. . . .

Jim Roberts saying, as we left the course after a losing day: "At least I know that most of the horses we backed were goers. The majority of horses backed by other punters either weren't trying to win or couldn't have won even if they were."

I learned to know what lay behind that remark.

Owners, trainers and jockeys often pull up horses, in collusion or independently. They are in the game to make money. Sometimes they wait for a better price, or for an easier race. Or they just decide to back another horse. Also, they have a habit of running a horse into form and out of form. After a horse is spelled, it comes back above itself in condition. It is then raced into condition. It runs two or three times unfancied, dead because it couldn't win even if it tried, and the jockey is instructed not to knock it about. It reaches the peak of condition and perhaps wins a race or two, then it begins to lose condition again, it trains off. Before being spelled, it races out of condition.

"They do that to get weight off a horse's back," Jim explained. "They have to do it. The handicapper raises a horse's weight when it wins, and weight will beat the best of them, eventually. Even the few honest owners and trainers have to stop the handicapper from getting a horse's measure."

Dapper Dan coming back from the Bird Cage and calling Jim aside furtively: "So and so, Jim. Be a moral. Been given every assistance." Dapper Dan narrowed his eyes and touched his upper lip with the tip of his tongue – an expression he adopted only when he really knew something.

Jim laughing and saying: "Been sniffing round the stalls again, have yer, you old bloodhound?" Then he became serious: "A jigger job, eh?"

My curiosity getting the better of me. "A jigger job? What do you mean by that, Jim?"

He told me. A jigger is a battery. It is not used in the actual race. A horse is "hit with it" on the training tracks.

"But what did you mean about sniffing round the stalls?"

Again Jim was quite frank. He knew I could be trusted. I only reveal this sordid story now because he told me to do so during our remand yard talks.

"Well, Paul, horse-racing is not a kindergarten. A horse is hit with the battery on the track, usually on the morning of the actual race. They rub a mixture called Penetaine on the horse's sides. This acts as a conductor. In the actual race, the jockey hits the horse with the spurs or the whip at the same point of the track, and the sensation is like that of the battery. You can smell the mixture a mile off, but it doesn't show in a swab."

That horse won by three lengths. And I think I saw the point at which it received the spurs, the imitation of the dreaded battery. After turning into the straight, the horse bounded as if struck by lightning.

Jim told me afterwards that the use of the battery is rare. A horse is soon worn out by the frantic exertion and develops some immunity to the treatment.

Not so rare, commonplace, in fact, is the use of dope.

One day at Caulfield, Jim introduced me to the foreman of a well-known training stable. A strong, clean-cut fellow and an expert horse-breaker, he appealed to me as a good type of man. A non-bettor himself (he was engaged to be married and his fiancée would not permit him to gamble), he often gave Jim inside information.

As we left the stall, I said to Jim: "He seems a nice fellow."

"One of the best," Jim replied.

Tom Sparks endorsed this opinion with a characteristically crude expression. At first his bawdy slang had offended my susceptibilities – but I was getting used to it.

"He really is a good bloke," Jim reiterated, "as racing men go. But he dopes horses. Look now. See that fellow talking to him; the bloke in the homburg hat?"

"Yes."

"Well, that's the mad doctor. Used to be a Collins Street surgeon. Took to punting. Lost all his money. Now he prepares dope for horse trainers. He makes more money this way than by cutting out appendixes – but loses it all punting horses. Bet on two flies crawling up a wall, he would. He dopes the horses and can't win – what hope have we got. . . ."

Jim insisted then, and later here inside the jail walls, that the majority of race winners are doped. So prevalent is doping, that the most honest trainer in Australia dare not risk a horse in an important race without "assistance." Jim said that all the champion horses of the Australian turf in the past twenty-five years have been treated with dope.

Jim Roberts saying: "Dope can't make a slow horse fast, but it can make a fast horse faster, make a good horse do better than its best."

Jim explained to me in the yard that a horse must be absolutely fit and up to the class of his opponents before dope can be used effectively.

"What about the stewards?"

Jim replied that the stewards act against dope rings (usually operated by bookmakers) which dope horses to make them lose.

"What about the two horses that lost those races in Sydney," I persisted, quite unable to believe that this sordid aspect of racing really existed.

"They were Victorian horses," Jim said. "Their trainers used the old-fashioned Melbourne stings. In Sydney the stewards take swabs of every placed horse."

"So they can't dope horses in Sydney," I replied somewhat triumphant.

My feeling of triumph was short lived. Jim convinced me that doping remained just as prevalent in Sydney as Melbourne. Swabbing of horses was introduced in an attempt to restore public confidence in racing, but the "smarties" soon found stings that didn't show on a swab.

The old-fashioned stings included nicotine acid to accentuate the horse's heart beat; strychnine to make the horse's muscles contract better; caffeine and heroin to dull the nerve centres of fatigue in the horse's brain, these being a safety valve which lets a horse know when it has had enough. All of these drugs can be detected in saliva or urinal tests. In Sydney, their use has been supplanted by hormone drugs which cannot be detected in any test. Cortisone, for instance, is already in the horse's system; additional doses improve the horse's performance without producing a positive swab. There are other drugs which normally produce a positive swab, but this can be prevented if an antidote is fed to the horse. Tranquilliser drugs are used on horses that are highly strung and shy of crowds. Many trainers have come to view the use of drugs as a natural extension of scientific feeding.

Jim Roberts saying: "Bookmakers can't get along without horse-racing, but horse-racing can get along without book-makers."

Infamous instances of nobbling horses were often discussed. Cheery Jack, the great nimble-footed steeplechaser discovered blinded with dope on the way to the post for the Melbourne Grand National. Bookmakers could not have met their commitments had he won the race, as he assuredly would have done, ridden by the one-and-only Laurie Meenan. And the attempt to shoot the mighty Phar-Lap. . . .

Tom Sparks advising: "Don't back that horse, Paul. It's been bagged."

"Bagged?"

This can be done by the owner or the jockey, but more often it's done by the trainer, sometimes without the knowledge of either the owner or the jockey. A trainer gets a horse "in the market". He approaches a bookmaker or a group of bookmakers through an intermediary. The horse will not win if they pay up; he is prepared to "bag it", to run it for the bookmakers. This horse drifts in the market. Those bookmakers in the know and eventually their shrewd confrères, are anxious to lay it. Its price gradually increases. It gets the "Joe Blows" as the punters put it. Of course, a dead horse which has not been bagged will also drift in the market but in that case the bookmakers are lengthening its price just because there is no money for it. Occasionally, a horse might drift and still win. An SP job (a horse backed aw£y from the course); or a horse from a non-betting stable that drifts in the market because of pressure of money for other horses.

"But what about the stewards? Surely they know this goes on!"

Occasionally, the stewards enquire into inconsistent running. The trainer asserts that he has backed the horse – and produces betting tickets to prove it. Bookmakers in the know have supplied the trainer with fictitious betting tickets to prove the horse has been backed. Usually, the explanation is accepted. Occasionally a jockey might be disqualified for rough riding but inconsistent running is more difficult to prove, so action against it is rare.

Jim Roberts standing in front of the stand of a rails bookmaker, explaining how a book is made to collect a percentage whichever horse wins. This percentage varies from, say, $12\frac{1}{2}$ per cent if a well-backed horse wins to 100 per cent if a rank outsider gives a "skinner". A bookmaker applies the "over-round" method as it is called in England, or the "round-robbin", as it is called in Australia. A hypothetical case: if a bookmaker, in a four horse race, bets odds of five to two about each horse, he would win $12\frac{1}{2}$ per cent of his turnover whichever horse won, provided he held the same amount for each horse. Of course, the extent to which the over-round can be operated varies from race to race and there are occasions when weight of money for a winner leaves a bookmaker losing on a race. But, in the long run, the over-round makes it a mathematical impossibility for a bookmaker to lose.

Jim Roberts and Tom Sparks revealing to me the flotsam and jetsam of the racecourses.

The urgers.

A man accosting me at Flemington saying: "I've got the winner of this next race. So-and-so. Don't tell a soul."

Tom Sparks intervening: "Don't listen to him, Paul. That's old 'Don't tell a soul', the urger. He gives you a tip and then persuades you to put a few quid on it for him. Gives a different horse to every victim. Must pick a winner occasionally."

The mail-order tipsters.

Jim Roberts pointing out a gaudily dressed man in the Caulfield Hotel:

"That's 'please find enclosed'. He sends out tips to people on a mug's list. Sends a different horse to every customer. Got his nickname because he reckons he only reads letters that begin with the words 'please find enclosed'."

The punch-drunk jockeys.

Me laughing aloud at a humorous remark of Tom Sparks or a bitter Australian slang term of Harry Walton's. A man nearby interjecting: "Don't laugh at me. I'll get a good ride one of these days and win a big race."

Jim Roberts explaining: "That fella's what we call a punch drunk jockey. A good apprentice years ago, got too heavy, dreams of the day he'll stage a come back."

The phoney "nod-bettors".

A man rushing headlong scattering people, to make a large bet "on the nod".

Jim Roberts warning: "Don't follow his lead, Paul. He's employed by the bookies to start a rush on a dead horse. Used to be a big professional punter, went broke, now works for the bookies to get the mugs in."

The pie-eaters.

Tom Sparks commenting: "Look at 'em. Here, out on the Flat, on the Hill, even in the members' enclosure. Pie and tomato sauce. Gravy running down one side of the sleeve, sauce down the other. Leaning forward away from the wind. . . . Hoo. Hoo. A nation of bloody pie-eaters."

The talking jockeys.

Jim Roberts taking me back of the course in the Flat enclosure to hear the boys debate during a race.

Experienced riders shouting angry words to intimidate apprentice boys. Top jockeys buying a run: "Let me through for twenty quid." Collusion: "Where's the favourite? I'm supposed to finish behind it."

The incredible skill of Australian horsemen:

Darby Munro stealing a weight for age race on a moke. Snozzle Purtell timing his run, getting up in a punishing photo finish. Nevvie Selwood, a great judge of pace, clocking the horses in his mind, during a race. George Moore, a better businessman than he is a rider – and that's saying something. "Professor" Thompson never beaten in a photo finish, nudging the favourite over the line to win by a hair on its chin. Billy Williamson coldly planning his race, riding mean and winning. Ronnie Hutchison, a specialist in long distance races, getting the wrap up from his mates, Des

Hoysted and Frank O'Brien – "ridden in copy-book style by Hutchie". "Scobie" Breasley going the shortest way home. "Digger" McGrowdie with the temperament for the big occasion: "Big-Race" McGrowdie has won more cups than a champion golfer.

The battling trainers.

Jim Roberts telling me: "That bloke just tipped me one of his horses. It couldn't win if it started now. A battler. Got a few scrubbers. Picks up a race in the bush occasionally. Likes to run his horses in the city. Dreams of the day he'll buy a horse for twenty quid and win a Derby. But those days are gone. If one of his mokes is sick he sleeps in the stall with it and gets the best vet in Melbourne. If his missus got sick he'd give her a couple of Aspros."

The system punters.

Tom Sparks nodding his head towards a mild-looking man: "Get a gander at the little bloke with the black exercise book. A system punter with his records. Spends more time at the library than a university professor."

The women punters.

Jim Roberts saying: "Have an eyeful of those two old sheilas beside the five quid tote queue. They stand there and note every bet made before making their selections. Manage to lose their housekeeping money every week, just the same. And look there at that young woman with the little boy, slapping the kid round the legs because it's tired and crying. Fancy bringing a kid that age to the racecourse."

And Jim Roberts observing: "Take a look round at the ages of people on the course. The majority between thirty-five and forty-five. The depression-bred generation. The younger generation brought up during the war and after don't gamble as much as we do – society has found other ways of demoralising them, like the bodgie cult, for instance."

Jim Roberts and Tom Sparks, their hands full of form guides analysing a race, seeking the winner. An education in misplaced shrewdness, and in Australian humour.

Comparing the weights with those carried in previous races, handicapping one horse against the other. "Purtell's mount is in well; the handicapper has said 'yes'." The jockeys: "A change of rider here; he'd be dead last start with the apprentice on top." The state of the track: "That filly is a definite mud-runner." Barrier position: "That favourite is drawn wide. They have to draw in close at this barrier." The breeding; "That favourite is bred for stamina." The betting habits of trainers. "They generally bet about every third run when the price is right." Horses for courses. "They usually send this one off at the Valley" or "So-and-so is a straight-six specialist". And watching the market. "There's money for this one" or "The favourite's got the Joe Blows."

Tom Sparks rolling his head on one side, pursing his lips: "Hoo! Hoo! It'll be a massacre!" And Jim Roberts saying with mock gravity: "Well, now, we'd better be careful. If the bag boys see us looking shrewd, they'll smell a rat. P'raps we'd better get Paul to put the money on."

Jim Roberts saying to me, when I told him I intended, as a man of mathematical turn of mind, to bet on a system: "That's a sure way to go broke."

"But there are systems advertised in the paper. One guarantees you will win five thousand a year. All a matter of mathematics, it says."

Jim laughing scornfully: "If you had a system as good as that, would you advertise it in the papers?"

Jim advising: "Avoid systems like a plague."

Winners cannot be profitably selected on the basis of mathematics, or by backing favourites, or second favourites, or the mounts of a leading jockey or the selections of a given newspaper. Making selections by any predetermined method cannot succeed. For example, over a period, a certain newspaper tipster might select the winner of one race in every four. To use these selections as the basis of a system, a punter would have to increase the number of units invested on each horse selected until one of them won, then revert to his original unit. All manner of permutations of the one in four are possible. The tipster sooner or later will have a run of twenty or thirty losing tips in succession. If the punter is determined to follow the system to the bitter end he will lose his money, his house and motor car, and perhaps his employer's money as well. The law of averages will destroy all systems and staking plans.

Jim Roberts explaining in all seriousness that punters must replace the law of averages, with what he called the law of probability. The example of a method of betting at two-up. In an honestly conducted two-up school, an equal number of heads and tails will be thrown over a long period; both head and tail bettors must lose because the man conducting the school takes a percentage, just as the bookmakers and the tote do at the races. But this law can be overcome in various ways. For instance, a tail better can back the tail on every spin – only for two throws, doubling his stake on the second throw if the spinner heads them first time. In this way he defeats the law of averages. He wins a unit every time a spinner throws a flat tail or one head and one tail. His only losing bets are made when a spinner throws two or more heads.

And me asking Jim: "Can that be done on the horses?"

Something like it.

A punter must first minimise the average number of losing bets. This can only be achieved by not betting on every race or, more precisely, by not betting on difficult races. And there are harder and easier races. Hard races can be recognised in various ways: by the number of horses under ten to one in the market, by large variations in the selections of newspapers, by the size of the field or by the class of horse engaged. Some successful punters take all these factors into account. Others only take the last one. They don't bet on maiden, novice, or welter handicaps because the fields are usually large and the market wide, and they don't bet on weight-for-age races because these are usually won by odds-on favourites or bolters.

Having deleted the races in which he is least likely to select the winner, the punter has taken a step towards defeating the law of averages.

But, in the final analysis, successful forecasting is the only way a punter can win at horse-racing. And to select winners with any degree of consistency takes years of fanatical study and costs much in money and heartaches.

Jim Roberts reciting his formula: "Only back a horse that is fit, that is racing in his own class, that is favourably handicapped, that has a good barrier position, that is ridden by a good jockey, that is suited by the track, that is firm in the market! And even then, remember! Horses don't bet on people, that's why they never go broke."

And Tom Sparks commenting: "And never back a dead 'un! A man should only bet when he's got inside information – and if it's information from a stable with a jigger or a good sting, all the better."

Genuine tips are hard to come by. Most trainers and jockeys are tight-lipped. Harry Walton saying: "Wouldn't tell their blind grandmother the way to the lavatory."

In return for information, they often want "the odds to a tenner" if the horse wins. In any case the majority of trainers think their horse is a goose that will lay a golden egg when it is, in fact, often only an ugly duckling. And always check an owner's tip – the owner isn't always told when his horse is trying.

Having made a deliberate, intelligent selection or selections, the punter should then seek what Jim called value. Some favourites are value, others are not. This is an imponderable factor, but some punters develop an instinct for it. They won't back a favourite at even money which appears to have only a two to one chance. Again, they might consider a horse at eight to one better value "each way" than the favourite at six to four straight out. Yet again, they will sometimes back two or even three horses straight out to show a profit, rather than back one horse each way. This they call "making a book against the bookmaker". Such punters rarely bet on a race in which the favourite is odds-on. They argue that it is unprofitable either to back odds on favourites, or bet against them.

Having reduced the number of races on which he bets and sought value, a punter should then stake intelligently, putting his largest bets on horses which his gambling intelligence tells him are most likely to win. The race tracks are strewn with the corpses of gamblers who back many winners but still lose because they have not staked intelligently.

Tom Sparks telling me: "There was once a way of betting so you couldn't lose. Trust an Australian to invent it. A punter approached a bookmaker and backed say, Hairy Legs, in the first race provided that, say, Goldilocks won the last race. Then approached another bookmaker and backed Goldilocks in the last race, provided Hairy Legs won the first race. Get it? It was a 'budy'! But the bookies soon saw through the ruse and introduced a no betting backwards rule to meet the situation!"

In the yard, Jim Roberts often echoed or amplified remarks I had heard his brother make.

He told me that the commercial racket of horse-racing could not survive long without press and radio publicity. "But," I replied, "they cater for a public need." "Which came first?" Jim asked by way of reply. "The chicken or the egg?" He and Gerald claimed that the press and radio debased public taste in this and in other fields.

Near the end, I asked Jim: "As Australians love to gamble, how can the game be cleaned up?"

"Well," he replied, "the first thing to do is to wipe out all bookmaking, on and off the course. A crooked jockey or trainer can't do business with the tote machine; the tote can't rig a race. The second thing is that stewards must be forced to act against the practice of racing horses dead. Then, at least, the punter would have some chance."

"Do you think that's ever likely to come?"

"Not until the whole social system is changed. Then horse-racing could really be cleaned up, and become a true sport again. There would be less gambling; people would feel secure and be encouraged to do better things with their time and money."

"And meantime, the game can't be beaten," I said.

"Well, I s'pose it can be beaten. After all, I beat it for a few years and I've met a few punters who beat it for longer. What beat me and will beat them all is the psychology of the true gambler. Even when he learns all the rules, he can't resist gambling for gambling's sake; he breaks his own rules and often bets against his own better judgement."

After some thought, he added: "I've advised many punters to give it up, but not one took the advice. They were all convinced they would beat the game one day."

Only one punter in tens of thousands ever becomes a professional or semi-professional, or even gets ahead of the game, Jim asserted more than once. To do so, that punter must spend half a lifetime losing his money and living often in a state of dread and remorse.

Even assuming a punter continued winning indefinitely, where would he end up? As a fanatic who has given his soul over to the devil of gambling. He would lose the taste for the fine things of life. He would be dehumanised by his very success. He would have bought a ticket in the four-legged lottery, running the risk of winning a major prize. . . .

THE MEMOIRS OF BARRY LYNDON

William Thackeray

Thackeray's satire is very acute but is not bitter, a rare quality that is demonstrated in the following extract from *The Memoirs of Barry Lyndon*. The hero has just met up with his uncle, a professional gambler, in Berlin, and he is invited to become a partner in his gambling "firm." Barry takes naturally to the life. . . .

"MY LAD, I have been in every service; and between ourselves, owe money in every capital in Europe. I made a campaign or two with the Pandours under Austrian Trenck. I was captain in the Guard of his Holiness the Pope. I made the campaign of Scotland with the Prince of Wales – a bad fellow, my dear, caring more for his mistress and his brandy-bottle than for the crowns of the three kingdoms. I have served in Spain and in Piedmont; but I have been a rolling stone, my good fellow. Play – play has been my ruin! that and beauty" (here he gave a leer which made him, I must confess, look anything but handsome; besides, his rouged cheeks were all beslobbered with the tears which he had shed on receiving me). "The women have made a fool of me, my dear Redmond. I am a soft-hearted creature, and this minute, at sixty-two, have no more command of myself than when Peggy O'Dwyer made a fool of me at sixteen."

"'Faith, sir," says I, laughing, "I think it runs in the family!" and described to him, much to his amusement, my romantic passion for my cousin, Nora Brady. He resumed his narrative:

"The cards now are my only livelihood. Sometimes I am in luck, and then I lay out my money in these trinkets you see. It's property, look you, Redmond; and the only way I have found of keeping a little about me. When the luck goes against me, why, my dear, my diamonds go to the pawnbrokers, and I wear paste. Friend Moses the goldsmith will pay me a visit this very day; for the chances have been against me all the week past, and I must raise money for the bank to-night. Do you understand the cards?"

I replied that I could play as soldiers do, but had no great skill.

"We will practise in the morning, my boy," said he, "and I'll put you up to a thing or two worth knowing."

Of course I was glad to have such an opportunity of acquiring knowledge, and professed myself delighted to receive my uncle's instruction.

The chevalier's account of himself rather disagreeably affected me. All his show was on his back, as he said. His carriage, with the fine gilding, was a part of his stock in trade. He *had* a sort of mission from the Austrian court: – it was to discover whether a certain quantity of alloyed ducats, which had been traced to Berlin, were from the king's treasury. But the real end of Monsieur de Balibari was play. There was a young *attaché* of the English embassy, my Lord Deuceace, afterwards Viscount and Earl of Crabs in the English peerage, who was playing high; and it was after hearing of the passion of this young English nobleman that my uncle, then at Prague, determined to visit Berlin and engage him. For there is a sort of chivalry among the knights of the dice-box: the fame of great players is known all over Europe. I have known the Chevalier de Casanova, for instance, to travel six hundred miles, from Paris to Turin, for the purpose of meeting Mr Charles Fox, then only my Lord Holland's dashing son, afterwards the greatest of European orators and statesmen.

It was agreed that I should keep my character of valet; that in the presence of strangers I should not know a word of English; that I should keep a good look-out on the trumps when I was serving the champagne and punch about; and, having a remarkably fine eyesight and a great natural aptitude, I was speedily able to give my dear uncle much assistance against his opponents at the green table. Some prudish persons may affect indignation at the frankness of these confessions, but heaven pity them! Do you suppose that any man who has lost or won a hundred thousand pounds at play will not take the advantages which his neighbour enjoys? They are all the same. But it is only the clumsy fool who *cheats*; who resorts to the vulgar expedients of cogged dice and cut cards. Such a man is sure to go wrong some time or other, and is not fit to play in the society of gallant gentlemen; and my advice to people who see such a vulgar person at his pranks is, of course, to back him while he plays, but never – never to have anything to do with him. Play grandly, honourably. Be not, of course, cast down at losing; but above all, be not eager at winning, as mean souls are. And, indeed, with all one's skill and advantages winning is often problematical; I have seen a sheer ignoramus that knows no more of play than of Hebrew, blunder you out of five thousand pounds in a few turns of the cards. I have seen a gentleman and his confederate play against another and *his* confederate. One never is secure in these cases: and when one considers the time and labour spent, the genius, the anxiety, the outlay of money required, the multiplicity of bad debts that one meets with (for dishonourable rascals are to be found at the play-table, as everywhere else in the world), I say, for my part, the profession is a bad one; and, indeed, have scarcely ever met a man who, in the end, profited by it. I am writing now with the experience of a man of the world. At the time I speak of I was a lad, dazzled by the idea of wealth, and respecting, certainly too much, my uncle's superior age and station in life.

There is no need to particularize here the little arrangements made between us; the play-men of the present day want no instruction, I take it, and the public have little interest in the matter. But simplicity was our secret. Everything successful is simple. If, for instance, I wiped the dust off a chair with my napkin, it was to show that the enemy was strong in diamonds; if I pushed it, he had ace, king; if I said, "Punch or wine, my lord?" hearts was meant; if "Wine or punch?" clubs. If I blew my nose, it was to indicate that there was another confederate employed by the adversary; and *then*, I warrant you, some pretty trials of skill would take place. My Lord Deuceace, although so young, had a very great skill and cleverness with the cards in every way; and it was only from hearing Frank Punter, who came with him, yawn three times when the chevalier had the ace of trumps that I knew we were Greek to Greek, as it were. . . .

. . . I came into it at once, and as if I had never done anything else all my life. I had a gentleman to wait upon me, a French *friseur* to dress my hair of a morning; I knew the taste of chocolate as by intuition almost, and could distinguish between the right Spanish and the French before I had been a week in my new position; I had rings on all my fingers, watches in both my fobs, canes, trinkets, and snuff-boxes of all sorts, and each outvying the other in elegance. I had the finest natural taste for lace and china of any man I ever knew; I could judge a horse as well as any Jew dealer in Germany; in shooting and athletic exercises I was unrivalled; I could not spell, but I could speak German and French cleverly. I had at the least twelve suits of clothes; three richly embroidered with gold, two laced with silver, a garnet-coloured velvet pelisse lined with sable; one of French grey, silver-laced and lined with chinchilla. I had damask morning-robes. I took lessons on the guitar, and sang French catches exquisitely. Where, in fact, was there a more accomplished gentleman than Redmond de Balibari?

All the luxuries becoming my station could not, of course, be purchased without credit and money: to procure which, as our patrimony had been wasted by our ancestors, and we were above the vulgarity and slow returns and doubtful chances of trade, my uncle kept a faro-bank. We were in partnership with a Florentine, well known in all the courts of Europe, the Count Alessandro Pippi, as skilful a player as ever was seen; but he turned out a sad knave latterly, and I have discovered that his countship was a mere imposture. My uncle was maimed, as I have said; Pippi, like all impostors, was a coward; it was my unrivalled skill with the sword, and readiness to use it, that maintained the reputation of the firm, so to speak, and silenced many a timid gambler who might have hesitated to pay his losings. We always played on parole with anybody: any person, that is, of honour and noble lineage. We never pressed for our winnings or declined to receive promissory notes in lieu of gold. But woe to the man who did not pay when the note became due! Redmond de Balibari was sure to wait upon him with his bill, and I promise you there were very few bad debts: on the contrary, gentlemen were grateful to us for our forbearance, and our character for honour stood unimpeached. In later times, a vulgar national prejudice has chosen to cast a slur upon the character of men of honour engaged in the profession of play; but I speak of the good old days in Europe, before the cowardice of the French aristocracy (in the shameful Revolution, which served them right) brought discredit and ruin upon our order. They cry fie now upon men engaged in play; but I should like to know how much more honourable *their* modes of livelihood are than ours. The broker of the Exchange who bulls and bears, and buys and sells, and dabbles with lying loans, and trades on state-secrets, what is he but a gamester? The merchant who deals in teas and tallow, is he any better? His bales of dirty indigo are his dice, his cards come up every year instead of every ten minutes, and the sea is his green table. You call the profession of the law an honourable one, where a man will lie for any bidder: lie down poverty for the sake of a fee from wealth, lie down right because wrong is in his brief. You call a doctor an honourable man, a swindling quack, who does not believe in the nostrums which he prescribes, and takes your guinea for whispering in your ear that it is a fine morning; and yet, forsooth, a gallant man who sits him down before the baize and challenges all comers, his money against theirs, his fortune against theirs, is proscribed by your modern moral world. It is a conspiracy of the middle classes against gentlemen: it is only the shopkeeper cant which is to go down nowadays. I say that play was an institution of chivalry: it has been wrecked, along with other privileges of men of birth. When Seingalt engaged a man for six-and-thirty hours without leaving the table, do you think he showed no courage? How have we had the best blood, and the brightest eyes, too, of Europe throbbing round the table, as I and my uncle have held the cards and the bank against some terrible player, who was matching some thousands out of his millions against our all which was there on the baize! When we engaged that daring Alexis Kossloffsky, and won seven thousand louis in a single coup, had we lost, we should have been beggars the next day; when *he* lost, he was only a village and a few hundred serfs in pawn the worse. When at Toeplitz, the Duke of Courland brought fourteen lacqueys, each with four bags of florins, and challenged our bank to play against the sealed bags, what did we ask? "Sir," said we, "we have but eighty thousand florins in bank, or two hundred thousand at three months. If your highness's bags do not contain more than eighty thousand, we will meet you." And we did, and after eleven hours' play, in which our bank was at one time reduced to two hundred and three ducats, we won seventeen thousand florins of him. Is *this* not something like boldness? does *this* profession not require skill, and perseverance, and bravery? Four crowned heads looked on at the game, and an imperial princess, when I turned up the ace of hearts and made Paroli, burst into tears. No man on the European Continent held a higher position than Redmond Barry then; and when the Duke of Courland lost, he was pleased to say that we had won nobly: and so we had, and spent nobly what we won.

At this period my uncle, who attended mass every day regularly, always put ten florins into the box. Wherever we went, the tavern-keepers made us more welcome than royal princes. We used to give away the broken meat from our suppers and dinners to scores of beggars who blessed us. Every man who held my horse or cleaned my boots got a ducat for his pains. I was, I may say, the author of our common good fortune, by putting boldness into our play. Pippi was a faint-hearted fellow, who was always cowardly when he began to win. My uncle (I speak with great respect of him) was too much of a devotee and too much of a martinet at play ever to win *greatly*. His moral courage was unquestionable, but his daring was not sufficient. Both of these my seniors very soon acknowledged me to be their chief, and hence the style of splendour I have described.

I have mentioned H.I.H. the Princess Frederica Amelia, who was affected by my success, and shall always think with gratitude of the protection with which that exalted lady honoured me. She was passionately fond of play, as indeed were the ladies of almost all the courts in Europe in those days, and hence would often arise no small trouble to us; for the truth must be told, that ladies love to play certainly, but not to *pay*. The point of honour is not understood by the charming sex, and it was with the greatest difficulty, in our peregrinations to the various courts of Northern Europe, that we could keep them from the table, could get their money if they lost, or, if they paid, prevent them from using the most furious and extraordinary means of revenge. In those great days of our fortune, I calculate that we lost no less than fourteen thousand louis by such failures of payment. A princess of a ducal house gave us paste instead of diamonds, which she had solemnly pledged to us; another organized a robbery of the crown jewels, and would have charged the theft upon us, but for Pippi's caution, who had kept back a note of hand "her High Transparency" gave us, and sent it to his ambassador; by which precaution I do believe our necks were saved. A third lady of high (but not princely) rank, after I had won a considerable sum in diamonds and pearls from her, sent her lover with a band of cut-throats to waylay me; and it was only by extraordinary courage, skill, and good luck, that I escaped from these villains, wounded myself, but leaving the chief aggressor dead on the ground: my sword entered his eye and broke there, and the villains who were with him fled, seeing their chief fall. They might have finished me else, for I had no weapon of defence.

Thus it will be seen that our life, for all its splendour, was one of extreme danger and difficulty, requiring high talents and courage for success; and often, when we were in a full vein of success, we were suddenly driven from our ground on account of some freak of a reigning prince, some intrigue of a disappointed mistress, or some quarrel with the police minister. If the latter personage were not bribed or won over, nothing was more common than for us to receive a sudden order of departure; and so, perforce, we lived a wandering and desultory life.

Though the gains of such a life are, as I have said, very great, yet the expenses are enormous. Our appearance and retinue was too splendid for the narrow mind of Pippi, who was always crying out at my extravagance, though obliged to own that his own meanness and parsimony would never have achieved the great victories which my generosity had won. With all our success, our capital was not very great. That speech to the Duke of Courland, for instance, was a mere boast as far as the two hundred thousand florins at three months were concerned. We had no credit, and no money beyond that on our table, and should have been forced to fly if his Highness had won and accepted our bills. Sometimes, too, we were hit very hard. A bank is a certainty, *almost*; but now and then a bad day will come; and men who have the courage of good fortune, at least, ought to meet bad luck well: the former, believe me, is the harder task of the two.

One of these evil chances befell us in the Duke of Baden's territory, at Mannheim. Pippi, who was always on the look-out for business, offered to make a bank at the inn where we put up, and where the officers of the duke's cuirassiers supped; and some small play accordingly took place, and some wretched crowns and louis changed hands: I trust, rather to the advantage of these poor gentlemen of the army, who are surely the poorest of all devils under the sun.

But, as ill luck would have it, a couple of young students from the neighbouring University of Heidelberg, who had come to Mannheim for their quarter's revenue, and so had some hundred of dollars between them, were introduced to the table, and having never played before, began to win (as is always the case). As ill luck would have it, too, they were tipsy, and against tipsiness I have often found the best calculations of play fail entirely. They played in the most perfectly insane way, and yet won always. Every card they backed turned up in their favour. They had won a hundred louis from us in ten minutes; and, seeing that Pippi was growing angry and the luck against us, I was for shutting up the bank for the night, saying the play was only meant for a joke, and that now we had had enough.

But Pippi, who had quarrelled with me that day, was determined to proceed, and the upshot was, that the students played and won more; then they lent money to the officers, who began to win too; and in this ignoble way in a tavern room thick with tobacco-smoke, across a deal table besmeared with beer and liquor, and to a parcel of hungry sub-alterns and a pair of beardless students, three of the most skilful and renowned players in Europe lost seventeen hundred louis! I blush now when I think of it. It was like Charles XII. or Richard Coeur de Lion falling before a petty fortress and an unknown hand (as my friend Mr Johnson wrote), and was, in fact, a most shameful defeat.

Nor was this the only defeat. When our poor conquerors had gone off, bewildered with the treasure which fortune had flung in their way (one of these students was called the Baron de Clootz, perhaps he who afterwards lost his head at Paris), Pippi resumed the quarrel of the morning, and some exceedingly high words passed between us. Among other things I recollect I knocked him down with a stool, and was for flinging him out of window; but my uncle, who was cool, and had been keeping Lent with his usual solemnity, interposed between us, and a reconciliation took place, Pippi apologizing and confessing he had been wrong.

I ought to have doubted, however, the sincerity of the treacherous Italian: indeed, as I never before believed a word that he said in his life, I know not why I was so foolish as to credit him now, and go to bed, leaving the keys of our cash-box with him. It contained, after our loss to the cuirassiers, in bills and money, near upon 8,000*l.* sterling. Pippi insisted that our reconciliation should be ratified over a bowl of hot wine, and I have no doubt put some soporific drug into the liquor; for my uncle and I both slept till very late the next morning, and woke with violent headaches and fever: we did not quit our beds till noon. He had been gone twelve hours, leaving our treasury empty; and behind him a sort of calculation, by which he strove to make out that this was his share of the profits, and that all the losses had been incurred without his consent.

Thus, after eighteen months, we had to begin the world again. But was I cast down? No. Our wardrobes still were worth a very large sum of money; for gentlemen did not dress like parish-clerks in those days, and a person of fashion would often wear a suit of clothes and a set of ornaments that would be a shop-boy's fortune; so, without repining for one single minute, or saying a single angry word (my uncle's temper in this respect was admirable), or allowing the secret of our loss to be known to a mortal soul, we pawned three-fourths of our jewels and clothes to Moses Löwe the banker, and with the produce of the sale, and our private pocket-money, amounting in all to something less than 800 louis, we took the field again.

GAMBLERS
COURAGEOUS

IN A SAN FRANCISCO
GAMBLING SALOON

Bret Harte

Beginning as a reporter for the San Francisco *Golden Era* during the heyday of the Californian gold mining boom, Bret Harte rapidly established himself as the chronicler of the American West.

Gambling was quite simply an integral part of life in the Californian saloons and mining camps and a man's conduct in a poker game could make or break his reputation. "In a San Francisco Gambling Saloon" shows how important gambling was regarded as a test of manhood especially by a young man on his first visit.

PERHAPS FROM MY Puritan training I experienced a more fearful joy in the gambling saloons. They were the largest and most comfortable, even as they were the most expensively decorated rooms in San Franscisco. Here again the gravity and decorum which I have already alluded to were present at that earlier period – though perhaps from concentration of another kind. People staked and lost their last dollar with a calm solemnity and a resignation that was almost Christian. The oaths, exclamations, and feverish interruptions which often characterized more dignified assemblies were absent here. There was no room for the lesser vices; there was little or no drunkenness; the gaudily dressed and painted women who presided over the wheels of fortune or performed on the harp and piano attracted no attention from those ascetic players. The man who had won ten thousand dollars and the man who had lost everything rose from the table with equal silence and imperturbability. *I* never witnessed any tragic sequel to those losses; *I* never heard of any suicide on account of them. Neither can I recall any quarrel or murder directly attributable to this kind of gambling. It must be remembered that these public games were chiefly *rouge et noir, monté, faro*, or *roulette*, in which the antagonist was Fate, Chance, Method, or the impersonal "bank," which was supposed to represent them all; there was no individual opposition or rivalry; nobody challenged the decision of the "croupier," or dealer.

I remember a conversation at the door of one saloon which was as characteristic for its brevity as it was a type of the prevailing stoicism. "Hello!" said a departing miner, as he recognized a brother miner coming in, "when did you come down?" "This morning," was the reply. "Made a strike on the bar?" suggested the first speaker. "You bet!" said the other, and passed in. I chanced an hour later to be at the same place as they met again – their relative positions changed. "Hello! What now?" said the incomer. "Back to the bar." "Cleaned out?" "You bet!" not a word more explained a common situation.

My first youthful experience at those tables was an accidental one. I was watching roulette one evening, intensely absorbed in the mere movement of the players. Either they were so preoccupied with the game, or I was really older looking than my actual years, but a by-stander laid his hand familiarly on my shoulder, and said, as to an ordinary *habitué*, "Ef you're not chippin' in yourself, pardner, s'pose you give *me* a show." Now I honestly believe that up to that moment I had no intention, nor even a desire, to try my own fortune. But in the embarrassment of the sudden address I put my hand in my pocket, drew out a coin, and laid it, with an attempt at carelessness, but a vivid consciousness that I was blushing, upon a vacant number. To my horror I saw that I had put down a large coin – the bulk of my possessions! I did not flinch, however; I think any boy who reads this will understand my feeling; it was not only my coin but my manhood at stake. I gazed with a miserable show of indifference at the players, at the chandelier – anywhere but at the dreadful ball spinning round the wheel. There was a pause; the game was declared, the rake rattled up and down, but still I did not look at the table. Indeed, in my inexperience of the game and my embarrassment, I doubt if I should have known if I had won or not. I had made up my mind that I should lose, but I must do so like a man, and, above all, without giving the least suspicion that I was a greenhorn. I even affected to be listening to the music. The wheel spun again; the game was declared, the rake was busy, but I did not move. At last the man I had displaced touched me on the arm and whispered, "Better make a straddle and divide your stake this time." I did not understand him, but as I saw he was looking at the board, I was obliged to look, too. I drew back dazed and bewildered! Where my coin had lain a moment before was a glittering heap of gold.

My stake had doubled, quadrupled, and doubled again. I did not know how much then – I do not know now – it may have been not more than three or four hundred dollars – but it dazzled and frightened me. "Make your game, gentlemen," said the croupier monotonously. I thought he looked at me – indeed, everybody seemed to be looking at me – and my companion repeated his warning. But here I must again appeal to the boyish reader in defense of my idiotic obstinacy. To have taken advice would have shown my youth. I shook my head – I could not trust my voice. I smiled, but with a sinking heart, and let my stake remain. The ball again sped round the wheel, and stopped. There was a pause. The croupier indolently advanced his rake and swept my whole pile with others into the bank! I had lost it all. Perhaps it may be difficult for me to explain why I actually felt relieved, and even to some extent triumphant, but I seemed to have asserted my grown-up independence – possibly at the cost of reducing the number of my meals for days; but what of that! I was a man! I wish I could say that it was a lesson to me. I am afraid it was not. It was true that I did not gamble again, but then I had no especial desire to – and there was no temptation. I am afraid it was an incident without a moral. Yet it had one touch characteristic of the period which I like to remember. The man who had spoken to me, I think, suddenly realized, at the moment of my disastrous *coup*, the fact of my extreme youth. He moved toward the banker, and leaning over him whispered a few words. The banker looked up, half impatiently, half kindly – his hand straying tentatively toward the pile of coin. I instinctively knew what he meant, and, summoning my determination, met his eyes with all the indifference I could assume, and walked away.

FIVE WHITE MICE

Stephen Crane

Famed for his masterpiece about the Civil War *The Red Badge of Courage*, Stephen Crane is another eminent American writer who learned his craft as a reporter and war correspondent.

Like Bret Harte, he knows that gambling, like violence, is as American as cherry pie. In "Five White Mice" he shows that the courage which enables a young man to carry through a bluff against all the odds in a dice game can be turned to good account in the life and death situation of a gunfight.

F REDDIE was mixing a cock-tail. His hand with the long spoon was whirling swiftly, and the ice in the glass hummed and rattled like a cheap watch. Over by the window, a gambler, a millionaire, a railway conductor, and the agent of a vast American syndicate were playing seven-up. Freddie surveyed them with the ironical glance of a man who is mixing a cock-tail.

From time to time a swarthy Mexican waiter came with his tray from the rooms at the rear, and called his orders across the bar. The sounds of the indolent stir of the city, awakening from its siesta, floated over the screens which barred the sun and the inquisitive eye. From the far-away kitchen could be heard the roar of the old French *chef*, driving, herding, and abusing his Mexican helpers.

A string of men came suddenly in from the street. They stormed up to the bar. There were impatient shouts. "Come now, Freddie, don't stand there like a portrait of yourself. Wiggle!" Drinks of many kinds and colors, amber, green, mahogany, strong and mild, began to swarm upon the bar with all the attendants of lemon, sugar, mint and ice. Freddie, with Mexican support, worked like a sailor in the provision of them, sometimes talking with that scorn for drink and admiration for those who drink which is the attribute of a good bar-keeper.

At last a man was afflicted with a stroke of dice-shaking. A herculean discussion was waging, and he was deeply engaged in it, but at the same time he lazily flirted the dice. Occasionally he made great combinations. "Look at that, would you?" he cried proudly. The others paid little heed. Then violently the craving took them. It went along the line like an epidemic and involved them all. In a moment they had arranged a carnival of dice-shaking with money penalties and liquid prizes. They clamorously made it a point of honour with Freddie that he should play and take his chance of sometimes providing this large group with free refreshment. With bended heads like football players, they surged over the tinkling dice, jostling, cheering, and bitterly arguing. One of the quiet company playing seven-up at the corner table said profanely that the row reminded him of a bowling contest at a picnic.

After the regular shower, many carriages rolled over the smooth calle, and sent musical thunder through the Casa Verde. The shop-windows became aglow with light, and the walks were crowded with youths, callow and ogling, dressed vainly according to supposititious fashions. The policemen had muffled themselves in their gnome-like cloaks, and placed their lanterns as obstacles for the carriages in the middle of the street. The city of Mexico gave forth the deep organ-mellow tones of its evening resurrection.

But still the group at the bar of the Casa Verde were shaking dice. They had passed beyond shaking for drinks for the crowd, for Mexican dollars, for dinners, for the wine at dinner. They had even gone to the trouble of separating the cigars and cigarettes from the dinner's bill, and causing a distinct man to be responsible for them. Finally they were aghast. Nothing remained in sight of their minds which even remotely suggested further gambling. There was a pause for deep consideration.

"Well . . ."

"Well . . ."

A man called out in the exuberance of creation. "I know! Let's shake for a box to-night at the circus! A box at the circus!" The group was profoundly edified. "That's it! That's it! Come on now! Box at the circus!" A dominating voice cried – "Three dashes – high man out!" An American, tall, and with a face of copper red from the rays that flash among the Sierra Madres and burn on the cactus deserts, took the little leathern cup and spun the dice out upon the polished wood. A fascinated assemblage hung upon the bar-rail. Three kings turned their pink faces upward. The tall man flourished the cup, burlesquing, and flung the two other dice. From them he ultimately extracted one more pink king. "There," he said. "Now, let's see! Four kings!" He began to swagger in a sort of provisional way.

The next man took the cup, and blew softly in the top of it. Posing it in his hand he then surveyed the company with a stony eye and paused. They knew perfectly well that he was applying the magic of deliberation and ostentatious indifference, but they could not wait in tranquillity during the performance of all these rites. They began to call out impatiently. "Come now – hurry up." At last the man, with a gesture that was singularly impressive, threw the dice. The others set up a howl of joy. "Not a pair!" There was another solemn pause. The men moved restlessly. "Come, now, go ahead!" In the end, the man, induced and abused, achieved something that was nothing in the presence of four kings. The tall man climbed on the foot-rail and leaned hazardously forward. "Four kings! My four kings are good to go out," he bellowed into the middle of the mob, and although in a moment he did pass into the radiant region of exemption, he continued to bawl advice and scorn.

The mirrors and oiled woods of the Casa Verde were now dancing with blue flashes from a great buzzing electric lamp. A host of quiet members of the Anglo-Saxon colony had come in for their pre-dinner cock-tails. An amiable person was exhibiting to some tourists this popular American saloon. It was a very sober and respectable time of day. Freddie reproved courageously the dice-shaking brawlers, and, in return, he received the choicest advice in a tumult of seven combined vocabularies. He laughed; he had been compelled to retire from the game, but he was keeping an interested, if furtive, eye upon it.

Down at the end of the line there was a youth at whom everybody railed for his flaming ill-luck. At each disaster, Freddie swore from behind the bar in a sort of affectionate contempt. "Why, this kid has had no luck for two days. Did you ever see such throwin'?"

The contest narrowed eventually to the New York kid and an individual who swung about placidly on legs that moved in nefarious circles. He had a grin that resembled a bit of carving. He was obliged to lean down and blink rapidly to ascertain the facts of his venture, but fate presented him with five queens. His smile did not change, but he puffed gently like a man who has been running.

The others, having emerged unscathed from this part of the conflict, waxed hilarious with the kid. They smote him on either shoulders. "We've got you stuck for it, kid! You can't beat that game! Five queens!"

Up to this time the kid had displayed only the temper of the gambler, but the cheerful hoots of the players, supplemented now by a ring of guying non-combatants, caused him to feel profoundly that it would be fine to beat the five queens. He addressed a gambler's slogan to the interior of the cup.

> *Oh, five white mice of chance,*
> *Shirts of wool and corduroy pants,*
> *Gold and wine, women and sin,*
> *All for you if you let me come in –*
> *Into the house of chance.*

Flashing the dice sardonically out upon the bar, he displayed three aces. From two dice in the next throw he achieved one more ace. For his last throw, he rattled the single dice for a long time. He already had four aces; if he accomplished another one, the five queens were vanquished and the box at the circus came from the drunken man's pocket. All the kid's move-ments were slow and elaborate. For the last throw he planted the cup bottom-down on the bar with the one dice hidden under it. Then he turned and faced the crowd with the air of a conjuror or a cheat.

"Oh, maybe it's an ace," he said in boastful calm. "Maybe it's an ace."

Instantly he was presiding over a little drama in which every man was absorbed. The kid leaned with his back against the bar-rail and with his elbows upon it.

"Maybe it's an ace," he repeated.

A jeering voice in the background said – "Yes, maybe it is, kid!"

The kid's eyes searched for a moment among the men. "I'll bet fifty dollars it is an ace," he said.

Another voice asked – "American money?"

"Yes," answered the kid.

"Oh!" There was a genial laugh at this discomfiture. However, no one came forward at the kid's challenge, and presently he turned to the cup. "Now, I'll show you." With the manner of a mayor unveiling a statue he lifted the cup. There was revealed naught but a ten-spot. In the roar which arose could be heard each man ridiculing the cowardice of his neighbour, and above all the din rang the voice of Freddie be-rating every one. "Why, there isn't one liver to every five men in the outfit. That was the greatest cold bluff I ever saw worked. He wouldn't know how to cheat with dice if he wanted to. Don't know the first thing about it. I could hardly keep from laughin' when I seen him drillin' you around. Why, I tell you, I had that fifty dollars right in my pocket if I wanted to be a chump. You're an easy lot . . ."

Nevertheless the group who had won in the theatre-box game did not relinquish their triumph. They burst like a storm about the head of the kid, swinging at him with their fists. " 'Five white mice'!" they quoted, choking. " 'Five white mice'!"

"Oh, they are not so bad," said the kid.

Afterward it often occurred that a man would jeer a finger at the kid and derisively say – " 'Five white mice.' "

On the route from the dinner to the circus, others of the party often asked the kid if he had really intended to make his appeal to mice. They suggested other animals – rabbits, dogs, hedgehogs, snakes, opossums. To this banter the kid replied with a serious expression of his belief in the fidelity and wisdom of the five white mice. He presented a most eloquent case, decorated with fine language and insults, in which he proved that if one was going to believe in anything at all, one might as well choose the five white mice. His companions, however, at once and unanimously pointed out to him that his recent exploit did not place him in the light of a convincing advocate.

The kid discerned two figures in the street. They were making imperious signs at him. He waited for them to approach, for he recognized one as the other kid – the Frisco kid: there were two kids. With the Frisco kid was Benson. They arrived almost breathless. "Where you been?" cried the Frisco kid. It was an arrangement that upon a meeting the one that could first ask this question was entitled to use a tone of limitless injury. "What you been doing? Where you going? Come on with us. Benson and I have got a little scheme."

The New York kid pulled his arm from the grapple of the other. "I can't. I've got to take these sutlers to the circus. They stuck me for it shaking dice at Freddie's. I can't, I tell you."

The two did not at first attend to his remarks. "Come on! We've got a little scheme."

"I can't. They stuck me. I've got to take 'm to the circus."

At this time it did not suit the men with the scheme to recognize these objections as important. "Oh, take 'm some other time. Well, can't you take 'm some other time? Let 'em go. Damn the circus. Get cold feet. What did you get stuck for? Get cold feet."

But despite their fighting, the New York kid broke away from them. "I can't, I tell you. They stuck me." As he left them, they yelled with rage. "Well, meet us, now, do you hear? In the Casa Verde as soon as the circus quits! Hear?" They threw maledictions after him.

In the city of Mexico, a man goes to the circus without descending in any way to infant amusements, because the Circo Teatro Orrin is one of the best in the world, and too easily surpasses anything of the kind in the United States, where it is merely a matter of a number of rings, if possible, and a great professional agreement to lie to the public. Moreover, the American clown, who in the Mexican arena prances and gabbles, is the clown to whom writers refer as the delight of their childhood, and lament that he is dead. At this circus the kid was not debased by the sight of mournful prisoner elephants and caged animals forlorn and sickly. He sat in his box until late, and laughed and swore when past laughing at the comic foolish-wise clown.

When he returned to the Casa Verde there was no display of the Frisco kid and Benson. Freddie was leaning on the bar listening to four men terribly discuss a question that was not plain. There was a card-game in the corner, of course. Sounds of revelry pealed from the rear rooms.

When the kid asked Freddie if he had seen his friend and Benson, Freddie looked bored. "Oh, yes, they were in here just a minute ago, but I don't know where they went. They've got their skates on. Where've they been? Came in here rolling across the floor like two little gilt gods. They wobbled around for a time, and then Frisco wanted me to send six bottles of wine around to Benson's rooms, but I didn't have anybody to send this time of night, and so they got mad and went out. Where did they get their loads?"

In the first deep gloom of the street the kid paused a moment debating. But presently he heard quavering voices. "Oh, kid! kid! Com'ere!" Peering, he recognized two vague figures against the opposite wall. He crossed the street, and they said – "Hello-kid."

"Say, where did you get it?" he demanded sternly. "You Indians better go home. What did you want to get scragged for?" His face was luminous with virtue.

As they swung to and fro, they made angry denials. "We ain' load'! We ain' load'. Big chump. Comonangetadrink."

The sober youth turned then to his friend. "Hadn't you better go home, kid? Come on, it's late. You'd better break away."

The Frisco kid wagged his head decisively. "Got take Benson home first. He'll be wallowing around in a minute. Don't mind me. I'm all right."

"Cerly, he's all right," said Benson, arousing from deep thought. "He's all right. But better take'm home, though. That's ri—right. He's load'. But he's all right. No need go home any more'n you. But better take'm home. He's load'." He looked at his companion with compassion. "Kid, you're load'."

The sober kid spoke abruptly to his friend from San Francisco. "Kid, pull yourself together, now. Don't fool. We've got to brace this ass of a Benson all the way home. Get hold of his other arm."

The Frisco kid immediately obeyed his comrade without a word or a glower. He seized Benson and came to attention like a soldier. Later, indeed, he meekly ventured – "Can't we take cab?" But when the New York kid snapped out that there were no convenient cabs he subsided to an impassive silence. He seemed to be reflecting upon his state, without astonishment, dismay, or any particular emotion. He submitted himself woodenly to the direction of his friend.

Benson had protested when they had grasped his arms. "Washa doing?" he said in a new and guttural voice. "Washa doing? I ain' load'. Commonangetadrink. I . . ."

"Oh, come along, you idiot," said the New York kid. The Frisco kid merely presented the mien of a stoic to the appeal of Benson, and in silence dragged away at one of his arms. Benson's feet came from that particular spot on the pavement with the reluctance of roots and also with the ultimate suddenness of roots. The three of them lurched out into the street in the abandon of tumbling chimneys. Benson was meanwhile noisily challenging the others to produce any reasons for his being taken home. His toes clashed into the kerb when they reached the other side of the calle, and for a moment the kids hauled him along with the points of his shoes scraping musically on the pavement. He balked formidably as they were about to pass the Casa Verde. "No! No! Leshavanothdrink! Anothdrink! Onemore!"

But the Frisco kid obeyed the voice of his partner in a manner that was blind but absolute, and they scummed Benson on past the door. Locked together the three swung into a dark street. The sober kid's flank was continually careering ahead of the other wing. He harshly admonished the Frisco child, and the latter promptly improved in the same manner of unthinking complete obedience. Benson began to recite the tale of a love affair, a tale that didn't even have a middle. Occasionally the New York kid swore. They toppled on their way like three comedians playing at it on the stage.

At midnight a little Mexican street burrowing among the walls of the city is as dark as a whale's throat at deep sea. Upon this occasion heavy clouds hung over the capital and the sky was a pall. The projecting balconies could make no shadows.

"Shay," said Benson, breaking away from his escort suddenly, "what want gome for? I ain't load'. You got reg'lar spool-fact'ry in your head – you N'York kid there. Thish oth' kid, he's mos' proper shober, mos' proper shober. He's drunk, but – but he's shober."

"Ah, shup up, Benson," said the New York kid. "Come along now. We can't stay here all night." Benson refused to be corralled, but spread his legs and twirled like a dervish, meanwhile under the evident impression that he was conducting himself most handsomely. It was not long before he gained the opinion that he was laughing at the others. "Eight purple dogsh – dogs! Eight purple dogs. Thas what kid'll see in the morn'. Look ou' for 'em. They . . ."

As Benson, describing the canine phenomena, swung wildly across the sidewalk, it chanced that three other pedestrians were passing in shadowy rank. Benson's shoulder jostled one of them.

A Mexican wheeled upon the instant. His hand flashed to his hip. There was a moment of silence, during which Benson's voice was not heard raised in apology. Then an indescribable comment, one burning word, came from between the Mexican's teeth.

Benson, rolling about in a semi-detached manner, stared vacantly at the Mexican, who thrust his lean face forward while his fingers played nervously at his hip. The New York kid could not follow Spanish well, but he understood when the Mexican breathed softly: "Does the señor want to fight?"

Benson simply gazed in gentle surprise. The woman next to him at dinner had said something inventive. His tailor had presented his bill. Something had occurred which was mildly out of the ordinary, and his surcharged brain refused to cope with it. He displayed only the agitation of a smoker temporarily without a light.

The New York kid had almost instantly grasped Benson's arm, and was about to jerk him away, when the other kid, who up to this time had been an automaton, suddenly projected himself forward, thrust the rubber Benson aside, and said – "Yes."

There was no sound nor light in the world. The wall at the left happened to be of the common prison-like construction – no door, no window, no opening at all. Humanity was enclosed and asleep. Into the mouth of the sober kid came a wretched bitter taste as if it had filled with blood. He was transfixed as if he was already seeing the lightning ripples on the knife-blade.

But the Mexican's hand did not move at that time. His face went still further forward and he whispered – "So?" The sober kid saw this face as if he and it were alone in space – a yellow mask smiling in eager cruelty, in satisfaction, and above all it was lit with sinister decision. As for the features, they were reminiscent of an unplaced, a forgotten type, which really resembled with precision those of a man who had shaved him three times in Boston in 1888. But the expression burned his mind as sealing-wax burns the palm, and fascinated, stupefied, he actually watched the progress of the man's thought toward the point where a knife would be wrenched from its sheath. The emotion, a sort of mechanical fury, a breeze made by electric fans, a rage made by vanity, smote the dark countenance in wave after wave.

Then the New York kid took a sudden step forward. His hand was at his hip. He was gripping there a revolver of robust size. He recalled that upon its black handle was stamped a hunting scene in which a sportsman in fine leggings and a peaked cap was taking aim at a stag less than one-eighth of an inch away.

His pace forward caused instant movement of the Mexicans. One immediately took two steps to face him squarely. There was a general adjustment, pair and pair. This opponent of the New York kid was a tall man and quite stout. His sombrero was drawn low over his eyes. His serape was flung on his left shoulder. His back was bended in the supposed manner of a Spanish grandee. This concave gentleman cut a fine and terrible figure. The lad, moved by the spirits of his modest and perpendicular ancestors, had time to feel his blood roar at sight of the pose.

He was aware that the third Mexican was over on the left fronting Benson, and he was aware that Benson was leaning against the wall sleepily and peacefully eying the convention. So it happened that these six men stood, side fronting side, five of them with their right hands at their hips and with their bodies lifted nervously, while the central pair exchanged a crescendo of provocations. The meaning of their words rose and rose. They were travelling in a straight line toward collision.

The New York kid contemplated his Spanish grandee. He drew his revolver upward until the hammer was surely free of the holster. He waited immovable and watchful while the garrulous Frisco kid expended two and a half lexicons on the middle Mexican.

The eastern lad suddenly decided that he was going to be killed. His mind leaped forward and studied the aftermath. The story would be a marvel of brevity when first it reached the far New York home, written in a careful hand on a bit of cheap paper, topped and footed and backed by the printed fortifications of the cable company. But they are often as stones flung into mirrors, these bits of paper upon which are laconically written all the most terrible chronicles of the times. He witnessed the uprising of his mother and sister and the invincible calm of his hard-mouthed old father, who would probably shut himself in his library and smoke alone. Then his father would come, and they would bring him here and say – "This is the place." Then, very likely, each would remove his hat. They would stand quietly with their hats in their hands for a decent minute. He pitied his old financing father, unyielding and millioned, a man who commonly spoke twenty-two words a year to his beloved son. The kid understood it at this time. If his fate was not impregnable, he might have turned out to be a man and have been liked by his father.

The other kid would mourn his death. He would be preternaturally correct for some weeks, and recite the tale without swearing. But it would not bore him. For the sake of his dead comrade he would be glad to be preternaturally correct, and to recite the tale without swearing.

These views were perfectly stereopticon, flashing in and away from his thought with an inconceivable rapidity until after all they were simply one quick dismal impression. And now here is the unreal real: into this kid's nostrils, at the expectant moment of slaughter, had come the scent of new-mown hay, a fragrance from a field of prostrate grass, a fragrance which contained the sunshine, the bees, the peace of meadows, and the wonder of a distant crooning stream. It had no right to be supreme, but it was supreme, and he breathed it as he waited for pain and a sight of the unknown.

But in the same instant, it may be, his thought flew to the Frisco kid, and it came upon him like a flicker of lightning that the Frisco kid was not going to be there to perform, for instance, the extraordinary office of respectable mourner. The other kid's head was muddled, his hand was unsteady, his agility was gone. This other kid was facing the determined and most ferocious gentleman of the enemy. The New York kid became convinced that his friend was lost. There was going to be a screaming murder. He was so certain of it that he wanted to shield his eyes from sight of the leaping arm and the knife. It was sickening, utterly sickening. The New York kid might have been taking his first sea-voyage. A combination of honourable manhood and inability prevented him from running away.

He suddenly knew that it was possible to draw his own revolver, and by a swift manoeuvre face down all three Mexicans. If he was quick enough he would probably be victor. If any hitch occurred in the draw he would undoubtedly be dead with his friends. It was a new game; he had never been obliged to face a situation of this kind in the Beacon Club in New York. In this test, the lungs of the kid still continued to perform their duty.

Oh, five white mice of chance,
Shirts of wool and corduroy pants,
Gold and wine, women and sin,
All for you if you let me come in —
Into the house of chance.

He thought of the weight and size of his revolver, and dismay pierced him. He feared that in his hands it would be as unwieldy as a sewing-machine for this quick work. He imagined, too, that some singular providence might cause him to lose his grip as he raised his weapon. Or it might get fatally entangled in the tails of his coat. Some of the eels of despair lay wet and cold against his back.

But at the supreme moment the revolver came forth as if it were greased and it arose like a feather. This somnolent machine, after months of repose, was finally looking at the breasts of men.

Perhaps in this one series of movements, the kid had unconsciously used nervous force sufficient to raise a bale of hay. Before he comprehended it he was standing behind his revolver glaring over the barrel at the Mexicans, menacing first one and then another. His finger was tremoring on the trigger. The revolver gleamed in the darkness with a fine silver light.

The fulsome grandee sprang backward with a low cry. The man who had been facing the Frisco kid took a quick step away. The beautiful array of Mexicans was suddenly disorganized.

The cry and the backward steps revealed something of great importance to the New York kid. He had never dreamed that he did not have a complete monopoly of all possible trepidations. The cry of the grandee was that of a man who suddenly sees a poisonous snake. Thus the kid was able to understand swiftly that they were all human beings. They were unanimous in not wishing for too bloody combat. There was a sudden expression of the equality. He had vaguely believed that they were not going to evince much consideration for his dramatic development as an active factor. They even might be exasperated into an onslaught by it. Instead, they had respected his movement with a respect as great even as an ejaculation of fear and backward steps. Upon the instant he pounced forward and began to swear, unreeling great English oaths as thick as ropes, and lashing the faces of the Mexicans with them. He was bursting with rage, because these men had not previously confided to him that they were vulnerable. The whole thing had been an absurd imposition. He had been seduced into respectful alarm by the concave attitude of the grandee. And after all there had been an equality of emotion, an equality: he was furious. He wanted to take the serape of the grandee and swaddle him in it.

The Mexicans slunk back, their eyes burning wistfully. The kid took aim first at one and then at another. After they had achieved a certain distance they paused and drew up in a rank. They then resumed some of their old splendour of manner. A voice hailed him in a tone of cynical bravado as if it had come from between lips of smiling mockery. "Well, señor, it is finished?"

The kid scowled into the darkness, his revolver drooping at his side. After a moment he answered – "I am willing." He found it strange that he should be able to speak after this silence of years.

"Good-night, señor."

"Good-night."

When he turned to look at the Frisco kid he found him in his original position, his hand upon his hip. He was blinking in perplexity at the point from whence the Mexicans had vanished.

"Well," said the sober kid crossly, "are you ready to go home now?"

The Frisco kid said – "Where they gone?" His voice was undisturbed but inquisitive.

Benson suddenly propelled himself from his dreamful position against the wall. "Frishco kid's all right. He's drunk's fool and he's all right. But you New York kid, you're shober." He passed into a state of profound investigation. "Kid shober 'cause didn't go with us. Didn't go with us 'cause went to damn circus. Went to damn circus 'cause lose shakin' dice. Lose shakin' dice 'cause – what make lose shakin' dice, kid?"

The New York kid eyed the senile youth. "I don't know. The five white mice, maybe."

Benson puzzled so over this reply that he had to be held erect by his friends. Finally the Frisco kid said – "Let's go home."

Nothing had happened.

THE OUTCASTS OF POKER FLAT

Bret Harte

Another story by Bret Harte, "The Outcasts of Poker Flat" shows that the professional gambler can be a man of great character and integrity. Mr John Oakhurst is one of his best loved characters and in this story he demonstrates a far greater degree of courage and compassion than the so-called respectable members of the community of Poker Flat.

As Mr John Oakhurst, gambler, stepped into the main street of Poker Flat on the morning of the twenty-third of November, 1850, he was conscious of a change in its moral atmosphere since the preceding night. Two or three men, conversing earnestly together, ceased as he approached, and exchanged significant glances. There was a Sabbath lull in the air, which, in a settlement unused to Sabbath influences, looked ominous.

Mr Oakhurst's calm, handsome face betrayed small concern in these indications. Whether he was conscious of any predisposing cause, was another question. "I reckon they're after somebody," he reflected; "likely it's me." He returned to his pocket the handkerchief with which he had been whipping away the red dust of Poker Flat from his neat boots, and quietly discharged his mind of any further conjecture.

In point of fact, Poker Flat was "after somebody." It had lately suffered the loss of several thousand dollars, two valuable horses, and a prominent citizen. It was experiencing a spasm of virtuous reaction, quite as lawless and ungovernable as any of the acts that had provoked it. A secret committee had determined to rid the town of all improper persons. This was done permanently in regard of two men who were then hanging from the boughs of a sycamore in the gulch, and temporarily in the banishment of certain other objectionable characters. I regret to say that some of these were ladies. It is but due to the sex, however, to state that their impropriety was professional, and it was only in such easily established standards of evil that Poker Flat ventured to sit in judgment.

Mr Oakhurst was right in supposing that he was included in this category. A few of the committee had urged hanging him as a possible example, and a sure method of reimbursing themselves from his pockets of the sums he had won from them. "It's agin justice," said Jim Wheeler, "to let this yer young man from Roaring Camp – an entire stranger – carry away our money." But a crude sentiment of equity residing in the breasts of those who had been fortunate enough to win from Mr Oakhurst overruled this narrower local prejudice.

Mr Oakhurst received his sentence with philosophic calmness, none the less coolly that he was aware of the hesitation of his judges. He was too much of a gambler not to accept Fate. With him life was at best an uncertain game, and he recognised the usual per-centage in favour of the dealer.

A party of armed men accompanied the deported wickedness of Poker Flat to the outskirts of the settlement. Besides Mr Oakhurst, who was known to be a coolly desperate man, and for whose intimidation the armed escort was intended, the expatriated party consisted of a young woman familiarly known as "The Duchess;" another, who had bore the title of "Mother Shipton;" and "Uncle Billy," a suspected sluice-robber and confirmed drunkard. The cavalcade provoked no comments from the spectators, nor was any word uttered by the escort. Only when the gulch which marked the uttermost limit of Poker Flat was reached, the leader spoke briefly and to the point. The exiles were forbidden to return at the peril of their lives.

As the escort disappeared, their pent-up feelings found vent in a few hysterical tears from the Duchess, some bad language from Mother Shipton, and a Parthian volley of expletives from Uncle Billy. The philosophic Oakhurst alone remained silent. He listened calmly to Mother Shipton's desire to cut somebody's heart out, to the repeated statements of the Duchess that she would die in the road, and to the alarming oaths that seemed to be bumped out of Uncle Billy as he rode forward. With the easy good-humour characteristic of his class, he insisted upon exchanging his own riding-horse, "Five Spot," for the sorry mule which the Duchess rode. But even this act did not draw the party into any closer sympathy. The young woman readjusted her somewhat draggled plumes with a feeble, faded coquetry; Mother Shipton eyed the possessor of "Five Spot" with malevolence; and Uncle Billy included the whole party in one sweeping anathema.

The road to Sandy Bar – a camp that, not having as yet experienced the regenerating influences of Poker Flat, consequently seemed to offer some invitation to the emigrants – lay over a steep mountain range. It was distant a day's severe travel. In that advanced season, the party soon passed out of the moist, temperate regions of the foot-hills into the dry, cold, bracing air of the Sierras. The trail was narrow and difficult. At noon the Duchess, rolling out of her saddle upon the ground, declared her intention of going no farther, and the party halted.

The spot was singularly wild and impressive. A wooded amphitheatre, surrounded on three sides by precipitous cliffs of naked granite, sloped gently towards the crest of another precipice that overlooked the valley. It was, undoubtedly, the most suitable spot for a camp, had camping been advisable. But Mr Oakhurst knew that scarcely half the journey to Sandy Bar was accomplished, and the party were not equipped or provisioned for delay. This fact he pointed out to his companions curtly, with a philosophic commentary on the folly of "throwing up their hand before the game was played out." But they were furnished with liquor, which in this emergency stood them in place of food, fuel, rest, and prescience. In spite of his remonstrances, it was not long before they were more or less under its influence. Uncle Billy passed rapidly from a bellicose state into one of stupor, the Duchess became maudlin, and Mother Shipton snored. Mr Oakhurst alone remained erect, leaning against a rock, calmly surveying them.

Mr Oakhurst did not drink. It interfered with a profession which required coolness, impassiveness, and presence of mind, and, in his own language, he "couldn't afford it." As he gazed at his recumbent fellow-exiles, the loneliness begotten of his pariah-trade, his habits of life, his very vices, for the first time seriously oppressed him. He bestirred himself in dusting his black clothes, washing his hands and face, and other acts characteristic of his studiously neat habits, and for a moment forgot his annoyance. The thought of deserting his weaker and more pitiable companions never perhaps occurred to him. Yet he could not help feeling the want of that excitement which, singularly enough, was most conducive to that calm equanimity for which he was notorious. He looked at the gloomy walls that rose a thousand feet sheer above the circling pines around him; at the sky, ominously clouded; at the valley below, already deepening into shadow. And, doing so, suddenly he heard his own name called.

A horseman slowly ascended the trail. In the fresh, open face of the new-comer, Mr Oakhurst recognized Tom Simson, otherwise known as "The Innocent" of Sandy Bar. He had met him some months before over a "little game," and had, with perfect equanimity, won the entire fortune – amounting to some forty dollars – of that guileless youth. After the game was finished, Mr Oakhurst drew the youthful speculator behind the door, and thus addressed him: "Tommy, you're a good little man, but you can't gamble worth a cent. Don't try it over again." He then handed him his money back, pushed him gently from the room, and so made a devoted slave of Tom Simson.

There was a remembrance of this in his boyish and enthusiastic greeting of Mr Oakhurst. He had started, he said, to go to Poker Flat to seek his fortune. "Alone?" No, not exactly alone; in fact (a giggle), he had run away with Piney Woods. Didn't Mr Oakhurst remember Piney? She that used to wait on the table at the Temperance House? They had been engaged a long time, but old Jake Woods had objected, and so they had run away, and were going to Poker Flat to be married; and here they were. And they were tired out, and how lucky it was they had found a place to camp and company. All this the Innocent delivered rapidly, while Piney, a stout, comely damsel of fifteen, emerged from behind the pine-tree, where she had been blushing unseen, and rode to the side of her lover.

Mr Oakhurst seldom troubled himself with sentiment, still less with propriety; but he had a vague idea that the situation was not fortunate. He retained, however, his presence of mind sufficiently to kick Uncle Billy, who was about to say something, and Uncle Billy was sober enough to recognize in Mr Oakhurst's kick a superior power that would not bear trifling. He then endeavoured to dissuade Tom Simson from delaying further, but in vain. He even pointed out the fact that there was no provision, nor means of making a camp. But, unluckily, the Innocent met this objection by assuring the party that he was provided with an extra mule loaded with provisions, and by the discovery of a rude attempt at a log-house near the trail. "Piney can stay with Mrs Oakhurst," said the Innocent, pointing to the Duchess, "and I can shift for myself."

Nothing but Mr. Oakhurst's admonishing foot saved Uncle Billy from bursting into a roar of laughter. As it was, he felt compelled to retire up the cañon until he could recover his gravity. There he confided the joke to the tall pine-trees, with many slaps of his leg, contortions of his face, and the usual profanity. But when he returned to the party, he found them seated by a fire – for the air had grown strangely chill, and the sky overcast – in apparently amicable conversation. Piney was actually talking in an impulsive, girlish fashion to the Duchess, who was listening with an interest and animation she had not shown for many days. The Innocent was holding forth, apparently with equal effect, to Mr Oakhurst and Mother Shipton, who was actually relaxing into amiability. "Is this yer a d—d pic-nic?" said Uncle Billy, with inward scorn, as he surveyed the sylvan group, the glancing firelight, and the tethered animals in the foreground. Suddenly an idea mingled with the alcoholic fumes that disturbed his brain. It was apparently of a jocular nature, for he felt impelled to slap his leg again and cram his fist into his mouth.

As the shadows crept slowly up the mountain, a slight breeze rocked the tops of the pine-trees, and moaned through their long and gloomy aisles. The ruined cabin, patched and covered with pine-boughs, was set apart for the ladies. As the lovers parted, they unaffectedly exchanged a kiss, so honest and sincere that it might have been heard above the swaying pines. The frail Duchess and the malevolent Mother Shipton were probably too stunned to remark upon this last evidence of simplicity, and so turned without a word to the hut. The fire was replenished, the men lay down before the door, and in a few minutes were asleep.

Mr Oakhurst was a light sleeper. Toward morning he awoke benumbed and cold. As he stirred the dying fire, the wind, which was now blowing strongly, brought to his cheek that which caused the blood to leave it, – snow!

He started to his feet with the intention of awakening the sleepers, for there was no time to lose. But turning to where Uncle Billy had been lying, he found him gone. A suspicion leaped to his brain and a curse to his lips. He ran to the spot where the mules had been tethered; they were no longer there. The tracks were already rapidly disappearing in the snow.

The momentary excitement brought Mr Oakhurst back to the fire with his usual calm. He did not waken the sleepers. The Innocent slumbered peacefully, with a smile on his good-humoured, freckled face; the virgin Piney slept beside her frailer sisters as sweetly as though attended by celestial guardians, and Mr Oakhurst, drawing his blanket over his shoulders, stroked his mustaches and waited for the dawn. It came slowly in a whirling mist of snow-flakes, that dazzled and confused the eye. What could be seen of the landscape appeared magically changed. He looked over the valley, and summed up the present and future in two words – "snowed in!"

A careful inventory of the provisions, which, fortunately for the party, had been stored within the hut, and so escaped the felonious fingers of Uncle Billy, disclosed the fact that with care and prudence they might last ten days longer. "That is," said Mr Oakhurst, *sotto voce* to the Innocent, "if you're willing to board us. If you ain't – and perhaps you'd better not – you can wait till Uncle Billy gets back with provisions." For some occult reason Mr Oakhurst could not bring himself to disclose Uncle Billy's rascality, and so offered the hypothesis that he had wandered from the camp and had accidentally stampeded the animals. He dropped a warning to the Duchess and Mother Shipton, who of course knew the facts of their associate's defection. "They'll find out the truth about us *all* when they find out anything" he added, significantly, "and there's no good frightening them now."

Tom Simson not only put his worldly store at the disposal of Mr Oakhurst, but seemed to enjoy the prospect of their enforced seclusion. "We'll have a good camp for a week, and then the snow'll melt, and we'll all go back together." The cheerful gaiety of the young man and Mr Oakhurst's calm infected the others. The Innocent, with the aid of pine-boughs, extemporized a thatch for the roofless cabin, and the Duchess directed Piney in the rearrangement of the interior with a taste and tact that opened the blue eyes of that provincial maiden to their fullest extent. "I reckon now you're used to fine things at Poker Flat," said Piney. The Duchess turned away sharply to conceal something that reddened her cheeks through its professional tint, and Mother Shipton requested Piney not to "chatter." But when Mr Oakhurst returned from a weary search for the trail, he heard the sound of happy laughter echoed from the rocks. He stopped in some alarm, and his thoughts first naturally reverted to the whiskey, which he had prudently *cachéd*. "And yet it don't somehow sound like whiskey," said the gambler. It was not until he caught sight of the blazing fire through the still blinding storm and the group around it, that he settled to the conviction that it was "square fun."

Whether Mr Oakhurst had *cachéd* his cards with the whiskey as something debarred the free access of the community, I cannot say. It was certain that, in Mother Shipton's words, he "didn't say cards once" during that evening. Haply the time was beguiled by an accordion, produced somewhat ostentatiously by Tom Simson from his pack. Notwithstanding some difficulties attending the manipulation of this instrument, Piney Woods managed to pluck several reluctant melodies from its keys, to an accompaniment by the Innocent on a pair of bone castinents. But the crowning festivity of the evening was reached in a rude camp-meeting hymn, which the lovers, joining hands, sang with great earnestness and vociferation. I fear that a certain defiant tone and Convenanter's swing to its chorus, rather than any devotional quality, caused it speedily to infect the others, who at last joined in the refrain: –

I'm proud to live in the service of the Lord,
And I'm bound to die in His army.

The pines rocked, the storm eddied and whirled above the miserable group, and the flames of their altar leaped heavenward, as if in token of the vow.

At midnight the storm abated, the rolling clouds parted, and the stars glittered keenly above the sleeping camp. Mr Oakhurst, whose professional habits had enabled him to live on the smallest possible amount of sleep, in dividing the watch with Tom Simson, somehow managed to take upon himself the greater part of that duty. He excused himself to the Innocent by saying that he had "often been a week without sleep." "Doing what?" asked Tom. "Poker!" replied Oakhurst, sententiously; "when a man gets a streak of luck – nigger-luck – he don't get tired. The luck gives in first. Luck," continued the gambler, reflectively, "is a mighty queer thing. All you know about it for certain is that it's bound to change. And it's finding out when it's going to change that makes you. We've had a streak of bad luck since we left Poker Flat – you come along, and slap you get into it too. If you can hold your cards right along you're all right. For," added the gambler, with cheerful irrelevance –

> I'm proud to live in the service of the Lord,
> And I'm bound to die in His army.

The third day came, and the sun, looking through the white-curtained valley, saw the outcasts divide their slowly decreasing store of provisions for the morning meal. It was one of the peculiarities of that mountain climate that its rays diffused a kindly warmth over the wintry landscape, as if in regretful commiseration of the past. But it revealed drift on drift of snow piled high around the hut – a hopeless, unchartered, trackless sea of white lying below the rocky shores to which the castaways still clung. Through the marvellously clear air the smoke of the pastoral village of Poker Flat rose miles away. Mother Shipton saw it, and from a remote pinnacle of her rocky fastness, hurled in that direction a final malediction. It was her last vituperative attempt, and perhaps for that reason was invested with a certain degree of sublimity. It did her good, she privately informed the Duchess. "Just you go out there and cuss, and see." She then set herself to the task of amusing, "the child," as she and the Duchess were pleased to call Piney. Piney was no chicken, but it was a soothing and original theory of the pair thus to account for the fact that she didn't swear and wasn't improper.

When night crept up again through the gorges, the reedy notes of the accordion rose and fell in fitful spasms and long-drawn gasps by the flickering camp-fire. But music failed to fill entirely the aching void left by insufficient food, and a new diversion was proposed by Piney – story-telling. Neither Mr Oakhurst nor his female companions caring to relate their personal experiences, this plan would have failed, too, but for the Innocent. Some months before he had chanced upon a stray copy of Mr Pope's ingenious translation of the Iliad. He now proposed to narrate the principal incidents of that poem – having thoroughly mastered the argument and fairly forgotten the words – in the current vernacular of Sandy Bar. And so for the rest of that night the Homeric demigods again walked the earth. Trojan bully and wily Greek wrestled in the winds, and the great pines in the cañon seemed to bow to the wrath of the son of Peleus.

206

Mr Oakhurst listened with quiet satisfaction. Most especially was he interested in the fate of "Ash-heels," as the Innocent persisted in denominating the "swift-footed Achilles."

So with small food and much of Homer and the accordion, a week passed over the heads of the outcasts. The sun again forsook them, and again from leaden skies the snow-flakes were sifted over the land. Day by day closer around them drew the snowy circle, until at last they looked from their prison over drifted walls of drizzling white, that towered twenty feet above their heads. It became more and more difficult to replenish their fires, even from the fallen trees beside them, now half hidden in the drifts. And yet no one complained. The lovers turned from the dreary prospect, and looked into each other's eyes, and were happy. Mr Oakhurst settled himself coolly to the losing game before him. The Duchess, more cheerful than she had been, assumed the care of Piney. Only Mother Shipton – once the strongest of the party – seemed to sicken and fade. At midnight on the tenth day she called Oakhurst to her side. "I'm going," she said, in a voice of querulous weakness, "but don't say anything about it. Don't waken the kids. Take the bundle from under my head and open it." Mr Oakhurst did so. It contained Mother Shipton's rations for the last week, untouched. "Give 'em to the child," she said, pointing to the sleeping Piney. "You've starved yourself," said the gambler. "That's what they call it," said the woman, querulously, as she lay down again, and, turning her face to the wall, passed quietly away.

The accordion and the bones were put aside that day, and Homer was forgotten. When the body of Mother Shipton had been committed to the snow, Mr Oakhurst took the Innocent aside, and showed him a pair of snow-shoes, which he had fashioned from the old pack-saddle. "There's one chance in a hundred to save her yet," he said, pointing to Piney; "but it's there," he added, pointing toward Poker Flat. "If you can reach there in two days she's safe." "And you?" asked Tom Simson. "I'll stay here," was the curt reply.

The lovers parted with a long embrace. "You are not going, too?" said the Duchess, as she saw Mr Oakhurst apparently waiting to accompany him. "As far as the cañon," he replied. He turned suddenly, and kissed the Duchess, leaving her pallid face aflame, and her trembling limbs rigid with amazement.

Night came, but not Mr Oakhurst. It brought the storm again and the whirling snow. Then the Duchess, feeding the fire, found that some one had quietly piled beside the hut enough fuel to last a few days longer. The tears rose to her eyes, but she hid them from Piney.

The women slept but little. In the morning, looking into each other's faces, they read their fate. Neither spoke; but Piney, accepting the position of the stronger, drew near and placed her arm around the Duchess's waist. They kept this attitude for the rest of the day. That night the storm reached its greatest fury, and, rendering asunder the protecting pines, invaded the very hut.

Toward morning they found themselves unable to feed the fire, which gradually died away. As the embers slowly blackened, the Duchess crept closer to Piney, and broke the silence of many hours: "Piney, can you pray?" "No, dear," said Piney, simply. The Duchess, without knowing exactly why, felt relieved, and, putting her head upon Piney's shoulder, spoke no more. And so reclining, the younger and purer pillowing the head of her soiled sister upon her virgin breast, they fell asleep.

The wind lulled as if it feared to waken them. Feathery drifts of snow, shaken from the long pine-boughs, flew like white-winged birds, and settled about them as they slept. The moon through the rifted clouds looked down upon what had been the camp. But all human stain, all trace of earthly travail, was hidden beneath the spotless mantle mercifully flung from above.

They slept all that day and the next, nor did they waken when voices and footsteps broke the silence of the camp. And when pitying fingers brushed the snow from their wan faces, you could scarcely have told, from the equal peace that dwelt upon them, which was she that had sinned. Even the law of Poker Flat recognized this, and turned away, leaving them still locked in each other's arms.

But at the head of the gulch, on one of the largest pine-trees, they found the deuce of clubs pinned to the bark with a bowie-knife. It bore the following, written in pencil, in a firm hand: –

Beneath this tree
Lies the body
of
JOHN OAKHURST,
who struck a streak of bad luck
on the 23rd of November 1850,
and
handed in his checks
on the 7th December, 1850

And pulseless and cold, with a Derringer by his side and a bullet in his heart, though still calm as in life, beneath the snow lay he who was at once the strongest and yet the weakest of the outcasts of Poker Flat.

THE HORSES AND THE SEA

William Saroyan

Like many American writers, William Saroyan is fond of making a comparison between the risks involved in gambling and those in other and more gainful pursuits. In "The Horses and the Sea," a sailor comes to realise that the excitement of betting on the horses is nothing when compared with that he experiences in his own profession.

DRINKING BEER in *The Kentucky* on Third Street, I met a fellow named Drew, father English, mother Italian, and he said he had just got off the boat, straight from Australia, assistant engineer. He was a tall dark half-breed with a solid chin and a long horsey face. Like most seamen ashore he seemed to be in a daze, and although he'd hear something I'd say, he wouldn't understand the meaning immediately. It would take him thirty seconds or maybe a little longer to make out what I was talking about. It looked as if he had something important on his mind, but in reality he was only becoming adjusted to land, to the city, and what was going on. In reality he still had the sea in him and it was taking him time to get the land back into his brain. He wasn't liking it, either: it wasn't pleasing him very much. He had gone to sea when he was fourteen and, on and off, man and boy, he had been to sea ever since. He was nearing his fortieth year, but appeared to be in his middle twenties: it is like this with some seamen: they lead a hard life, they drink, they go away in ships, they walk in the streets of alien cities, they do a lot of swift living, and yet they keep young. Drew was one of these men, and we were drinking beer together, talking.

We got to be friends casually, the way it happens in saloons, and Drew began to talk about himself, how it had been with him from the beginning, feeling restless, dreaming of cities, wanting to walk in them, and all that. Regular Joseph Conrad stuff, a young fellow from inland longing for the sea. I said I had an idea how it had been with him. I myself had gone off with a circus when I was fifteen, but with me it had been something different, the grace of the lady who stood on the horses and went around in a ring. Something like that. Boyish adoration for something hard to define, part woman, part horse. But in the end I went back home and forgot all about it. A horse is a horse, and a woman – well, a boy is apt to learn in a circus. So I went back home and got a job in a grocery store. The inside of a circus tent may appear to be the universe while the circus is going on, but when the show is over and the tent is taken down it is not so wonderful: everybody in a hurry, wagons rolling, poles falling, canvas coming down, elephants walking to the trains: it is not so fine, taking the universe to pieces every other day. Everything gets to have too much impermanence, and after a while the ferocious restlessness of the jungle animals becomes frightening. Either this, or I wasn't cut out to be a circus man.

Anyway, I said I had an idea how it had been with Drew. We drank another beer and all of a sudden he said, Do you understand horses? I want to gamble a little because I haven't much money and winter is coming.

You could have knocked me over with a feather, as they say. The things we had been talking about, and all of a sudden this sort of talk.

I don't know a thing about horses, I said.

But Mac winked at Drew and said, Don't believe it. He's the best handicapper on Third Street.

Drew wasn't very alert mentally, as I've said, and he wanted to know if I ever played the horses. It seemed he hadn't quite understood what Mac had said. I told him I had been playing the horses regularly for over seven years and that all in all I was about eleven dollars and sixty-five cents ahead of the game.

Drew said, I'm feeling lucky to-day. I'd like to make a little bet.

We went around to Number One Opera Alley, through *The Kentucky* to the alley. It was Belmont that day, Arlington Park in Chicago, and Tia Juana, across the border. I began to look over the racing sheets to get a line on distances, odds, weights, and jockeys, and it looked like a bad day at every track. Not one race looked like a business proposition: everything was even-stephen, three horses in every race that might win, and these kind of races are no good. I want a horse to be there to win alone, by two lengths at least, at good odds. My object is not to make the bookies rich, but Drew came up with the name *Sea Bird*.

That horse, he said, sounds good.

What do you mean, good? I said.

The name, he said. *Sea Bird*.

I had to laugh: it was damn funny. I happened to know. *Sea Bird* was a no-good worthless piece of female horse-flesh. She hadn't won a race since she had gone to the barrier two years ago. I liked her name myself but horses with fancy names don't win races. Names have nothing to do with it, although once in a long while a man may win a few dollars by following name hunches. It isn't often though. I told Drew to lay off the horse.

Nevertheless, he liked the name so much he bet a half dollar on her across the board, dollar and a half in all, four bits to win, four bits to place, and four bits to show, and *Sea Bird* ran eighth in a nine-horse race. If she had won, Drew would have got a potful of money. He made the remark himself. If she had won, etc.

Then he said, She sounded good to me. Too bad a horse with a name like that has to be so slow.

I said she was probably a very handsome horse, but not of the running breed, the fast running, the nervous, hysterical kind, the kind that know a race is a race and like to win.

Drew was holding a dollar in his hand and looking bewildered. All those names. It was confusing. What horse do you like up there? he asked.

I said that I didn't like any horse that day. Not one race looked O.K. to me. I told him I wasn't betting.

Well, said Drew, make a suggestion.

I asked if he had money and he told me he had about twelve dollars. He had been in town four days and he had bought a suit of clothes, a pair of shoes, and a few other things: he had been drinking a little and now all he had was twelve dollars. I suggested he ought to hang on to it and forget the horses for the time being, but no, he wanted to make another bet, at least one more.

I named the horse *Unencumbered*.

Then Drew gave me the surprise of my life. What's it mean? he asked. That word?

It means, I said, why, it means *un* encumbered. Do you know what encumbered means?

Drew said he did not.

Well, I asked him what the hell difference it made what the word meant.

The horse was pretty good. It ought to win. It would win, if the race was on the up and up, if it wasn't a dope-race.

The odds were six to one. I told him to bet a half dollar to win and quit whether the horse won or not.

Drew bet two dollars on *Unencumbered* to win: he was a gambler, I could see that. He said, You like this horse. I think she'll win.

Now I am sorry I ever suggested the horse because it did win and it sort of made a tramp of Drew. We left the joint and he was full of gratitude. Now, he kept saying, if we could only make one bet a day like this, he would be able to get through the winter in good style. He said, Will you meet me every noon at *The Kentucky*?

I told him I would, but that it wouldn't be wise for him to have too much confidence in the horses. It didn't always work out so nicely. Sometimes you didn't win a bet in a week, sometimes two weeks.

The next day he had very good luck. I gave him a horse that won, and Pete, the unemployed Southern Pacific engineer, gave him a horse that won, and Drew himself bet only two of his own hunches that lost, so that at the end of the day, he was three dollars to the good.

I could tell he was going haywire because he bought a copy of *The Racing Form* and said he was going to go at the thing scientifically, and the next day when I saw him he said, I've got this racket all figured out. I've got eight winners for to-day.

It isn't impossible to pick eight winners in one day, but I never knew anybody who ever bet eight horses that won, and didn't bet any others.

I didn't say anything and Drew bet his eight horses and two of them won, and the two that won paid very little, and at the end of the day he was out seven dollars.

Afterwards he took it easier and made only one or two bets a day, and one day, about two weeks later, he was broke and I lent him a dollar.

I'm waiting for a boat, he said.

What happened to your boat? I said.

It went back to Australia, he said. Five days ago. I lost my job. They got another assistant engineer.

I didn't see him again for a month. Then he came tearing into Number One Opera Alley in a way that made me know he had money.

I been painting houses, he said. Making six, seven dollars a day.

He had on a brand-new suit and there was a smell of paint with him.

Giving up the sea? I said.

Sure, he said. Seven dollars a day is a lot of money.

He made three swift bets, the kind guys with lots of money and lots of faith in luck make, and lost.

He felt pretty good, though.

I thought I'd lose, he said. I just wanted to find out.

That was funny. How much was it? I said.

Seventeen dollars, he said.

He went away in a hurry.

When I saw him again, about six weeks later, I knew he wasn't painting houses any more and didn't have much money, maybe five or six dollars.

He wasn't wearing a brand-new suit and he wasn't acting game. He was being very cautious about everything. He was looking at the form charts in a way that meant that he didn't want to make a bet just to find out if he was right in believing he would lose, he wanted to make a bet and win, although he was pretty sure no matter what horse he bet on he would lose, and he couldn't afford to lose, and looking at the form charts this way he was looking bewildered and confused and worried. Too many things could happen. He could bet on *Will Colinet* at two to one that ought to win, and it would lose; and *Bright Star* at six to one, that ought to come seventh would win; or he could bet on *Bright Star*, and *Will Colinet* would win, and no matter which horse he played he would lose, and he kept looking at the form chart and trying to make up his mind.

Then he walked away from the form chart and we bumped into each other.

Any luck? I said, but I didn't mean horses.

Haven't made a bet yet, he said. Can't make up my mind.

He stayed around till the races were over and didn't make a bet, and I knew he had very little money.

So many things could happen, it was beginning to scare him because he believed only one thing could happen so far as he was concerned: he would lose all his money.

The next day he was busy all day studying the form charts and looking up the past performances of the various horses, but at the end of the day he hadn't made a bet. After each race he would be amazed that he didn't have sense enough to bet on the winner. And at the end of the day his senselessness in not having bet on every winner and become rich was digusting to him, and he was all bawled up and couldn't make a bet, not even a small half dollar one.

And it was the same the next day. All the races were run, and all the winners came in, and he didn't pay out or collect a nickel, because he couldn't make up his mind to accept the challenge of possibility and win or go broke, although one or the other would be better than trying to get along every day on forty or fifty cents, two lousy meals, and one lousy room to sleep in.

And it was like this for five or six days, and I knew it was getting worse and worse with him: afraid to make up his mind, and all his money being spent carefully for things he needed, and now hardly anything left, so I took him to an Italian restaurant for a big dinner.

My ship is three days out of 'Frisco, he said.

I knew how he felt. He felt lousy. Here he was in the stinking city, in the stinking places of the city, doing no work, fretting about the comparative nervousness of horses, fretting about the infinite possibilities of a single event, a horse race, and three days out of 'Frisco, on the Pacific, was his ship, and on the ship were the men, working, doing the simple things that would bring the ship to port, doing the things that would bring about the happening of only one event, not a horse race, but a ship crossing an ocean from one city on one continent to another city on another continent, and no two ways about it, and all around the ship the clean sea, and above the ship the clean sky, and the simplicity of day, and the certainty of deep sleep at night because he had worked and because the sea could be heard, even when it was very silent, and no confusion in his mind.

The next day he told me frankly he was broke, and I told him I would lend him as much money as he needed each day, and I did, and in a couple of days *The Texan* came to port, and he went down and talked to the Captain and the Chief Engineer, and got his job back. They told him he had missed one of the best voyages of the ship, and when he came uptown to Number One Opera Alley to pay me the money I had loaned him, he said, This voyage I missed because I stayed in the city, painting houses and betting horses, was one of the finest *The Texan* ever made. Four days out of Sydney they hit a big storm and the ship rolled all over the place. Everybody ate standing and the coffee would spill out of your cup while you were drinking it, and nobody could stay in his bunk to sleep, and then they hit the calmest sea anybody had ever seen, sunshine and warm breezes, and the tables steady as tables in restaurants.

And then I knew how it was. It was the *kind* of challenge that he didn't like: it was a manufactured kind. It was fake. It didn't need to be one way or another in the first place, and that was why he couldn't figure it out. They dared you to pick one horse out of six or seven or eight or nine or ten or eleven or twelve, and if you did, you were a fool, even if you picked the right one, and if you didn't but were interested you were a greater fool, and the whole thing was goofy. Who cared about a horse race, anyway? And what if you did win? What if you got rich? It was the same. And the challenge wasn't worth accepting in the first place. But with the sea, with the ship, it was different. There was danger, but it was reasonable. There could be a storm and the ship could sink and everybody could drown, but there was sense to it because you were working to get a cargo to port and when the sea got rough and tried to leap over the ship you could know it was dangerous and still go on drinking coffee out of a half-empty cup and go on sleeping and the ship would go on moving, and you liked it even when it was dangerous because it was clean, the sea was clean, the job of getting the ship to port was a clean job, and there was a lot of sense to it and even if the ship sank and everybody was drowned it was all right because it was clean and the idea was a clean idea.

WHITE JACKET

Herman Melville

Although famous throughout the world for his epic *Moby Dick*, surprisingly Melville was not a success in his own lifetime. His writings were known but they brought him little financial reward or popular acclaim and he was forced to spend the last twenty years of his life as a customs inspector in the New York docks, ironically so near and yet so far from the seas on which he had passed so much of his early life and which had given birth to his greatest work.

White Jacket is a chronicle of life on board a man-of-war of the United States Navy in the middle of the nineteenth century. It is based on Melville's early experiences when he enlisted as an ordinary seaman in Hawaii after jumping ship from a whaler. It shows that clandestine gambling was as popular a pursuit in the armed forces of 1850 as it is today.

MENTION HAS ALREADY been made that the game of draughts, or checkers, was permitted to be played on board the Neversink. At the present time, while there was little or no ship-work to be done, and all hands, in high spirits, were sailing homeward over the warm, smooth sea of the tropics; so numerous became the players, scattered about the decks, that our First Lieutenant used ironically to say that it was a pity they were not tesselated with squares of white and black marble, for the express benefit and convenience of the players. Had this gentleman had his way, our checkerboards would very soon have been pitched out of the ports. But the Captain – unusually lenient in some things – permitted them, and so Mr Bridewell was fain to hold his peace.

But, although this one game was allowable in the frigate, all kinds of gambling were strictly interdicted, under the penalty of the gangway; nor were cards or dice tolerated in any way whatever. This regulation was indispensable, for, of all human beings, man-of-war's men are perhaps the most inclined to gambling. The reason must be obvious to any one who reflects upon their condition on shipboard. And gambling – the most mischievous of vices any where – in a man-of-war operates still more perniciously than on shore. But quite as often as the law against smuggling spirits is transgressed by the unscrupulous sailors, the statutes against cards and dice are evaded.

Sable night, which, since the beginning of the world, has winked and looked on at so many deeds of iniquity – night is the time usually selected for their operations by man-of-war gamblers. The place pitched upon is generally the berth-deck, where the hammocks are swung, and which is lighted so stintedly as not to disturb the sleeping seamen with any obtruding glare. In so spacious an area the two lanterns swinging from the stanchions diffuse a subdued illumination, like a night-taper in the apartment of some invalid. Owing to their position, also, these lanterns are far from shedding an impartial light, however dim, but fling long angular rays here and there, like burglar's dark-lanterns in the fifty-acre vaults of the West India Docks on the Thames.

It may well be imagined, therefore, how well adapted is this mysterious and subterranean Hall of Eblis to the clandestine proceedings of gamblers, especially as the hammocks not only hang thickly, but many of them swing very low, within two feet of the floor, thus forming innumerable little canvass glens, grottoes, nooks, corners, and crannies, where a good deal of wickedness may be practiced by the wary with considerable impunity.

Now the master-at-arms, assisted by his mates, the ship's corporals, reigns supreme in these bowels of the ship. Throughout the night these policemen relieve each other at standing guard over the premises; and, except when the watches are called, they sit in the midst of a profound silence, only invaded by trumpeter's snores, or the ramblings of some old sheet-anchor-man in his sleep.

The two ship's corporals went among the sailors by the names of Leggs and Pounce; Pounce had been a policeman, it was said, in Liverpool; Leggs, a turnkey attached to "The Tombs" in New York. Hence their education eminently fitted them for their stations; and Bland, the master-at-arms, ravished with their dexterity in prying out offenders, used to call them his two right hands.

When man-at-war's-men desire to gamble, they appoint the hour, and select some certain corner, in some certain shadow, behind some certain hammock. They then contribute a small sum towards a joint fund, to be invested in a bribe for some argus-eyed shipmate, who shall play the part of a spy upon the master-at-arms and corporals while the gambling is in progress. In nine cases out of ten these arrangements are so cunning and comprehensive, that the gamblers, eluding all vigilance, conclude their game unmolested. But now and then, seduced into unwariness, or perhaps, from parsimony, being unwilling to employ the services of a spy, they are suddenly lighted upon by the constables, remorselessly collared, and dragged into the *brig*, there to await a dozen lashes in the morning.

Several times at midnight I have been startled out of a sound sleep by a sudden, violent rush under my hammock, caused by the abrupt breaking up of some nest of gamblers, who have scattered in all directions, brushing under the tiers of swinging pallets, and setting them all in a rocking commotion.

It is, however, while laying in port that gambling most thrives in a man-of-war. Then the men frequently practice their dark deeds in the light of the day, and the additional guards which, at such times, they deem indispensable, are not unworthy of note. More especially, their extra precautions in engaging the services of several spies, necessitate a considerable expenditure, so that, in port, the diversion of gambling rises to the dignity of a nabob luxury.

During the day the master-at-arms and his corporals are continually prowling about on all three decks, eager to spy out iniquities. At one time, for example, you see Leggs switching his magisterial rattan, and lurking round the fore-mast on the spar-deck; the next moment, perhaps, he is three decks down, out of sight, prowling among the cable-tiers. Just so with his master, and Pounce his coadjutor; they are here, there, and every where, seemingly gifted with ubiquity.

In order successfully to carry on their proceedings by day, the gamblers must see to it that each of these constables is relentlessly dogged wherever he goes; so that, in case of his approach toward the spot where themselves are engaged, they may be warned of the fact in time to make good their escape. Accordingly, light and active scouts are selected to follow the constable about. From their youthful alertness and activity, the boys of the mizzen-top are generally chosen for this purpose.

But this is not all. On board of most men-of-war there is a set of sly, knavish foxes among the crew, destitute of every principle of honor, and on a par with Irish informers. In man-of-war parlance, they come under the denomination of *fancy-men* and *white-mice*. They are called *fancy-men*, because, from their zeal in craftily reporting offenders, they are presumed to be regarded with high favor by some of the officers. Though it is seldom that these informers can be certainly individualized, so secret and subtle are they in laying their information, yet certain of the crew, and especially certain of the marines, are invariably suspected to be *fancy-men* and *white-mice*, and are accordingly more or less hated by their comrades.

Now, in addition to having an eye on the master-at-arms and his aids, the day-gamblers must see to it, that every person suspected of being a *white-mouse* or *fancy-man*, is likewise dogged wherever he goes. Additional scouts are retained constantly to snuff at their trail. But the mysteries of man-of-war vice are wonderful; and it is now to be recorded, that, from long habit and observation, and familiarity with the *guardo moves* and *manoeuvres* of a frigate, the master-at-arms and his aids can almost invariably tell when any gambling is going on by day; though, in the crowded vessel, abounding in decks, tops, dark places, and outlandish corners of all sorts, they may not be able to pounce upon the identical spot where the gamblers are hidden.

During the period that Bland was suspended from his office as master-at-arms, a person who, among the sailors, went by the name of Sneak, having been long suspected to have been a *white-mouse*, was put in Bland's place. He proved a hang-dog, sidelong catch-thief, but gifted with a marvelous perseverance in ferreting out culprits; following in their track like an inevitable Cuba blood-hound, with his noiseless nose. When disconcerted, however, you sometimes heard his bay.

"The muffled dice are somewhere around," Sneak would say to his aids; "there are them three chaps, there, been dogging me about for the last half hour. I say, Pounce, has any one been scouting around *you* this morning?"

"Four on 'em," says Pounce. "I know'd it; I knowed the muffled dice was rattlin'!"

"Leggs!" says the master-at-arms to his other aid, "Leggs, how is it with *you* – any spies?"

"Ten on 'em," says Leggs. "There's one on 'em now – that fellow stitching a hat."

"Halloo, you sir!" cries the master-at-arms, "top your boom and sail large, now. If I see you about me again, I'll have you up to the mast."

"What am I a doin' now?" says the hat-stitcher, with a face as long as a rope-walk. "Can't a feller be workin' here, without being 'spected of Tom Coxe's traverse, up one ladder and down t'other?"

"Oh, I know the moves, sir; I have been on board a *guardo*. Top your boom, I say, and be off, or I'll have you hauled up and riveted in a clinch – both fore-tacks over the main-yard, and no bloody knife to cut the seizing. Sheer! or I'll pitch into you like a shin of beef into a beggar's wallet."

It is often observable, that, in vessels of all kinds, the men who talk the most sailor lingo are the least sailor-like in reality. You may sometimes hear even marines jerk out more salt phrases than the Captain of the Forecastle himself. On the other hand, when not actively engaged in his vocation, you would take the best specimen of a seaman for a landsman. When you see a fellow yawing about the docks like a homeward-bound Indiaman, a long Commodore's pennant of black ribbon flying from his mast-head, and fetching up at a grog-shop with a slew of his hull, as if an Admiral were coming alongside a three-decker in his barge; you may put that man down for what man-of-war's-men call a *damn-my-eyes-tar*, that is, a humbug. And many damn-my-eyes humbugs there are in this man-of-war world of ours.

THE FEMALE
OF THE SPECIES

THE GAMBLER (2)

Fedor Dostoevsky

In this further piece from *The Gambler*, Dostoevsky shows how totally gambling fever can take hold of a beginner, in this case a very rich and elderly countess. Her wealth had provided the principal expectations for her impoverished family who look on aghast as she makes her first sortie into the casino.

OUR VISIT to the Casino was a triumph. The porters and attendants displayed the same deference as in the hotel. They looked at us, however, with curiosity. Granny began by giving orders that she should be wheeled through all the rooms. Some she admired, others made no impression on her; she asked questions about them all. At last we came to the roulette room. The lackeys, who stood like sentinels at closed doors, flung the doors wide open as though they were impressed.

Granny's appearance at the roulette table made a profound impression on the public. At the roulette tables and at the other end of the room, where there was a table with *trente et quarante*, there was a crowd of a hundred and fifty or two hundred players, several rows deep. Those who had succeeded in squeezing their way right up to the table, held fast, as they always do, and would not give up their places to anyone until they had lost; for simple spectators were not allowed to stand at the tables and occupy space. Though there were chairs set round the table, few of the players sat down, especially when there was a great crowd, because standing one could get closer and consequently pick out one's place and put down one's stake more conveniently. The second and the third rows pressed up upon the first, waiting and watching for their turn; but sometimes a hand would be impatiently thrust forward through the first row to put down a stake. Even from the third row people managed to seize chances of poking forward their stakes; consequently every ten or even five minutes there was some "scene" over disputed stakes at one end of the hall or another. The police of the Casino were, however, fairly good. It was, of course, impossible to prevent crowding; on the contrary, the owners were glad of the rush of people because it was profitable, but eight croupiers sitting round the table kept a vigilant watch on the stakes: they even kept count of them, and when disputes arose they could settle them. In extreme cases they called in the police, and the trouble was over in an instant. There were police officers in plain clothes stationed here and there among the players, so that they could not be recognised. They were especially on the look-out for thieves and professional pickpockets, who are very numerous at the roulette tables, as it affords them excellent opportunity for exercising their skill. The fact is, elsewhere thieves must pick pockets or break locks, and such enterprises, when unsuccessful, have a very troublesome ending. But in this case the thief has only to go up to the roulette table, begin playing, and all at once, openly and publicly, take another person's winnings and put them in his pocket. If a dispute arises, the cheat insists loudly that the stake was his. If the trick is played cleverly and the witnesses hesitates, the thief may often succeed in carrying off the money, if the sum is not a very large one, of course. In that case the croupiers or some one of the other players are almost certain to have been keeping an eye on it. But if the sum is not a large one, the real owner sometimes actually declines to keep up the dispute, and goes away shrinking from the scandal. But if they succeed in detecting a thief, they turn him out at once with contumely.

All this Granny watched from a distance with wild curiosity. She was much delighted at a thief's being turned out. *Trente et quarante* did not interest her very much; she was more pleased at roulette and the rolling of the little ball. She evinced a desire at last to get a closer view of the game. I don't know how it happened, but the attendants and other officious persons (principally Poles who had lost, and who pressed their services on lucky players and foreigners of all sorts) at once, and in spite of the crowd, cleared a place for Granny in the very middle of the table beside the chief croupier, and wheeled her chair to it. A number of visitors who were not playing, but watching the play (chiefly Englishmen with their families), at once crowded round the table to watch Granny from behind the players. Numbers of lorgnettes were turned in her direction. The croupiers' expectations rose. Such an eccentric person certainly seemed to promise something out of the ordinary. An old woman of seventy, who could not walk, yet wished to play, was, of course, not a sight to be seen every day. I squeezed my way up to the table too, and took my stand beside Granny. Potapitch and Marfa were left somewhere in the distance among the crowd. The General, Polina, De Grieux, and Mlle Blanche stood aside, too, among the spectators.

At first Granny began looking about at the players. She began in a half whisper asking me abrupt, jerky questions. Who was that man and who was this woman? She was particularly delighted by a young man at the end of the table who was playing for very high stakes, putting down thousands, and had, as people whispered around, already won as much as forty thousand francs, which lay before him in heaps of gold and banknotes. He was pale; his eyes glittered and his hands were shaking; he was staking now without counting, by handfuls, and yet he kept on winning and winning, kept raking in the money. The attendants hung about him solicitously, set a chair for him, cleared a place round him that he might have more room, that he might not be crowded – all this in expectation of a liberal tip. Some players, after they have won, tip the attendants without counting a handful of coins in their joy. A Pole had already established himself at his side, and was deferentially but continually whispering to him, probably telling him what to stake on, advising and directing his play – of course, he, too, expected a tip later on! But the player scarcely looked at him. He staked at random and kept winning. He evidently did not know what he was doing.

Granny watched him for some minutes.

"Tell him," Granny said suddenly, growing excited and giving me a poke, "tell him to give it up, to take his money quickly and go away. He'll lose it all directly, he'll lose it all!" she urged, almost breathless with agitation. "Where's Potapitch? Send Potapitch to him. Come, tell him, tell him," she went on, poking me. "Where is Potapitch? *Sortez! Sortez!*" – she began herself shouting to the young man.

I bent down to her and whispered resolutely that she must not shout like this here, that even talking aloud was forbidden, it hindered counting and that we should be turned out directly.

"How vexatious! The man's lost! I suppose it's his own doing. . . . I can't look at him, it quite upsets me. What a dolt!" and Granny made haste to turn in another direction.

On the left, on the other side of the table, there was conspicuous among the players a young lady, and beside her a sort of dwarf. Who this dwarf was, and whether he was a relation or brought by her for the sake of effect, I don't know. I had noticed the lady before; she made her appearance at the gambling table every day, at one o'clock in the afternoon, and went away exactly at two; she always played for an hour. She was already known, and a chair was set for her at once. She took out of her pocket some gold, some thousand-franc notes, and began staking quietly, coolly, prudently, making pencil notes on a bit of paper of the numbers about which the chances grouped themselves, and trying to work out a system. She staked considerable sums. She used to win every day – one, two, or at the most three thousand francs – not more, and instantly went away. Granny scrutinised her for a long time.

"Well, that one won't lose! That one there won't lose! Of what class is she? Do you know? Who is she?"

"She must be a Frenchwoman, of a certain class, you know," I whispered.

"Ah, one can tell the bird by its flight. One can see she has a sharp claw. Explain to me now what every turn means and how one has to bet!"

I explained as far as I could to Granny all the various points on which one could stake: *rouge et noir, pair et impair, manque et passe*, and finally the various subtleties in the system of the numbers. Granny listened attentively, remembered, asked questions, and began to master it. One could point to examples of every kind, so that she very quickly and readily picked up a great deal.

"But what about zéro? You see that croupier, the curly-headed one, the chief one, showed zéro just now? And why did he scoop up everything that was on the table? Such a heap, he took it all for himself. What is the meaning of it?"

"Zéro, Granny, means that the bank wins all. If the little ball falls on zéro, everything on the table goes to the bank. It is true you can stake your money so as to keep it, but the bank pays nothing."

"You don't say so! And shall I get nothing?"

"No, Granny, if before this you had staked on zéro you would have got thirty-five times what you staked."

"What! thirty-five times, and does it often turn up? Why don't they stake on it, the fools."

"There are thirty-six chances against it, Granny."

"What nonsense. Potapitch! Potapitch! Stay, I've money with me – here." She took out of her pocket a tightly packed purse, and picked out of it a friedrich d'or. "Stake it on the zéro at once."

"Granny, zéro has only just turned up," I said; "so now it won't turn up for a long time. You will lose a great deal; wait a little, anyway."

"Oh, nonsense; put it down!"

"As you please, but it may not turn up again till the evening. You may go on staking thousands; it has happened."

"Oh, nonsense, nonsense. If you are afraid of the wolf you shouldn't go into the forest. What? Have I lost? Stake again!"

A second friedrich d'or was lost: she staked a third. Granny could scarcely sit still in her seat. She stared with feverish eyes at the little ball dancing on the spokes of the turning wheel. She lost a third, too. Granny was beside herself, she could not sit still, she even thumped on the table with her fist when the croupier announced "trente-six" instead of the zéro she was expecting.

"There, look at it," said Granny angrily; "isn't that cursed little zéro coming soon? As sure as I'm alive, I'll sit here till zéro does come! It's that cursed curly-headed croupier's doing; he'll never let it come! Alexey Ivanovitch, stake two gold pieces at once! Staking as much as you do, even if zéro does come you'll get nothing by it."

"Granny!"

"Stake, stake! it is not your money."

I staked two friedrichs d'or. The ball flew about the wheel for a long time, at last it began dancing about the spokes. Granny was numb with excitement, and squeezed my fingers, and all at once. . . .

"Zéro!" boomed the croupier.

"You see, you see!" – Granny turned to me quickly, beaming and delighted. "I told you so. The Lord Himself put it into my head to stake those two gold pieces! Well, how much do I get now? Why don't they give it me? Potapitch, Marfa, where are they? Where have all our people got to? Potapitch, Potapitch!"

"Granny, afterwards," I whispered; "Potapitch is at the door, they won't let him in. Look, Granny they are giving you the money, take it!" A heavy roll of printed blue notes, worth fifty friedrichs d'or, was thrust towards Granny and twenty friedrich d'or were counted out to her. I scooped it all up in a shovel and handed it to Granny.

"Faites le jeu, messieurs! Faites le jeu, messieurs! Rien ne va plus!" called the croupier, inviting the public to stake, and preparing to turn the wheel.

"Heavens! we are too late. They're just going to turn it. Put it down, put it down!" Granny urged me in a flurry. "Don't dawdle, make haste!" She was beside herself and poked me with all her might.

"What am I to stake it on, Granny?"

"On zéro, on zéro! On zéro again! Stake as much as possible! How much have we got altogether? Seventy friedrichs d'or. There's no need to spare it. Stake twenty friedrichs d'or at once."

"Think what you are doing, Granny! sometimes it does not turn up for two hundred times running! I assure you, you may go on staking your whole fortune."

"Oh, nonsense, nonsense! Put it down! How your tongue does wag! I know what I'm about." Granny was positively quivering with excitement.

"By the regulations it's not allowed to stake more than twelve roubles on zéro at once, Granny; here I have staked that."

"Why is it not allowed? Aren't you lying? Monsieur! Monsieur!" – she nudged the croupier, who was sitting near her on the left, and was about to set the wheel turning. *"Combien zéro? Douze? Douze?"*

I immediately interpreted the question in French.

"Oui, madame," the croupier confirmed politely; "as the winnings from no single stake must exceed four thousand florins by the regulations," he added in explanation.

"Well, there's no help for it, stake twelve."

"Le jeu est fait," cried the croupier. The wheel rotated, and thirty turned up. She had lost.

"Again, again, again! Stake again!" cried Granny. I no longer resisted, and, shrugging my shoulders, staked another twelve friedrichs d'or. The wheel turned a long time. Granny was simply quivering as she watched the wheel. "Can she really imagine that zéro will win again?" I thought, looking at her with wonder. Her face was beaming with a firm conviction of winning, an unhesitating expectation that in another minute they would shout zéro. The ball jumped into the cage.

"Zéro!" cried the croupier.

"What!!!!" Granny turned to me with intense triumph.

I was a gambler myself, I felt that at the moment my arms and legs were trembling, there was a throbbing in my head. Of course, this was a rare chance that zéro should have come up three times in some dozen turns; but there was nothing particularly wonderful about it. I had myself seen zéro turn up three times *running* two days before, and a gambler who had been zealously noting down the lucky numbers, observed aloud that, only the day before, zéro had turned up only once in twenty-four hours.

Granny's winnings were counted out to her with particular attention and deference as she had won such a large sum. She received four hundred and twenty friedrichs d'or, that is, four thousand florins and seventy friedrichs d'or. She was given twenty friedrichs d'or in gold, and four thousand florins in banknotes.

This time Granny did not call Potapitch; she had other pre-occupations. She did not even babble or quiver outwardly! She was, if one may so express it, quivering inwardly. She was entirely concentrated on something, absorbed in one aim.

"Alexey Ivanovitch, he said that one could only stake four thousand florins at once, didn't he? Come, take it, stake the whole four thousand on the red," Granny commanded.

It was useless to protest; the wheel began rotating.

"Rouge", the croupier proclaimed.

Again she had won four thousand florins, making eight in all.

"Give me four, and stake four again on red," Granny commanded.

Again I staked four thousand.

"Rouge", the croupier pronounced again.

"Twelve thousand altogether! Give it me all here. Pour the gold here into the purse and put away the notes. That's enough! Home! Wheel my chair out. . . ."

Granny was in an impatient and irritable mood; it was evident that roulette had made a deep impression on her mind. She took no notice of anything else and was altogether absent-minded. For instance, she asked me no questions on the road as she had done before. Seeing a luxurious carriage whirling by, she was on the point of raising her hand and asking: What is it? Whose is it? – but I believe she did not hear what I answered: her absorption was continually interrupted by abrupt and impatient gesticulations. When I pointed out to her Baron and Baroness Burmerhelm, who were approaching the Casino, she looked absent-mindedly at them and said, quite indifferently, "Ah!" and, turning round quickly to Potapitch and Marfa, who were walking behind her, snapped out to them –

"Why are you hanging upon us? We can't take you every time! Go home! You and I are enough." she added, when they had hurriedly turned and gone home.

They were already expecting Granny at the Casino. They immediately made room for her in the same place, next to the croupier. I fancy that these croupiers, who are always so strictly decorous and appear to be ordinary officials who are absolutely indifferent as to whether the bank wins or loses, are by no means so unconcerned at the bank's losses and, of course, receive instructions for attracting players and for augmenting the profits – for which they doubtless receive prizes and bonuses. They looked upon Granny, anyway, as their prey.

Then just what we had expected happened.

This was how it was.

Granny pounced at once on zéro and immediately ordered me to stake twelve friedrichs d'or. She staked once, twice, three times – zéro never turned up.

"Put it down! Put it down!" Granny nudged me, impatiently. I obeyed.

"How many times have we staked?" she asked at last, grinding her teeth with impatience.

"I have staked twelve times, Granny. I have put down a hundred and forty-four friedrichs d'or. I tell you, Granny, very likely till evening . . ."

"Hold your tongue!" Granny interrupted. "Stake on zéro, and stake at once a thousand gulden on red. Here, take the note."

Red won, and zéro failed once more; a thousand gulden was gained.

"You see, you see!" whispered Granny, "We have gained almost all that we have lost. Stake again on zéro; we'll stake ten times more and then give it up."

But the fifth time Granny was thoroughly sick of it.

"The devil take that filthy zéro. Come, stake the whole four thousand gulden on the red," she commanded me.

"Granny! it will be so much; why, what if red does not turn up!" I besought her; but Granny almost beat me. (Indeed, she nudged me so violently that she might almost be said to have attacked me.) There was no help for it. I staked on red the whole four thousand won that morning. The wheel turned. Granny sat calmly and proudly erect, never doubting that she would certainly win.

"Zéro!" boomed the croupier.

At first Granny did not understand, but when she saw the croupier scoop up her four thousand gulden, together with everything on the table, and learned that zéro, which had not turned up for so long and on which we had staked in vain almost two hundred friedrichs d'or, had, as though to spite her, turned up just as Granny was abusing it, she groaned and flung up her hands in view of the whole hall. People around actually laughed.

"Holy saints! The cursed thing has turned up" Granny wailed, "the hateful, hateful thing! That's your doing! It's all your doing" – she pounced upon me furiously, pushing me. "It was you persuaded me."

"Granny, I talked sense to you; how can I answer for chance?"

"I'll chance you," she whispered angrily. "Go away."

"Good-bye, Granny." I turned to go away.

"Alexey Ivanovitch. Alexey Ivanovitch! stop. Where are you off to?

Come, what's the matter, what's the matter? Ach, he's in a rage! Stupid, come, stay, stay; come, don't be angry; I am a fool myself! Come, tell me what are we to do now!"

"I won't undertake to tell you, Granny, because you will blame me. Play for yourself, tell me and I'll put down the stakes."

"Well, well! Come, stake another four thousand gulden on red! Here, take my pocket-book." She took it out of her pocket and gave it me. "Come, make haste and take it, there's twenty thousand roubles sterling in it."

"Granny," I murmured, "such stakes . . ."

"As sure as I am alive, I'll win it back. . . . Stake."

We staked and lost.

"Stake, stake the whole eight!"

"You can't, Granny, four is the highest stake! . . ."

"Well, stake four!"

This time we won. Granny cheered up.

"You see, you see," she nudged me; "stake four again!"

She staked – she lost; then we lost again and again.

"Granny, the whole twelve thousand is gone," I told her.

"I see it's all gone," she answered with the calm of fury, if I may so express it. "I see, my good friend, I see," she muttered, with a fixed, as it were, absent-minded stare. "Ech, as sure I am alive, stake another four thousand gulden!"

"But there's no money, Granny; there are some of our Russian five per cents and some bills of exchange of some sort, but no money."

"And in the purse?"

"There's some small change, Granny."

"Are there any money-changers here? I was told one could change any of our notes." Granny inquired resolutely.

"Oh, as much as you like, but what you'll lose on the exchange . . . would horrify a Jew!"

"Nonsense! I'll win it all back. Take me! Call those blockheads!"

I wheeled away the chair; the porters appeared and we went out of the Casino.

"Make haste, make haste, make haste," Granny commanded. "Show us the way, Alexey Ivanovitch, and take us the nearest . . . Is it far?"

"Two steps, Granny."

But at the turning from the square into the avenue we were met by our whole party: the General, De Grieux, Mlle. Blanche and her mamma.

Polina Alexandrovna was not with them, nor Mr Astley either.

"Well! Don't stop us!" cried Granny. "Well, what do you want? I have no time to spare for you now!"

I walked behind; De Grieux ran up to me.

"She's lost all she gained this morning and twelve thousand gulden as well. We are going to change some five per cents," I whispered to him quickly.

De Grieux stamped and ran to tell the General. We went on wheeling Granny.

"Stop, stop!" the General whispered to me frantically.

"You try stopping her," I whispered.

"Auntie!" said the General, approaching, "Auntie . . . we are just . . . we are just . . ." his voice quivered and failed him, "hiring a horse and driving into the country . . . a most exquisite view . . . the peak . . . We were coming to invite you."

"Oh, bother you and your peak." Granny waved him off irritably.

"There are trees there . . . we will have tea . . ." the General went on, utterly desperate.

"Nous boirons du lait, sur l'herbe fraîche," added De Grieux, with ferocious fury.

Du lait, de l'herbe fraîche, that is the Paris bourgeois notion of the ideally idyllic; that is, as we all know, his conception of *nature et la vérité*!

"Oh, go on with you and your milk! Lap it up yourself; it gives me the bellyache. And why do you pester me?" cried Granny. "I tell you I've no time to waste."

"It's here, Granny," I said; "it's here!"

We had reached the house where the bank was. I went in to change the notes; Granny was left waiting at the entrance; De Grieux, the General and Blanche stood apart waiting, not knowing what to do. Granny looked wrathfully at them, and they walked away in the direction of the Casino.

They offered me such ruinous terms that I did not accept them, and went back to Granny for instructions.

"Ah, the brigands!" she cried, flinging up her hands, "Well, never mind! Change it," she cried resolutely; "stay, call the banker out to me!"

"One of the clerks, Granny, do you mean?"

"Yes, a clerk, it's all the same. Ach, the brigands!"

The clerk consented to come when he learned that it was an invalid and aged countess, unable to come in, who was asking for him. Granny spent a long time loudly and angrily reproaching him for swindling her, and haggled with him in a mixture of Russian, French and German, while I came to the rescue in translating. The grave clerk listened to us in silence and shook his head. He looked at Granny with an intent stare that was hardly respectful; at last he began smiling.

"Well, get along with you," cried Granny. "Choke yourself with the money! Change it with him, Alexey Ivanovitch; there's no time to waste, or we would go elsewhere. . . ."

"The clerk says that other banks give even less."

I don't remember the sums exactly, but the banker's charges were terrible. I received close upon twelve thousand florins in gold and notes, took the account and carried it to Granny.

"Well, well, well, it's no use counting it," she said, with a wave of her hand. "Make haste, make haste, make haste!"

"I'll never stake again on that damned zéro nor on the red either," she pronounced, as she was wheeled up to the Casino.

This time I did my very utmost to impress upon her the necessity of staking smaller sums, trying to persuade her that with the change of luck she would always be able to increase her stake. But she was so impatient that, though she agreed at first, it was impossible to restrain her when the play had begun; as soon as she had won a stake of ten, of twenty friedrichs d'ors –

"There, you see, there, you see," she would begin nudging me; "there, you see, we've won; if only we had staked four thousand instead of ten, we should have won four thousand, but, as it is, what's the good? It's all your doing, all your doing!"

And, vexed as I felt, watching her play, I made up my mind at last to keep quiet and to give no more advice.

Suddenly De Grieux skipped up.

The other two were close by; I noticed Mlle Blanche standing on one side with her mother, exchanging amenities with the Prince. The General was obviously out of favour, almost banished. Blanche would not even look at him, though he was doing his utmost to cajole her! The poor General! He flushed and grew pale by turns, trembled and could not even follow Granny's play. Blanche and the Prince finally went away; the General ran after them.

"Madame, madame," De Grieux whispered in a honeyed voice to Granny, squeezing his way close up to her ear. "Madame, such stakes do not answer. . . . No, no, it's impossible . . ." he said, in broken Russian. "No!"

"How, then? Come, show me!" said Granny, turning to him.

De Grieux babbled something rapidly in French, began excitedly advising, said she must wait for a chance, began reckoning some numbers. . . . Granny did not understand a word. He kept turning to me, for me to translate; tapped the table with his fingers, pointed; finally took a pencil and was about to reckon something on paper. At last Granny lost patience.

"Come, get away, get away! You keep talking nonsense! 'Madame, madame,' he doesn't understand it himself; go away."

"*Mais, Madame,*" De Grieux murmured, and he began once more showing and explaining.

"Well, stake once as he says," Granny said to me; "let us see: perhaps it really will answer."

All De Grieux wanted was to dissuade her from staking large sums; he suggested that she should stake on numbers, either individually or collectively. I staked us he directed, a friedrich d'or on each of the odd numbers in the first twelve and five friedrichs d'or respectively on the groups of numbers from twelve to eighteen and from eighteen to twenty-four, staking in all sixteen friedrichs d'or.

The wheel turned.

"Zéro," cried the croupier.

We had lost everything.

"You blockhead!" cried Granny, addressing De Grieux. "You scoundrelly Frenchman! So this is how he advises, the monster. Go away, go away! He knows nothing about it and comes fussing round!"

Fearfully offended, De Grieux shrugged his shoulders, looked contemptuously at Granny, and walked away. He felt ashamed of having interfered; he had been in too great a hurry.

An hour later, in spite of all our efforts, we had lost everything.

"Home," cried Granny.

She did not utter a single word till we got into the avenue. In the avenue and approaching the hotel she began to break into exclamations:

"What a fool! What a silly fool! You're an old fool, you are!"

As soon as we got to her apartments –

"Tea!" cried Granny. "And pack up at once! We are going!"

"Where does your honour mean to go?" Marfa was beginning.

"What has it to do with you? Mind your own business! Potapitch, pack up everything: all the luggage. We are going back to Moscow. I have thrown away fifteen thousand roubles!"

. . . In the first place, to finish with Granny. The following day she lost everything. It was what was bound to happen. When once anyone is started upon that road, it is like a man in a sledge flying down a snow mountain more and more swiftly. She played all day till eight o'clock in the evening; I was not present and only know what happened from what I was told.

Potapitch was in attendance on her at the Casino all day. Several Poles in succession guided Granny's operations in the course of the day. She began by dismissing the Pole whose hair she had pulled the day before and taking on another, but he turned out almost worse. After dismissing the second, and accepting again the first, who had never left her side, but had been squeezing himself in behind her chair and continually poking his head in during the whole period of his disgrace, she sank at last into complete despair. The second Pole also refused to move away; one stationed himself on her right and the other on her left. They were abusing one another the whole time and quarrelling over the stakes and the game, calling each other "*laidak*" and other Polish civilities, making it up again, putting down money recklessly and playing at random. When they quarrelled they put the money down regardless of each other – one, for instance, on the red and the other on the black. It ended in their completely bewildering and overwhelming Granny, so that at last, almost in tears, she appealed to the old croupier, begging him to protect her and to send them away. They were, in fact, immediately turned out in spite of their outcries and protests; they both shouted out at once and tried to prove that Granny owed them something, that she had deceived them about something and had treated them basely and dishonourably. The luckless Potapitch told me all this the same evening almost with tears, and complained that they stuffed their pockets with money, that he himself had seen them shamelessly steal and continually thrust the money in their pockets. One, for instance, would beg five friedrichs d'or for his trouble and begin putting them down on the spot side by side with Granny's stakes. Granny won, but the man shouted that his stake was the winning one and that Granny's had lost. When they were dismissed Potapitch came forward and said that their pockets were full of gold. Granny at once bade the croupier to look into it and, in spite of the outcries of the Poles (they cackled like two cocks caught in the hand), the police came forward and their pockets were immediately emptied for Granny's benefit. Granny enjoyed unmistakable prestige among the croupiers and the whole staff of the Casino all that day, until she had lost everything. By degrees her fame spread all over the town. All the visitors at the watering-place, of all nations, small and great, streamed to look on at *"une vielle comtesse russe tombée en enfance"*, who had already lost "some millions".

But Granny gained very, very little by being rescued from the two Poles. They were at once replaced by a third, who spoke perfectly pure Russian and was dressed like a gentleman, though he did look like a flunkey with a huge moustache and a sense of his own importance. He, too, "laid himself at his lady's feet and kissed them," but behaved haughtily to those about him, was despotic over the play; in fact, immediately behaved like Granny's master rather than her servant. Every minute, at every turn in the game, he turned to her and swore with awful oaths that he was himself a "*pan* of good position", and that he wouldn't take a kopeck of Granny's money. He repeated this oath so many times that Granny was completely intimidated. But as this *pan* certainly seemed at first to improve her luck, Granny was not willing to abandon him on her own account. An hour later the two Poles who had been turned out of the Casino turned up behind Granny's chair again, and again proffered their services if only to run errands for her. Potapitch swore that the "*pan* of good position" winked at them and even put something in their hands. As Granny had no dinner and could not leave her chair, one of the Poles certainly was of use: he ran off at once to the dining-room of the Casino and brought her a cup of broth and afterwards some tea. They both ran about, however. But towards the end of the day, when it became evident to everyone that she would stake her last banknote, there were behind her chair as many as six Poles who had never been seen or heard of before. When Granny was playing her last coin, they not only ceased to obey her, but took no notice of her whatever, squeezed their way up to the table in front of her, snatched the money themselves, put down the stakes and made their own play, shouted and quarrelled, talked to the "*pan* of good position" as to one of themselves, while the "*pan* of good position" himself seemed almost oblivious of Granny's existence. Even when Granny, after losing everything, was returning after eight o'clock to the hotel, three or four Poles ran at the side of her bath-chair, still unable to bring themselves to leave her; they kept shouting at the top of their voices, declaring in a hurried gabble that Granny had cheated them in some way and must give them something. They followed her in this way right up to the hotel from which they were at last driven away with blows.

By Potapitch's reckoning Granny had lost in all ninety thousand roubles that day, apart from what she had lost the day before. All her notes, her exchequer bonds, all the shares she had with her, she had changed, one after another. I marvelled how she could have stood those seven or eight hours sitting there in her chair and scarcely leaving the table, but Potapitch told me that three or four times she had begun winning considerably; and, carried on by fresh hope, she could not tear herself away. But gamblers know how a man can sit for almost twenty-four hours at cards, without looking to right or to left.

THE WAY TO THE DAIRY

Saki

Best known under his pseudonym "Saki" taken from *Omar Khayyam*, H.H. Munro was another journalist turned short story writer and novelist. Born in Burma but educated in England, he returned there briefly to take up a career in the colonial police but recurrent bouts of fever forced him to come back to London once again. After an apprenticeship with the *Westminster Gazette*, he became foreign correspondent for the *Morning Post* and spent six years in the Balkans, Russia and Paris. By 1908 Saki had become a professional writer, publishing his first novel in 1914. In that year he enlisted in the army and was killed in November 1916 during an attack at Beaumont-Hamel.

His writings are characterised by their whimsicality but they are often not without a satirical bite. "The Way to the Dairy" is a typical Saki story in which three impoverished nieces of a rich aunt plan to demonstrate the prodigality of her nephew by taking her to the casino where he regularly plays.

THE BARONESS and Clovis sat in a much-frequented corner of the Park exchanging biographical confidences about the long succession of passers-by.

"Who are those depressed-looking young women who have just gone by?" asked the Baroness; "they have the air of people who have bowed to destiny and are not quite sure whether the salute will be returned."

"Those," said Clovis, "are the Brimley Bomefields. I dare say you would look depressed if you had been through their experiences."

"I'm always having depressing experiences," said the Baroness, "but I never give them outward expression. It's as bad as looking one's age. Tell me about the Brimley Bomefields."

"Well," said Clovis, "the beginning of their tragedy was that they found an aunt. The aunt had been there all the time, but they had very nearly forgotten her existence until a distant relative refreshed their memory by remembering her very distinctly in his will; it is wonderful what the force of example will accomplish. The aunt, who had been unobtrusively poor, became quite pleasantly rich, and the Brimley Bomefields grew suddenly concerned at the loneliness of her life and took her under their collective wings. She had as many wings around her at this time as one of those beast-things in Revelation."

"So far I don't see any tragedy from the Brimley Bomefields' point of view," said the Baroness.

"We haven't got to it yet," said Clovis. "The aunt had been used to living very simply, and had seen next to nothing of what we should consider life, and her nieces didn't encourage her to do much in the way of making a splash with her money. Quite a good deal of it would come to them at her death, and she was a fairly old woman, but there was one circumstance which cast a shadow of gloom over the satisfaction they felt in the discovery and acquisition of this desirable aunt: she openly acknowledged that a comfortable slice of her little fortune would go to a nephew on the other side of her family. He was rather a deplorable thing in rotters, and quite hopelessly top-hole in the way of getting through money, but he had been more or less decent to the old lady in her unremembered days, and she wouldn't hear anything against him. At least, she wouldn't pay any attention to what she did hear, but her nieces took care that she should have to listen to a good deal in that line. It seemed such a pity, they said among themselves, that good money should fall into such worthless hands. They habitually spoke of their aunt's money as 'good money,' as though other people's aunts dabbled for the most part in spurious currency.

"Regularly after the Derby, St. Leger, and other notable racing events they indulged in audible speculations as to how much money Roger had squandered in unfortunate betting transactions.

"'His travelling expenses must come to a big sum,' said the eldest Brimley Bomefield one day; 'they say he attends every race-meeting in England, besides others abroad. I shouldn't wonder if he went all the way to India to see the race for the Calcutta Sweepstake that one hears so much about.'

"'Travel enlarges the mind, my dear Christine,' said her aunt.

"'Yes, dear aunt, travel undertaken in the right spirit,' agreed Christine; 'but travel pursued merely as a means towards gambling and extravagant living is more likely to contract the purse than to enlarge the mind. However, as long as Roger enjoys himself, I suppose he doesn't care how fast or unprofitably the money goes, or where he is to find more. It seems a pity, that's all.'

"The aunt by that time had begun to talk of something else, and it was doubtful if Christine's moralizing had been even accorded a hearing. It was her remark, however – the aunt's remark, I mean – about travel enlarging the mind, that gave the youngest Brimley Bomefield her great idea for the showing-up of Roger.

"'If aunt could only be taken somewhere to see him gambling and throwing away money,' she said, 'it would open her eyes to his character more effectually than anything we can say.'

"'My dear Veronique,' said her sisters, 'we can't go following him to race-meetings.'

"'Certainly not to race-meetings,' said Veronique, 'but we might go to some place where one can look on at gambling without taking part in it.'

"'Do you mean Monte Carlo?' they asked her, beginning to jump rather at the idea.

"'Monte Carlo is a long way off, and has a dreadful reputation,' said Veronique; 'I shouldn't like to tell our friends that we were going to Monte Carlo. But I believe Roger usually goes to Dieppe about this time of year, and some quite respectable English people go there, and the journey wouldn't be expensive. If aunt could stand the Channel crossing the change of scene might do her a lot of good.'

"And that was how the fateful idea came to the Brimley Bomefields.

"From the very first set-off disaster hung over the expedition, as they afterwards remembered. To begin with, all the Brimley Bromefields were extremely unwell during the crossing, while the aunt enjoyed the sea air and made friends with all manner of strange travelling companions. Then, although it was many years since she had been on the Continent, she had served a very practical apprenticeship there as a paid companion, and her knowledge of colloquial French beat theirs to a standstill. It became increasingly difficult to keep under their collective wings a person who knew what she wanted and was able to ask for it and to see that she got it. Also, as far as Roger was concerned, they drew Dieppe blank; it turned out that he was staying at Pourville, a little watering-place a mile or two further west. The Brimley Bomefields discovered that Dieppe was too crowded and frivolous, and persuaded the old lady to migrate to the comparative seclusion of Pourville.

"'You won't find it dull, you know,' they assured her; 'there is a little casino attached to the hotel, and you can watch the people dancing and throwing away their money at *petits chevaux*.'

"It was just before *petits chevaux* had been supplanted by *boule*.

"Roger was not staying in the same hotel, but they knew that the casino would be certain of his patronage on most afternoons and evenings.

"On the first evening of their visit they wandered into the casino after a fairly early dinner, and hovered near the tables. Bertie van Tahn was staying there at the time, and he described the whole incident to me. The Brimley Bomefields kept a furtive watch on the doors as though they were expecting some one to turn up, and the aunt got more and more amused and interested watching the little horses whirl round and round the board.

"'Do you know, poor little number eight hasn't won for the last thirty-two times,' she said to Christine; 'I've been keeping count. I shall really have to put five francs on him to encourage him.'

"'Come and watch the dancing, dear,' said Christine nervously. It was scarcely a part of their strategy that Roger should come in and find the old lady backing her fancy at the *petits chevaux* table.

"'Just wait while I put five francs on number eight,' said the aunt, and in another moment her money was lying on the table. The horses commenced to move round; it was a slow race this time, and number eight crept up at the finish like some crafty demon and placed his nose just a fraction in front of number three, who had seemed to be winning easily. Recourse had to be had to measurement, and the number eight was proclaimed the winner. The aunt picked up thirty-five francs. After that the Brimley Bomefields would have had to have used concerted force to get her away from the tables. When Roger appeared on the scene she was fifty-two francs to the good; her nieces were hovering forlornly in the background, like chickens that have been hatched out by a duck and are despairingly watching their parent disporting herself in a dangerous and uncongenial element. The supper-party which Roger insisted on standing

238

that night in honour of his aunt and the three Miss Brimley Bomefields was remarkable for the unrestrained gaiety of two of the participants and the funereal mirthlessness of the remaining guests.

"'I do not think,' Christine confided afterwards to a friend, who re-confided it to Bertie van Tahn, 'that I shall ever be able to touch *pâté de foie gras* again. It would bring back memories of that awful evening.'

"For the next two or three days the nieces made plans for returning to England or moving on to some other resort where there was no casino. The aunt was busy making a system for winning at *petits chevaux*. Number eight, her first love, had been running rather unkindly for her, and a series of plunges on number five had turned out even worse.

"'Do you know, I dropped over seven hundred francs at the tables this afternoon,' she announced cheerfully at dinner on the fourth evening of their visit.

"'Aunt! Twenty-eight pounds! And you were losing last night too.'

"'Oh, I shall get it all back,' she said optimistically; 'but not here. These silly little horses are no good. I shall go somewhere where one can play comfortably at roulette. You needn't look so shocked. I've always felt that, given the opportunity, I should be an inveterate gambler, and now you darlings have put the opportunity in my way. I must drink your very good healths. Waiter, a bottle of *Pontet Canet*. Ah, it's number seven on the wine list; I shall plunge on number seven to-night. It won four times running this afternoon when I was backing that silly number five.'

"Number seven was not in a winning mood that evening. The Brimley Bomefields, tired of watching disaster from a distance, drew near to the table where their aunt was now an honoured habituée, and gazed mournfully at the successive victories of one and five and eight and four, which swept 'good money' out of the purse of seven's obstinate backer. The day's losses totalled something very near two thousand francs.

"'You incorrigible gamblers,' said Roger chaffingly to them, when he found them at the tables.

"'We are not gambling,' said Christine freezingly; 'we are looking on.'

"'I *don't* think,' said Roger knowingly; 'of course you're a syndicate and aunt is putting the stakes on for all of you. Anyone can tell by your looks when the wrong horse wins that you've got a stake on.'

"Aunt and nephew had supper alone that night, or at least they would have if Bertie hadn't joined them; all the Brimley Bomefields had headaches.

"The aunt carried them all off to Dieppe the next day and set cheerily about the task of winning back some of her losses. Her luck was variable; in fact, she had some fair streaks of good fortune, just enough to keep her thoroughly amused with her new distraction; but on the whole she was a loser. The Brimley Bomefields had a collective attack of nervous prostration on the day when she sold out a quantity of shares in Argentine rails. 'Nothing will ever bring that money back,' they remarked lugubriously to one another.

"Veronique at last could bear it no longer, and went home; you see, it had been her idea to bring the aunt on this disastrous expedition, and though the others did not cast the fact verbally in her face, there was a certain lurking reproach in their eyes which was harder to meet than actual upbraidings. The other two remained behind, forlornly mounting guard over their aunt until such time as the waning of the Dieppe season should at last turn her in the direction of home and safety. They made anxious calculations as to how little 'good money' might, with reasonable luck, be squandered in the meantime. Here, however, their reckoning went far astray; the close of the Dieppe season merely turned their aunt's thoughts in search of some other convenient gambling resort. 'Show a cat the way to the dairy—' I forget how the proverb goes on, but it summed up the situation as far as the Brimley Bomefields' aunt was concerned. She had been introduced to unexplored pleasures, and found them greatly to her liking, and she was in no hurry to forgo the fruits of her newly acquired knowledge. You see, for the first time in her life the old thing was thoroughly enjoying herself; she was losing money, but she had plenty of fun and excitement over the process, and she had enough left to do very comfortably on. Indeed, she was only just learning to understand the art of doing oneself well. She was a popular hostess, and in return her fellow-gamblers were always ready to entertain her to dinners and suppers when their luck was in. Her nieces, who still remained in attendance on her, with the pathetic unwillingness of a crew to leave a foundering treasure ship which might yet be steered into port, found little pleasure in these Bohemian festivities; to see 'good money' lavished on good living for the entertainment of a nondescript circle of acquaintances who were not likely to be in any way socially useful to them, did not attune them to a spirit of revelry. They contrived, whenever possible, to excuse themselves from participation in their aunt's deplored gaieties; the Brimley Bomefield headaches became famous.

"And one day the nieces came to the conclusion that, as they would have expressed it, 'no useful purpose would be served' by their continued attendance on a relative who had so thoroughly emancipated herself from the sheltering protection of their wings. The aunt bore the announcement of their departure with a cheerfulness that was almost disconcerting.

"'It's time you went home and had those headaches seen to by a specialist,' was her comment on the situation.

"The homeward journey of the Brimley Bomefields was a veritable retreat from Moscow, and what made it the more bitter was the fact that the Moscow, in this case, was not overwhelmed with fire and ashes, but merely extravagantly over-illuminated.

"From mutual friends and acquaintances they sometimes get glimpses of their prodigal relative, who has settled down into a confirmed gambling maniac, living on such salvage of income as obliging moneylenders have left at her disposal.

"So you need not be surprised," concluded Clovis, "if they do wear a depressed look in public."

"Which is Veronique?" asked the Baroness.

"The most depressed-looking of the three," said Clovis.

A MATTER OF SENTIMENT

Saki

"A Matter of Sentiment" is another tale by Saki neatly illustrating a situation that happens all too frequently to the dismay of the practised gambler.

IT WAS THE EVE of the great race, and scarcely a member of Lady Susan's house-party had as yet a single bet on. It was one of those unsatisfactory years when one horse held a commanding market position, not by reason of any general belief in its crushing superiority, but because it was extremely difficult to pitch on any other candidate to whom to pin one's faith. Peradventure II was the favourite, not in the sense of being a popular fancy, but by virtue of a lack of confidence in any one of his rather undistinguished rivals. The brains of clubland were much exercised in seeking out possible merit where none was very obvious to the naked intelligence, and the house-party at Lady Susan's was possessed by the same uncertainty and irresolution that infected wider circles.

"It is just the time for bringing off a good coup," said Bertie van Tahn.

"Undoubtedly. But with what?" demanded Clovis for the twentieth time.

The women of the party were just as keenly interested in the matter, and just as helplessly perplexed; even the mother of Clovis, who usually got good racing information from her dressmaker, confessed herself fancy free on this occasion. Colonel Drake, who was professor of military history at a minor cramming establishment, was the only person who had a definite selection for the event, but as his choice varied every three hours he was worse than useless as an inspired guide. The crowning difficulty of the problem was that it could only be fitfully and furtively discussed. Lady Susan disapproved of racing. She disapproved of many things; some people went as far as to say that she disapproved of most things. Disapproval was to her what neuralgia and fancy needlework are to many other women. She disapproved of early morning tea and auction bridge, of ski-ing and the two-step, of the Russian ballet and the Chelsea Arts Club ball, of the French policy in Morocco and the British policy everywhere. It was not that she was particularly strict or narrow in her views of life, but she had been the eldest sister of a large family of self-indulgent children, and her particular form of indulgence had consisted in openly disapproving of the foibles of the others. Unfortunately the hobby had grown up with her. As she was rich, influential, and very, very kind, most people were content to count their early tea as well lost on her behalf. Still, the necessity for hurriedly dropping the discussion of an enthralling topic, and suppressing all mention of it during her presence on the scene, was an affliction at a moment like the present, when time was slipping away and indecision was the prevailing note.

After a lunch-time of rather strangled and uneasy conversation, Clovis managed to get most of the party together at the further end of the kitchen gardens, on the pretext of admiring the Himalayan pheasants. He had made an important discovery. Motkin, the butler, who (as Clovis expressed it) had grown prematurely grey in Lady Susan's service, added to his other excellent qualities an intelligent interest in matters connected with the Turf. On the subject of the forthcoming race he was not illuminating, except in so far that he shared the prevailing unwillingness to see a winner in Peradventure II. But where he outshone all the members of the house-party was in the fact that he had a second cousin who was head stable-lad at a neighbouring racing establishment, and usually gifted with much inside information as to private form and possibilities. Only the fact of her ladyship having taken it into her head to invite a house-party for the last week of May had prevented Mr Motkin from paying a visit of consultation to his relative with respect to the big race; there was still time to cycle over if he could get leave of absence for the afternoon on some specious excuse.

"Let's jolly well hope he does," said Bertie van Than; "under the circumstances a second cousin is almost as useful as second sight."

"That stable ought to know something, if knowledge is to be found any-where," said Mrs Packletide hopefully.

"I expect you'll find he'll echo my fancy for Motorboat," said Colonel Drake.

At this moment the subject had to be hastily dropped. Lady Susan bore down upon them, leaning on the arm of Clovis's mother, to whom she was confiding the fact that she disapproved of the craze for Pekingese spaniels. It was the third thing she had found time to disapprove of since lunch, without counting her silent and permanent disapproval of the way Clovis's mother did her hair.

"We have been admiring the Himalayan pheasants," said Mrs Packletide suavely.

"They went off to a bird-show at Nottingham early this morning," said Lady Susan, with the air of one who disapproves of hasty and ill-considered lying.

"Their house, I mean; such perfect roosting arrangements, and all so clean," resumed Mrs Packletide, with an increased glow of enthusiasm. The odious Bertie van Tahn was murmuring audible prayers for Mrs Packletide's ultimate estrangement from the paths of falsehood.

"I hope you don't mind dinner being a quarter of an hour late to-night," said Lady Susan; "Motkin has had an urgent summons to go and see a sick relative this afternoon. He wanted to bicycle there, but I am sending him in the motor."

"How very kind of you! Of course we don't mind dinner being put off." The assurances came with unanimous and hearty sincerity.

At the dinner-table that night an undercurrent of furtive curiosity directed itself towards Motkin's impassive countenance. One or two of the guests almost expected to find a slip of paper concealed in their napkins, bearing the name of the second cousin's selection. They had not long to wait. As the butler went round with the murmured question, "Sherry?"

he added in an even lower tone the cryptic words, "Better not." Mrs Packletide gave a start of alarm, and refused the sherry; there seemed some sinister suggestion in the butler's warning, as though her hostess had suddenly become addicted to the Borgia habit. A moment later the explanation flashed on her that "Better Not" was the name of one of the runners in the big race. Clovis was already pencilling it on his cuff, and Colonel Drake, in his turn, was signalling to every one in hoarse whispers and dumb-show the fact that he had all along fancied "B.N."

Early next morning a sheaf of telegrams went Townward, representing the market commands of the house-party and servants' hall.

It was a wet afternoon, and most of Lady Susan's guests hung about the hall, waiting apparently for the appearance of tea, though it was scarcely yet due. The advent of a telegram quickened every one into a flutter of expectancy; the page who brought the telegram to Clovis waited with unusual alertness to know if there might be an answer.

Clovis read the message and gave an exclamation of annoyance.

"No bad news, I hope," said Lady Susan. Every one else knew that the news was not good.

"It's only the result of the Derby," he blurted out; "Sadowa won; an utter outsider."

"Sadowa!" exclaimed Lady Susan; "you don't say so! How remarkable! It's the first time I've ever backed a horse; in fact I disapprove of horse-racing, but just for once in a way I put money on this horse, and it's gone and won."

"May I ask," said Mrs Packletide, amid the general silence, "why you put your money on this particular horse? None of the sporting prophets mentioned it as having an outside chance."

"Well," said Lady Susan, "you may laugh at me, but it was the name that attracted me. You see, I was always mixed up with the Franco-German war; I was married on the day that the war was declared, and my eldest child was born the day that peace was signed, so anything connected with the war has always interested me. And when I saw there was a horse running in the Derby called after one of the battles in the Franco-German war, I said I *must* put some money on it, for once in a way, though I disapprove of racing. And it's actually won."

There was a general groan. No one groaned more deeply than the professor of military history.

MOLL FLANDERS

Daniel Defoe

Daniel Defoe was one of the great satirical journalists of his time, but he has become much more than just a figure of interest to English political and social historians thanks to the extraordinary success of his novel *Robinson Crusoe* based on the real life experiences of a Scottish castaway.

Moll Flanders is another of Defoe's most popular works and the adventures of his heroine afford a remarkable insight into English society of the period from the highest to the lowest levels. In this episode, Moll finds herself in a gaming house in London's Covent Garden. . . .

I MADE another adventure after this, of a nature different from all I had been concerned in yet, and this was at a gaming-house near Covent Garden.

I saw several people go in and out; and I stood in the passage a good while with another woman with me, and seeing a gentleman go up that seemed to be of more than ordinary fashion, I said to him, "Sir, pray don't they give women leave to go up?" "Yes, madam," says he, " and to play too, if they please." "I mean so, sir," said I. And with that he said he would introduce me if I had a mind; so I followed him to the door, and he looking in, "There, madam," says he, "are the gamesters, if you have a mind to venture." I looked in, and said to my comrade aloud, "Here's nothing but men; I won't venture." At which one of the gentlemen cried out, "You need not be afraid, madam, here's none but fair gamesters; you are very welcome to come and set what you please." So I went a little nearer and looked on, and some of them brought me a chair, and I sat down and saw the box and dice go round apace; then I said to my comrade, "The gentlemen play too high for us; come, let us go."

The people were all very civil, and one gentleman encouraged me, and said, "Come, madam, if you please to venture, if you dare trust me, I'll answer for it you shall have nothing put upon you here." "No, sir," said I, smiling, "I hope the gentlemen would not cheat a woman." But still I declined venturing, though I pulled out a purse with money in it that they might see I did not want money.

After I had sat awhile, one gentleman said to me, jeering, "Come, madam, I see you are afraid to venture for yourself; I always had good luck with the ladies, you shall set for me, if you won't set for yourself." I told him, "Sir, I should be very loath to lose your money," though I added, "I am pretty lucky too; but the gentlemen play so high, and I dare not venture my own."

"Well, well," says he, "there's ten guineas, madam; set them for me"; so I took the money and set, himself looking on. I run out the guineas by one and two at a time, and then the box coming to the next man to me, my gentleman gave me ten guineas more, and made me set five of them at once, and the gentleman who had the box threw out, so there was five guineas of his money again. He was encouraged at this, and made me take the box, which was a bold venture: however, I held the box so long that I gained him his whole money, and had a handful of guineas in my lap; and which was the better luck, when I threw out, I threw but at one or two of those that had set me, and so went off easy.

When I was come this length, I offered the gentleman all the gold, for it was his own; and so would have had him play for himself, pretending that I did not understand the game well enough. He laughed, and said if I had but good luck, it was no matter whether I understood the game or no; but I should not leave off. However, he took out the fifteen guineas that he had put in first, and bade me play with the rest. I would have him to have seen how much I had got, but he said, "No, no, don't tell them, I believe you are very honest, and 'tis bad luck to tell them"; so I played on.

I understood the game well enough, though I pretended I did not, and played cautiously, which was to keep a good stock in my lap, out of which I every now and then conveyed some into my pocket, but in such a manner as I was sure he could not see it.

I played a great while, and had very good luck for him; but the last time I held the box they set me high, and I threw boldly at all, and held the box till I had gained near fourscore guineas, but lost above half of it back at the last throw; so I got up, for I was afraid I should lose it all back again, and said to him, "Pray come, sir, now, and take it and play for yourself; I think I have done pretty well for you." He would have had me play on, but it grew late, and I desired to be excused. When I gave it up to him, I told him

I hoped he would give me leave to tell it now, that I might see what he had gained, and how lucky I had been for him; when I told them, there were threescore and three guineas. "Ay," says I, "if it had not been for that unlucky throw, I had got you a hundred guineas." So I gave him all the money, but he would not take it till I had put my hand into it, and taken some for myself, and bid me please myself. I refused it, and was positive I would not take it myself; if he had a mind to do anything of that kind, it should be all his own doings.

The rest of the gentlemen seeing us striving, cried, "Give it her all"; but I absolutely refused that. Then one of them said, "D—n ye, Jack, halve it with her; don't you know you should be always on even terms with the ladies." So, in short, he divided it with me, and I brought away thirty guineas, besides about forty-three which I had stole privately which I was sorry for, because he was so generous.

Thus I brought home seventy-three guineas, and let my old governess see what good luck I had at play. However, it was her advice that I should not venture again, and I took her counsel, for I never went there any more; for I knew as well as she, if the itch of play came in, I might soon lose that, and all the rest of what I had got.

MAMMON & CO. (1)

E. F. Benson

English novelist and biographer, E.F. Benson's first novel *Dodo* created something of a sensation not so much because it was urbane and witty and a little irreligious for its time, but more because its author was the son of the reigning Archbishop of Canterbury.

His writing has been described as redolent of "silks and satins still fragrant with crumpled roses that recall what never can be again," but the following story from *Mammon & Co.* shows that Benson was capable of taking a cynical though still kindly view of Edwardian high society. Kit, Lady Conybeare and Lady Haslemere believe that they have detected Mr

Alington, an Autralian financier, cheating at baccarat. They plan to set a trap for him the next time they play together, but it is not Mr Alington who is caught. . . .

'YOU PLAY BACCARAT, I think, Mr Alington?''

Mr Alington paused, as usual, before replying, and looked benevolently at Kit and Lady Haslemere in turn.

"I shall be delighted to play," he said. "I find it very soothing after a tiring day; one does not have to think at all. I used to play a good deal in Australia, and, dear me, yes! I had the pleasure of playing the other night at your house, Lady Haslemere. Odd games we used to have in Australia. One had to keep both eyes open to see that nobody cheated. Indeed, that was not very soothing work. I have seen five nines on the table before now, which really is an excessive number. Embarrassing almost."

He had the manner of taking everybody into his confidence, and as the others were standing together as he spoke, and he a few steps from them, he had an easy opportunity to look several people in the face. Kit and Alice again received a special share of his kind and intelligent glance, and, as he finished speaking, he laughed in his pleasant voice, as if with considerable inward amusement. So, when they sat down at the card-table, out of the dozen of them there were at least two disconcerted people present, for it was not certain whether Jack had heard.

"I think he scored," said Alice, in a low voice to Kit; and Kit looked impatient, and thought so too.

When they had all taken their seats, Alington was found, as Kit and Alice had wished (and he also, if they had known it), to be opposite them. There were a few moments' delay, as the table was lined, and, playing idly with the counters he had purchased, he looked up at them.

"It is so simple to cheat at baccarat, without the clumsy device of five nines," he said. "One need only lay one's stake just on the white line, neither over it nor behind it. Then, if you win, the slightest touch and the counters will go over, and it appears that you have staked; if not, you leave them as they are. A touch of the cards will do it. So!"

He put a couple of cards face upwards on the table, as if showing his hand, and as he did it, drew his stake over the line so gently and imperceptibly that it was impossible to see that the counters moved. Kit laughed, not very pleasantly. Her laughter sounded a trifle cracked.

"Take care, all of you!" she cried. "There is a brilliant sharper present.

Mr Alington, how stupid of you to tell us! You might have won all our money without any of us being the wiser."

Alington laughed, and Alice told Kit in a low voice not to lose her temper. Alington's laugh was a great contrast to Kit's, pleasant and amused.

"I make the company a present of the only safe way to cheat at baccarat," he said. "The bank? Ah, I see Lord Conybeare takes the bank."

Death and baccarat are great levellers, and Kit in her more sententious moments used to call the latter an escape from the trammels of civilization, and a return to the natural savage instincts. Certainly nothing can be simpler; the cave-men, provided they could count as far as nine, might have played at it. And indeed, unalloyed gambling is not a bad second, considered as a leveller, to death itself. Rich men win, poor men lose; the Countess rubs shoulders (it is not meant that she did at Kit's house) with the cocotte; Jew spoils Jew, and Gentile Gentile. The simple turn of the cards is an affair as haphazard as life. If anyone it must be the devil who knows where and when the nines will come up, and he is incorruptible on this point. The brute loses; the honest man wins; the honest man is made a pauper; the brute a millionaire. There is certainly something fascinating about what we call Luck. No virtue or vice invented by the asceticism or perverted corruptness of man has yet made a bait that she will take. Mathematicians tell us that she is purely mathematical; yet how emphatic a denial she gives to this shallow description of her if one tries to woo her on a system! One might as well make love on the prescriptions of the "Complete Letter-writer."

On this particular night she showed herself the opposite of all the epithets with which her unintelligent worshippers have plastered her. She is called fickle – she was a pattern of devotion; she is called changeable – she exhibited an immutable face. Wherever Alington sat, whether to the right or to the left of the dealer, or whether he took the bank himself, she favoured him with a fixed, unalterable smile, a smile nailed to her features, as if her photograph was being taken. Like the two-faced Jannet, as Mrs Murchison had once called that heathen deity, she kept the benignant aspect for him.

Now, it is one of the rules without exception in this world, that nobody likes losing at cards. People have been heard to say that they do not like winning. This statement is certainly incorrect. It is possible to play an interesting set at tennis, an enjoyable round of golf, an entrancing football match, a really memorable game of chess, and lose, but it is not humanly possible to enjoy losing at baccarat. The object of the game is to win the money of your friends in an exciting and diverting manner, but the diversion tends to become something worse than tedium if they consistently win yours. Excuses and justifications may be found for most unprofitable pursuits, and perhaps the only thing to be said in favour of gambling is that there is no nonsense about it, and, as a rule, no nonsense about those who indulge in it. No one as yet has said that it improves the breed of cards, or that he has the prosperity of the card-makers at heart. The card-table is still a place where hypocrites do not win credence from anybody.

The great goddess Luck ignored Lady Haslemere that night (for she is no respecter of persons, and cuts people whenever she chooses), merely letting her lose a few inglorious sovereigns, and devoted her attentions to Alington and Kit. The latter she visited with every mark of her peculiar disfavour, and the nest-egg in her jewel-case upstairs had to be heavily unyoked. Kit seldom enjoyed herself less than she did this evening; as a rule, she had distinctly good luck at cards, and it was little short of maddening to sit there hour after hour, just to watch her stake being firmly and regularly taken away. Like most people who are generally lucky at cards, she was considered admirably good form at play; but when she was losing in this unexampled manner, she found it difficult to remain cordial, and more than once she had to force herself with an effort to remember that a hostess had duties. Alington's mild, intelligent face opposite her roused in her a kind of frenzy, and his unassumed quietness and utter absence of any signs of satisfaction at his huge winnings seemed to her in the worst taste. Both she and Lady Haslemere had seen how completely their scheme of watching him to see whether he cheated had miscarried; indeed, from the moment when he gave his little exhibition of the ease with which it was possible to defraud the table, they had realized that they might play the detective till their eyes dropped out of their heads from weariness without catching him. Lady Haslemere had given it up at once, concluding that Kit and she must have been mistaken before; Kit continued to watch him furtively and angrily, but the little detective game was not nearly so amusing as she had anticipated.

Meantime, as her stakes vanished and revanished, Kit found herself thinking absently of what Alington had shown them. It was so simple, and she almost wished that she was one of the people who cheated at cards. But she was not. Then occurred an incident.

Alington was taking the bank. Nearly opposite him, and belonging to the party on the dealer's right, was Kit. She had just been upstairs to get all that remained of her nest-egg, and in front of her lay several small counters, two of fifty pounds, and two of a hundred. She had just lost once, and counting up what remained to her, she put all her counters in a heap near the line. Again she staked fifty pounds, and on receiving her cards took them up and looked at them. She was rather excited; her hand trembled a little, and the lower edge of her cards twitched forward. Then she laid them on the table.

"Natural," she said, and as she said it, she saw that she had flicked one of her hundred-pound counters over the line, and it was staked. Almost simultaneously she caught Alington's eye; almost simultaneously Tom's voice said:

"One fifty. Well done, Kit! You've had the worst of luck all the evening."

"A fine, bold stroke," said Alington in his precise tones, still looking at her. "Luck must turn, Lady Conybeare."

For one moment Kit paused, and in that pause she was lost. Alington counted out her stake, pushed it over to her, and rose.

"A thrilling end to my bank," he said. "The first big stake this evening. Thank you, Lady Conybeare, for introducing big stakes. The game was getting a little slow."

And he went to the side-table for a cigarette.

Kit had cheated, and she knew it, and she suspected Alington knew it. She had neither meant, intended, contemplated, nor conceived possible such a thing, yet the thing was done. In point of fact, she had done it quite unwittingly. She had never intended to push her counters over the line with the edge of her cards. But then had followed – and she knew this, too – an appreciable moment in which she perceived what had happened before Tom's voice broke in. But she had not been able to say *at once*, "I have made a mistake; I only staked fifty." After that each possible division of a single second made speech infinitely more impossible. To hesitate then was to be lost. Thirty seconds later her stake was paid, and to say then what had happened was not only impossible, but inconceivable. Besides she thought to herself with a sudden relief, it was wholly unnecessary. She would tell Alington about it quite candidly, and return the money. But it was a poor ending to the evening on which she and Alice were going to watch him to see if he cheated.

That moment when she did not speak was psychologically more important than Kit knew. She had lived in the world some five-and-twenty years, and for five-and-twenty years her instincts had been forming. But during those years she had not formed an instinct of absolute, unwavering, instantaneous honesty. Before now she had been in positions where there was a choice between the perfectly upright course and the course ever so slightly crooked, and had she known the history of her soul, she would have been aware that when she had stuck to the absolutely upright line she had done so after reflection. Then came this moment when there was no time for reflection, and the habit of looking at her decisions as ever so faintly debateable had asserted itself. She had paused to consider what she should do. That, in such circumstances, was quite sufficient.

That she was ashamed was natural; that she was angry was to her more natural still. She felt that the thing had been forced on her, and so in a manner, if we take into consideration all the instincts which were undoubtedly hers at that moment, it was; how far she was to be held responsible for those instincts is a question for psychologists and those who have got to the bottom of the problem of original sin, but not for story-tellers.

STRIKING
IT RICH...

TRENTE ET QUARANTE

Edmond About

French satirical novelist and journalist, Edmond About's writings have a characteristic wit and charm that makes the satire all the more effective and begs a comparison with the work of his English contemporary, William Thackeray.

In this extract from About's *Trente et Quarante*, M. Bitterlin, a retired army captain and a stern, unbending man, is touring Europe with his daughter, Emma, and her admirer, a timid young man called Meo M. Bitterlin is determinedly opposed to gambling in all its forms, but his vigorous denunciation of the vice prompts one of the company to wager that he will not be able to pass a day in the casino town of Baden-Baden without placing a bet. . . .

TOWARDS THE END of luncheon M. Le Roy announced his departure for Baden-Baden.

The Captain replied politely:

"A pleasant journey, gentlemen."

"But," stammered Meo, "we are not going – pardon me – M. Le Roy is going alone – that is to say, if there is no objection. . . ."

"What has that got to do with us?" replied the Captain. "Everyone goes his own way when travelling. M. Le Roy has business to attend to, and attends to it; other people do nothing. All right, let them be off, too!"

"Oh! as for me," said the Parisian, "my business is not complicated. I am going to pay 10,000 francs to a good fellow who will not give me a receipt; that is the Paris way. Since California, Australia, and all sorts of countries ending in 'ia' have been discovered, we got so much gold sent us that we do not know where to put it. It bores us, tires us, wears out our pockets, and makes our hands itch. I assure you one really cannot stand it! Well, what do people do? They go and drink the waters at Baden-Baden and return cured."

M. Bitterlin grew visibly sterner.

"You are a gambler," he said. "I could have believed that of many people – of that gentleman, for instance – but never of you! As for me, whenever I have been asked to play, I have always replied, 'I am neither poor enough to need your money, nor rich enough to make you a present of mine.'"

"I, sir, have got uncles enough to enable me to win without pleasure and to lose without regret. I began by playing in Paris, in the fast society of young and rich people. It is an understood thing that, after dining with friends, you must play cards in order to cool yourself again. This remedy has cost me dearer than any chemist's prescription. Sometimes I lost, sometimes I won; but as there were always ladies playing, I usually went home cleaned out, tired after a stupid evening, with dirty hands, a headache, and a yellow face, and then I slept till five o'clock the following afternoon. After two or three years of this amusement – by which I acquired a very bad reputation – I took a heroic resolve. I have now regulated my vice. Gambling cost me on an average about 500 louis a year, without counting loss to health, reputation, temper, and friends who disappear because they have borrowed your money. I prefer to go and lose my 10,000 francs at Baden-Baden; it is less dangerous, less tiring, more healthy, and quicker done. I know for certain that the bank has no cards all ready up its sleeve. I know that it will not want to borrow 25 louis from me to pay for a cab at six o'clock in the morning. If by some extraordinary chance I win, I shall go off without any sense of shame, and it will not afflict me to think that I carry away the means of support of an entire family. The bank is an impersonal being; you can relieve it of 50,000 francs at trente et quarante without fearing that it will blow its brains out. If, on the other hand, the bank wins my money, it will not go and boast about it all over Paris, destroying my credit and spreading the report that I am ruined. These are my reasons."

"What, sir!" rejoined the Captain. "You are young, intelligent, well educated – much better educated than this other gentleman, for instance – and yet you cannot find a better employment for your time and fortune! Take up some profession, by Jingo – take up a profession!"

"Unfortunately, sir, I have not been educated for the profession either of engineer, hosier, or lecturer at the Sorbonne. I might have asked for a place, like the many others who dance attendance at the public offices. That is a game which is more uncertain even than roulette. No, thank you! I might have gone on the Stock Exchange; I did even think of it. But the game is too difficult. Besides, I might lose more than I possess, and it would not be agreeable to me to leave my honour behind me. Finally, I had the resource of marriage. Ah! that is a poor kind of lottery, if you like, where one scarcely ever wins the prize one wants, and often wins a prize one would sooner not have. For these reasons, Captain, I invite you to drink a glass of chartreuse to the good town of Baden-Baden and to M. Bénazet, its prophet."

"You will please excuse me," said M. Bitterlin. "My convictions are immovable, and I am in hearty agreement with the noble object of the legislator who suppressed all gambling-houses in Paris."

"Well, no doubt he was quite right! Nobody denies it. Paris swarms with young fellows who carry about bags of money for their employers, either in offices or shops. If we possessed a Frascati, these youths would return empty-handed, and there would not be galleys enough in the whole of France to accommodate them. But Baden-Baden is five hundred miles from Paris; it costs money to go there, it costs money to stay there, it costs money to eat two meals a day there, and when a man has got means enough for expenses of this nature, the green table is doing no harm to anyone by relieving him of his money."

The Captain blew his nose with a certain amount of solemnity, and rejoined:

"You express yourself with facility, sir. You and your friend are the representatives of a society which some day will perish by the law of paradox. But an officer does not arrive at my time of life and then renounce his principles. Gambling is immoral, like all other methods of acquiring riches without work. I forbade it to my non-commissioned officers and privates, I forbade it to myself; and I will abandon the very name of Bitterlin if I ever step outside the line traced by honour. People may call me a blockhead if they like; but it was with blockheads like me that Lycurgus, the Spartan, conquered the whole world."

"Did he conquer the whole world?"

"Yes, sir. I shall not have the pleasure of meeting you at Baden-Baden. I had intended to include it in my tour, but now that you have explained what goes on there, it will have to do without me."

"Yes, sir," said M. Möring to the Captain, "you were quite right to change your route. However firm may be your will, it would be bent like a bar of iron in the forge. I will not quote you my own example, because every time that I have had to pass through Baden-Baden I have fallen a victim to roulette. But here is a case which perhaps will impress you. A clergyman of my native country, the Venerable M. Leuckel, went to Baden-Baden in 1854, in order to collect materials for a great sermon directed against gambling. His wife and two daughters accompanied him. Two days after their arrival I saw the whole four sitting at a trente et quarante table, a card in one hand and a pin in the other! The family had already lost 1,500 florins!"

"And the sermon?" asked M. Le Roy. "I heard it last winter. It was splendid, sir! It made the whole congregation weep, especially Mme Leuckel."

"Well, what does that prove?" replied the Captain roughly, "except that your clergyman was not a man of principle!" He added, with a modest lowering of the voice: "I am a man of principle."

"The righteous forget themselves seven times a day."

"Never in the regiment, sir. What control should I have over my men if I did not practise my own precepts? There is no better preacher than a blameless officer, such as I pride myself on having been. I know all games, and, indeed, excel at them. I can give lessons to the best of them at picquet, at Bezique, at dominoes, and at Billiards; but no one can boast of having ever seen me win or lose anything – not even a glass of absinthe or brandy."

"All the same," said M. Le Roy, "you are quite right not to go to Baden-Baden. The best way of avoiding sin is to fly from temptation."

"What temptation? I should never feel the least tempted."

Upon this there were protestations from all sides.

"No," he continued. "I should not be tempted in the least, and here is the proof. I will continue my tour just as if nothing had happened. I will go to Baden-Baden; I will pass a day in the gambling establishment with money in my pockets, and you shall see whether I risk a penny piece!"

"Will you have a bet with me about it?"

"No, sir. In the first place, I should be robbing you of your money; in the second place, I am a man of principle, and betting is the same as gambling."

The Captain held forth so loudly and with so much confidence that a change of opinion began to operate. M. Le Roy was certainly rather too much inclined to credit other people with his own weakness, and to maintain that a man who has abstained from all games of chance for sixty years would suddenly take to gambling was not far removed from impertinence. Mr Plum wagered £20 sterling that the Captain would not play. M. Le Roy took the bet, and bade farewell to the rest of the company.

In the meanwhile Meo had arrived at Baden-Baden and taken up his abode at the Hotel Victoria, where M. Le Roy had settled they should meet. He discovered the latter, about five o'clock in the evening, surrounded by the most extraordinary collection of furniture. The chest of drawers, the dressing-table, and even the floor, were completely hidden by a mass of objects in coloured glass; and a number of local works of art in deal in the form of cottages, boxes, paper-knives, and Black Forest clocks, completed this curious assortment. The owner of all these marvels was moving about amongst them in as melancholy a frame of mind as Marius at the ruins of Carthage. When he saw his old companion appear, he almost embraced him.

"By Jove!" he exclaimed, "you turn up like a perfect godsend! Have you got any money?"

"Eleven louis, which are at your service."

"What a Croesus you are!"

"Do you think so? It constitutes the whole of my present and future fortune."

"You have got eleven louis at Baden-Baden, and yet you grumble! My dear fellow in the first place you shall stand me a dinner to-night."

"Certainly."

"Wait a second. I will bring the Duke of S. and Prince D., two of my friends who, like me, have had no luncheon. Be civil to them; they are both millionaires!"

Meo opened his eyes wide.

"Don't you understand?" continued the Parisian. "I, my good fellow, am cleaned out, and so are the other two, besides plenty more whom I will not introduce to you, so as not to overdo it. For two days the bank has had extraordinary luck. And to think that if I had only gone off the day before yesterday, I should have taken away with me 60,000 francs! I began by winning every time; first a run on the red, then a run on black. I was backing black steadily, when all of a sudden, by inspiration, I felt that luck was going to turn. I first withdrew half my stake, then the whole of it. Crack! bang! A tie was dealt, and the bank collared all the stakes. My inspiration was true enough! I changed over to red, and the luck stuck to me. There were twelve reds running! I had a good headway on, and made good use of it, as did many other people. Everybody followed me, and there were barely a couple of louis on black. Unfortunately midnight struck. In another half-hour we should have broken the bank!"

"I ought to explain to you," said Meo, "that I do not understand the game of which you are speaking."

"You will learn it soon enough, my good friend; it is fearfully simple. So I came back to this room – this cursed room, with 70,000 francs in notes, in napoleons, and in fredericks; there was even one florin. Next day, as soon as I opened my eyes, I swore not to play any more this year. I visited all the shops so as to amuse myself harmlessly in making unimportant purchases. I gave the beggars five-franc pieces; I lent handfuls of money to ladies who had lost – that was an investment for the coming winter; I drove out in a carriage, and the country appeared to me charming; all the leaves on the trees looked as if they bore the signature of the governor of the Bank of France. Why on earth did I not go back to France? Why, indeed! Well, I will tell you why: it is all owing to you! I agreed to meet you here. You are the cause of my ruin. You have cost me 70,000 francs. The 10,000 francs I do not regret, because I had only brought them in order to lose them; but the other 60,000 were not born to be lost, and the proof is that I had actually won them. Well, if you feed me you will make me stop talking. I am waiting for funds; and there are many of us here who watch for the arrival of the postman. But the post is not up to much – a snail post, in fact. For one moment I thought of converting these rubbishy things into money, but the people who sold them to me will only take them back at eighty-five per cent. discount. They pointed out that all the things were ugly and in bad taste, and I begin to think they are right. Do you want a cottage, my good Narni? Do you fancy a cuckoo-clock? Would you like a blue glass trumpet? Hullo! it is broken. Everything is shoddy! Touch it, and it tumbles to pieces. Mind you don't step on the glass, my dear fellow. Select the cottages for choice amongst which to walk about; they are more rural. Ah, by the way, your love-affair! Is the fair-haired one all right? Have you tamed the old Red Indian? I will bet that you have not. Have they arrived here? I put 25 louis upon the tiger's head, and it would be very accommodating of him to let me win them as soon as possible. Ah, I forgot! There is a lady of your nationality at the Hotel Royal. She knows you; in fact, I think she has known you very well. A fine woman – Juno in person! On the turf she is known as 'big Aurelia.' She won 5,000 francs in following my luck, and has had sense enough to stick to them. I promised her you would go and see her. You had better go, my boy; it is always some sort of consolation. And sportsmen have a saying with regard to such things: 'If you can't get thrushes, you must be content with elephants.' Heavens! how you do make me laugh with your long face. Are you by any chance thinking of blowing your brains out?"

"Yes," replied Meo. "I only await the arrival of Mdlle Bitterlin, who has promised to die with me."

"Upon my word of honour, you are mad! But what would you do, wretch, if you had lost 70,000 francs?"

"I have lost ten times as much, and it never even grieved me. To-day it is quite different. My life is ruined; I have no longer any happiness to look forward to upon earth, and so I am going to take my departure."

"Not before giving us a dinner. I will just change my coat; we will then go and pick up our friends on the way, and after that we will try and pick up some new ideas at the Restauration."

An hour later Meo had completely unbosomed himself to M. Le Roy's friends. The young duke and the little prince consoled him to the best of their ability, while at the same time they devoured all the most substantial dishes they could find upon the bill of fare. These gambling victims were highly entertained at their own poverty; nothing amuses a young and rich man more than to find himself reduced to poverty for a day or two. They choked with laughter as they swallowed haricot beans; Meo's grief appeared to them rather more serious than their own misfortunes, but not much. They were acquainted with hundreds of remedies – all infallible – against the dejection of love. Each extolled the method which he considered the best or had found most effective, but all three guests were unanimous in asserting that the waters of Baden-Baden were the best in the world for curing maladies of the heart. Meo allowed them to talk on, and even took rather too much in drinking with them to his own health, but he would have taken poison at the end of the meal if Mdlle Bitterlin had been there to share it with him. They took him to the casino – that is to say, the gambling-rooms. He saw plenty of pretty women there of all sorts, but life with another woman seemed to him less desirable than death with Emma. M. Le Roy showed him the trente et quarante table from afar and the roulette close at hand.

"This," he said, "is a game of no importance, and intended for children who want amusement. You can stake the most modest sum at it, even as low as two francs. That is what is called 'florinating' in the language of Baden-Baden. Only men play at trente et quarante because the bank has fewer chances, and also because there is some scope for skill. However, if you would like to try this one, put a louis on the last six numbers – there, across the two lines. Good! thirty-three has come up. you get six times your stake. I told you so. Take them – take them! The six louis belong to you! Well, what do you think of roulette? Does it not strike you as an admirable institution, which for a few pence will enable you to forget all your annoyances? From the moment you put your money upon the table, up till the instant when that gentleman said, 'Thirty-three, red, pass, uneven,' you never thought of Mdlle Bitterlin, nor of the ineffable delight of dying with her in the convulsions of poison. And this recreation, the finest in the whole world, has cost you nothing at all. It has even earned you 120 francs. It is a splendid thing, is it not? And what will you say when you have tried trente et quarante?"

Meo made acquaintance with trente et quarante under the eye of his mentors. This game, the easiest of all, astonished him by its simplicity. It seemed to him astounding that 70,000 francs could be lost or won in the course of a few deals, because the banker had dealt thirty-seven points to red and thirty-eight to black. He played according to their advice: won, lost, won again, and remained just as indifferent to gain or loss as if there were nothing but mere pebbles on the table. When midnight struck he went sadly back to the hotel, although there were several hundred francs in his pockets and in those of his new friends. What use could money be to him? He was certain of having enough to last over the short time his life was likely to last.

Meo became the inseparable companion of M. Le Roy and the jovial crew of losers. These gentlemen obtained more money, lost it, re-established their financial positions by a few strokes of luck, and for three days managed to hold fortune in check. Meo, like his friends, rocked upon the see-saw of chance, losing, winning, and treating everything as a joke. People thought him changed for the better, and attributed the credit of this improvement to Mdlle Aurelia. This he vehemently denied, protesting his fidelity, and swearing that M. Bitterlin would have to reckon with him. So willingly did he relate the story of his infatuation that it became general property.

All the young men from Paris were aware that M. Bitterlin was on the way, and rumour already depicted him as a fabulous monster. Not a supper took place at the Restauration without toasting the decease of the ferocious Bitterlin. Emma figured as a medieval heroine, and Meo obtained celebrity under the pseudonym of Eginhard. Women interested themselves in his welfare, and more than one fair form fluttered sympathetically about him. The worthy man was fairly dazed; he sighed openly for his enchantress, shook his fist at the spectre of his father-in-law, and, whilst waiting for the enemy, played at trente et quarante. He had arrived at the stage of looking upon napoleons as counters merely utilized in the incidents of gambling, and credited them with no other use or importance. Fortune, who does not despise the rash, behaved kindly to him.

But Friday was ushered in as a day of disaster. From early morning trente et quarante set to work to despoil its victims. Diabolical luck upset the best-thought-out schemes and the most infallible precautions. Red and black lost alternatively, without method and without check. There were no runs in the game, and no possible sequence in the players' ideas. Things fell out in such a way that the bank, which had started with only 50,000 francs, had at seven o'clock in the evening 60,000 crowns before it. Mr Plum and Mr Wreck, who had arrived that morning, were obstinately backing, one the red, the other the black, and had dropped 10,000 francs apiece. Meo's new friends were dearly expiating their success of the previous day; he himself was paying back his three days' winnings at usurious interest. So exasperating was the luck that even the philosophical and apathetic lover had, like everyone else, more or less lost his temper. Standing up on the banker's right hand, he threw a louis each time upon red or black indifferently, shrugging his shoulders as the rake swept his money away.

Fresh cards had just been shuffled, he had cut them himself and was just placing his last stake upon the black, when a familiar cough made him turn his head, and it encountered M. Bitterlin's nose.

It is quite true that he had had time to anticipate this interview, and to prepare his weapons. An hour earlier he had even remarked to M. Le Roy:

"I will tame the Captain!"

He really had meant to face his father-in-law wherever the meeting-place might be. Moreover, the opportunity was an excellent one, and the pretext for defiance ready made, since M. Bitterlin had always declaimed against card-playing. But the big nose, suddenly projected into the midst of his amusements, completely disconcerted him. Fear born of respect and filial obedience of a fortnight's standing are not forgotten in a single instant. The Captain's fulminations against the immorality of gambling recurred to his memory. The habit of yielding, more potent than his resolves of the previous day, undermined his courage, and furtively he stole away, like a schoolboy surprised by the master.

M. Bitterlin had arrived by the six o'clock train, stiff and starched with morality. Ever since the declaration of faith made at Schaffhausen, he had almost come to look upon himself in the light of a reformer charged with a self-imposed mission. Upon the foundations of his virtue he had contracted a castle in Spain. Like Hercules, the conqueror of monsters, he intended to fell the hydra of gambling amidst the loud plaudits of domesticity.

His words and his example would convert plungers by hundreds, and the lessees themselves would come and renounce in his presence the worship of mammon. He scarcely waited to change his clothes and imprison his daughter in the hotel. He ascertained the way to the casino, and entered it with a march as resolute as that of Polycrates and Nearchus advancing into the Temple of Jupiter. The first heathen encountered in his progress was M. Le Roy, surrounded by a circle of friends. That young man, on catching sight of him, addressed him by name, exclaiming:

"Hurry up and start playing, so that I may win my 25 louis! You are as welcome here as the flowers in May!"

Bridling behind his black stock, the Captain rejoined:

"If I could induce you to restrain your passions and renounce card-playing, it would help you to make more than 500 francs."

Continuing his advance, he stopped to shrug his shoulders at M. and Mme Möring, who were playing at roulette. M. Le Roy's friends had spread the news of his arrival throughout the rooms. Every eye was turned towards him; fingers pointed at him; two hundred people followed and scrutinized him; they crowded up as he passed in order to get a closer view. On he marched, as if taking part in a procession, looking to right and left, and muttering under his moustache:

"They do not seem accustomed to the sight of men of principle here."

He recognised Meo, and took up his position in rear, so as to say something uncomplimentary when the latter should turn round. The pusillanimous flight of that unlucky man made him burst out with derision.

"Poor creature!" he exclaimed; "there isn't even courage in his vice! Why, he has forgotten his 20 francs! Twenty francs on a single chance! Two hundred pounds' weight of regulation bread!"

He felt tempted to pick up the louis and restore it to Meo, but a scruple restrained him. He was endowed with that species of brutal punctiliousness which carries respect for another person's property to an absurd pitch. Besides, he was looking forward to the joke of seeing the money raked in and the gambler taught a lesson. This pleasure did not come with the first deal; black won, and Meo's louis was joined by a companion coin.

"Well, what now?" thought the Captain. "The stupid ass will lose next time!"

With this hope he placed his elbows upon the table. But the second deal, like the first, resulted in favour of black. The Captain saw 80 francs before him.

Contemptuously he gazed upon this gold sullied by gambling. It was brand-new gold; the surface of the coins reflected the glitter of the lamps. As he observed their brilliancy, the Captain involuntarily recalled to memory the first four louis which he had ever possessed. They were coins of 24 francs apiece, of a yellow gold, very old, much worn and with edges slightly clipped. His mother had extracted them from the bottom of a stocking and slipped them into his hand on the day when he set out for the war.

"What a difference there is," he thought, "between these immoral counters and the honourable medals which my mother had sanctified by work and thrift!"

This reflection was interrupted by the arrival of the rake, which brought four more louis. Black had won for the third time.

"Now here," said he to himself, "is seen the justice of chance. When I was a second captain I strove for a whole month to earn the sum which this clumsy fellow has collared in three turns of the cards! Ah, the world is a nice sort of place! Happily black is 39 this time. Yes, but red is 40! That puts two months of my pay in M. Narni's pocket!"

He planked both arms firmly upon the table, determined to remain until black had lost. But both the fifth and sixth deals only served to double and redouble Meo's winnings. The pile of gold which glittered before the Captain began to assume majestic proportions, and amounted to neither more nor less than 1,280 francs. In view of a sum of such importance, M. Bitterlin began to regret that Meo was not there in order to come to some decision. He was not sure as to how far punctiliousness permitted 1,280 francs to be swept into the vortex of the bank. It was not that he cared in the least about the youthful foreigner, but he regretted the money.

"It can't go on like this for ever," he said to himself. "The banker is not going to spend the whole evening in adding to the pile before me; he would never make money in that fashion."

With these reflections he kept looking about for Meo, without, however, losing sight of the cards, in which he began to take a vague interest.

Black won for the seventh time, and a banknote accompanied by fourteen louis was added to the Italian's gains.

The game began to get interesting. It was the first run which had taken place since the morning. Black's unexpected success was bruited about through the rooms, and people some distance off now came up to see how long the luck would last. M. Bitterlin's fame, his grimaces, and, above all, the substantial stake which he had upon the board, drew attention to him. Two or three fair creatures had already come up to borrow five louis from him, and had been received much in the same way that hounds are received by a wild boar.

Black won for the eighth time, and he was left with a sum of 5,100 francs before him.

Never since his earliest childhood had he witnessed such a miracle. Sure enough this multiplying of gold scandalized him, but it astounded him still more. Five thousand francs! A whole year's income won in a few minutes through the caprice of chance! He experienced a certain amount of satisfaction in replacing a few louis which had gone astray upon either side. No doubt he felt proud at remaining the impartial spectator of the fray; from the bottom of his heart he pitied the unfortunate people waiting with panting breath for the decree of fate. But, all the same, he was not displeased to have seen the thing for himself upon the spot, and to have experienced some measure of their violent emotions. For one instant even he reflected that if the delirium of gambling can ever be excused, it is in the case of those big stakes which make or mar whole fortunes. Already in the far distance he beheld a precious moral lesson widely different from that narrow morality which he had been practising for sixty years. The money spread out before his eyes filled his brain with strange thoughts, and his ideas seemed to take, as it were, a new tinge of colour. One of the casino attendants brought him a chair. He declined it, alleging that he did not play. But as the chair imperceptibly tickled the back of his legs, and as the excitement of looking on caused his knees to bend, he sat down. The banker began to deal out the cards, and dealt black exactly thirty-one. M. Bitterlin noticed the sulky countenance of this official, who no doubt had an interest in the profits of the bank. It occurred to him that there might be some noble and chivalrous satisfaction in plundering such immoral enterprises, and in inflicting punishment upon the very spot where sin was committed every day. And when he had 10,240 francs under his nose, he looked upon himself as a champion of virtue, who had won a victory over the demon of gambling.

These events, so novel in the Captain's life, had taken place within less than a quarter of an hour: a properly-constituted bank does not require longer than that either to ruin or to enrich a man. Meo, driven away by fear, had not gone far. The recollection of Emma, the high resolves which he had formed, and the necessity of either conquering or dying, soon brought him back to the field of battle. He was in the roulette room endeavouring to screw up his courage, when one of the players whom he knew remarked as he passed:

"Well, this is how you take advantage of your luck! There has already been a run of nine in the hand which you cut!"

He then remembered the 20 francs which he had left upon the table. Although far from suspecting what a fortune he had won, he slipped furtively into the crowd surrounding the trente et quarante table, and sought for his father-in-law and for his money. He beheld both the former gloating upon the latter; and arrived just in time to hear the banker say to the Captain:

"How much do you stake, sir, please?"

I – don't know," replied the Captain, redder than a hundred prawns. "I – do not play. . . . My – principles. . . ."

"You are aware, sir," said a neighbouring croupier, "that 6,000 francs constitute a maximum?"

Everyone turned simultaneously to look at the audacious plunger who was staking more than the maximum, and M. Bitterlin felt himself giving way before the pressure of public curiosity. He cast a terrified glance around the room in the hope of seeing Meo, but not discovering him, and seeing that they were waiting for his decision before beginning to deal out the cards, replied in a stifled tone:

"Six thousand francs, sir – I – at least, I think so. . . . It does not belong to me. . . ."

His hand shook. He counted out six notes, left them on the black, and drew in the remainder. Contact with this treasure made him feel giddy. A swarm of golden butterflies seemed to be whirling about in his brain; firmly grasping the table with both hands, he closed his eyes. A buzzing from the crowd made him quickly reopen them; black had won for the tenth time!

"After all," thought the Captain, "I am not infringing my principles, for I am not playing for myself; I am not even playing for this young man, since I have made no arrangement with him. I leave his money where he put it down, merely taking away the excess over the regulation stake. If I did not perform this duty, the croupiers would discharge it."

Meanwhile play went on, without even giving him time to compound with his conscience. Black won fourteen times in succession, and he had only time enough to pick up 6,000 francs after each deal.

Meo, concealed behind Mr Wreck, was a prey to violent agitation. Distracted between surprise and delight, he watched his fortune growing under the captain's management, but in his perplexity he scarcely knew whether he wished to lose or to win. The sum might grow large enough to set the house of Miranda upon its legs again; it remained to be seen whether M. Bitterlin would bestow his daughter upon a Count. Would it not be better to lose all the winnings of the evening and remain a beggar? After having publicly ruined him, the Captain would no longer have the right to hound him from his family. Whatever happened, M. Bitterlin would become his partner, his man of straw, his agent, his comrade, and, according to some views, his accomplice. What joy! Bonds of such a nature are never broken; accomplices are in agreement upon everything.

At the fifteenth deal red won.

"Good!" thought Meo; "this is the beginning of the downfall. Oh, well-beloved Captain, accomplish my ruin, and manage to leave me penniless!"

But the Captain was far from reasoning after this fashion. His first impression was one of surprise and dejection. He was petrified at the loss of this money, which did not belong to him, and which he had no right to lose. In one instant a perfect mountain of scruples arose in his conscience. He asked himself whether he was not legally responsible for the misfortune which had occurred, and whether the foreigner would not be justified in claiming 6,000 francs from him. He opened his mouth in order to ask the banker to give back the money, urging the absence of its legitimate owner. But a loud hubbub hailed the triumph of red: the noise made by a hundred persons all speaking at once did not help to make his ideas any clearer. All around he heard people declaring that it was no real change in the luck; that it was only one of fortune's tricks for bewildering players; that black was good for another run of ten; that it would be folly to desert it for such a trifle. The idea of winning back for M. Narni the money which he had caused him to lose remained firmly fixed in the recesses of his brain. Mechanically he crumpled the notes which remained in his hands, like a General reckoning up his fresh troops in the midst of an engagement.

"What!" said he to himself, "I have won more than 30,000 francs, and am I not going to try and win 6,000 with all that I have still left? Six thousand francs! Why, what is that? Black is all right; everyone says so.

What would M. Narni do in my place? He would play on. He would try and win back what has been lost, and, after having recovered it, he would still continue playing. I, who am a prudent person, will risk only one more try to get back the 6,000 francs we are short of, and then I will shut up shop."

Perhaps he would have followed this sage resolve if he had got back his 6,000 francs at the first attempt. But the banker dealt a tie, and appropriated half the stakes. M. Bitterlin hurled forward fresh troops, and the first engagement resulted in his favour. He returned to the charge, lost, won again, forgot his prudent schemes, and threw himself blindly into the thick of the struggle. For some time he had found it impossible to keep still, and his chair, thrust back by a vigorous motion, was now a long way in the rear. On his legs, his hands full of gold and notes, he plunged on red, on black, on colour, obeying the inspiration of the moment. His face had turned pale; perspiration in small drops covered his forehead. As the banker dealt out the cards he counted the points in a whisper, without considering what an object he presented. He thought out loud, and occasionally swore between his teeth. Rest assured that he had forgotten all about the Italian, and that he no longer looked out for him. If Meo had been ill-advised enough to come and proffer advice, he would have been received at the bayonet's point. His attitude, his voice, and his gestures – everything about him, breathed the fury of a demoniac; he might have passed for a desperate lover delivering an assault upon Fortune.

He won often; he won much; thousand-franc notes came to him by handfuls. He crushed them up in his fists, thrust them into his pockets, piled them in heaps on the table; all this by jerks and with unpremeditated action. A moment came when the bank was reduced to its last resources; twice or thrice in the course of a single half-hour people thought that it might possibly break.

Dear reader, have you ever hunted the gazelle? It is the gentlest, the most harmless, and the most friendly animal in existence. Its very coat invites caresses, and the sight of the fair, pensive head and beautiful eyes almost impels one to embrace it. In the whole human race there is no being so unnatural as to wish harm to so charming a creature.

But when the greyhounds have started a gazelle, and when the horses are galloping in their track across the burning sands of the desert, the panting hunter drives the spurs into his horse, cracks his whip, and implores all the winds in turn to lend him their wings. Nothing stops him; neither shrubs, nor rocks, nor torrents, nor ravines, nor death gaping for him in the quagmires. He rushes after his enemy, he wears him down, he gains upon him, he draws nearer, he comes up to him with shouts of joy and victory; he seizes him in his arms, plants a knife in his throat, and slays, with ineffable delight, an innocent animal which if encountered in a drawing-room or garden he would proceed to fondle.

Thus did M. Bitterlin break the bank, in spite of all his reasons for disapproving of gambling.

THE SPECULATIONS OF JEFFERSON THORPE

Stephen Leacock

Described as the most popular humorist in America since Mark Twain, Stephen Leacock surprisingly was not a professional writer but an academic and head of the Department of Economics and Political Science at Canada's McGill University.

Sunshine Sketches of a Little Town was published in 1912 but the tale of the speculations of the town barber when the mining boom came to Mariposa is timeless.

IT WAS NOT until the mining boom, at the time when everybody went simply crazy over the Cobalt and Porcupine mines of the new silver country near the Hudson Bay, that Jefferson Thorpe reached what you might call public importance in Mariposa.

Of course everybody knew Jeff and his little barber shop that stood just across the street from Smith's Hotel. Everybody knew him and everybody got shaved there. From early morning, when the commercial travellers off the 6.30 express got shaved into the resemblance of human beings, there were always people going in and out of the barber shop.

Mullins, the manager of the Exchange Bank, took his morning shave from Jeff as a form of resuscitation, with enough wet towels laid on his face to stew him and with Jeff moving about in the steam, razor in hand, as grave as an operating surgeon.

Then, as I think I said, Mr Smith came in every morning and there was a tremendous out-pouring of Florida water and rums, essences and revivers and renovators, regardless of expense. What with Jeff's white coat and Mr Smith's flowered waistcoat and the red geranium in the window and the Florida water and the double extract of hyacinth, the little shop seemed multi-coloured and luxurious enough for the annex of a Sultan's harem.

But what I mean is that, till the mining boom, Jefferson Thorpe never occupied a position of real prominence in Mariposa. You couldn't for example, have compared him with a man like Golgotha Gingham, who, as undertaker, stood in a direct relation to life and death, or to Trelawney, the postmaster, who drew money from the Federal Government of Canada, and was regarded as virtually a member of the Dominion Cabinet.

Everybody knew Jeff and liked him, but the odd thing was that till he made money nobody took any stock in his ideas at all. It was only after he made the "clean up" that they came to see what a splendid fellow he was. "Level-headed" I think was the term; indeed in the speech of Mariposa, the highest form of endowment was to have the head set on horizontally as with a theodolite.

As I say, it was when Jeff made money that they saw how gifted he was, and when he lost it, – but still, there's no need to go into that. I believe it's something the same in other places, too.

The barber shop, you will remember, stands across the street from Smith's Hotel, and stares at it face to face.

It is one of those wooden structures – I don't know whether you know them – with a false front that sticks up above its real height and gives it an air at once rectangular and imposing. It is a form of architecture much used in Mariposa and understood to be in keeping with the pretentious and artificial character of modern business. There is a red, white and blue post in front of the shop and the shop itself has a large square window out of proportion to its little flat face.

Painted on the panes of the window is the remains of a legend that once spelt BARBER SHOP, executed with the flourishes that prevailed in the golden age of sign painting in Mariposa. Through the window you can see the geraniums in the window shelf and behind them Jeff Thorpe with his little black skull cap on and his spectacles drooped upon his nose as he bends forward in the absorption of shaving.

As you open the door, it sets in violent agitation a coiled spring up above and a bell that almost rings. Inside, there are two shaving chairs of the heavier, or electrocution pattern, with mirrors in front of them and pigeon holes with individual shaving mugs. There must be ever so many of them, fifteen or sixteen. It is the current supposition of each of Jeff's customers that everyone else but himself uses a separate mug. One corner of the shop is partitioned off and bears the sign: HOT AND COLD BATHS, 50 cents. There has been no bath inside the partition for twenty years – only old newspapers and a mop. Still, it lends distinction somehow, just as do the faded cardboard signs that hang against the mirror with the legends: TURKISH SHAMPOO, 75 cents, and ROMAN MASSAGE, $1.00.

They said commonly in Mariposa that Jeff made money out of the barber shop. He may have, and it may have been that that turned his mind to investment. But it's hard to see how he could. A shave cost five cents, and a hair-cut fifteen (or the two, if you liked, for a quarter), and at that it is hard to see how he could make money, even when he had both chairs going and shaved first in one and then in the other.

You see, in Mariposa, shaving isn't the hurried, perfunctory thing that it is in the city. A shave is looked upon as a form of physical pleasure and lasts anywhere from twenty-five minutes to three-quarters of an hour.

In the morning hours, perhaps, there was a semblance of haste about it, but in the long quiet of the afternoon, as Jeff leaned forward towards the customer and talked to him in a soft confidential monotone, like a portrait painter, the razor would go slower and slower, and pause and stop, move and pause again, till the shave died away into the mere drowse of conversation.

At such hours, the Mariposa barber shop would become a very Palace of Slumber, and as you waited your turn in one of the wooden arm-chairs beside the wall, what with the quiet of the hour, and the low drone of Jeff's conversation, the buzzing of the flies against the window pane and the measured tick of the clock above the mirror, your head sank dreaming on your breast, and the Mariposa Newspacket rustled unheeded on the floor. It makes one drowsy just to think of it!

The conversation, of course, was the real charm of the place. You see, Jefferson's forte, or specialty, was information. He could tell you more things within the compass of a half-hour's shave than you get in days of laborious research in an encyclopaedia. Where he got it all, I don't know, but I am inclined to think it came more or less out of the newspapers.

In the city, people never read the newspapers, not really, only little bits and scraps of them. But in Mariposa it's different. There they read the whole thing from cover to cover, and they build up on it, in the course of years, a range of acquirement that would put a college president to the blush. Anybody who has ever heard Henry Mullins and Peter Glover talk about the future of China will know just what I mean.

And of course, the peculiarity of Jeff's conversation was that he could suit it to his man every time. He had a kind of divination about it. There was a certain kind of man that Jeff would size up sideways as he stropped the razor, and in whose ear he would whisper: "I see where Saint Louis has took four straight games off Chicago," – and so hold him fascinated to the end.

In the same way he would say to Mr Smith: "I see where it says that this 'Flying Squirl' run a dead heat for the King's Plate."

To a humble intellect like mine he would explain in full the relations of the Keesar to the German Rich Dog.

But first and foremost, Jeff's specialty in the way of conversation was finance and the money market, the huge fortunes that a man with the right kind of head could make.

I've known Jefferson to pause in his shaving with the razor suspended in the air as long as five minutes while he described, with his eye half closed, exactly the kind of a head a man needed in order to make a "haul" or a "clean up." It was evidently simply a matter of the head, and as far as one could judge, Jeff's own was the very type required.

I don't know just at what time or how Jefferson first began his speculative enterprises. It was probably in him from the start. There is no doubt that the very idea of such things as Traction Stock and Amalgamated Asbestos went to his head: and whenever he spoke of Mr Carnegie and Mr Rockefeller, the yearning tone of his voice made it as soft as lathered soap.

I suppose the most rudimentary form of his speculation was the hens. That was years ago. He kept them out at the back of his house – which itself stood up a grass plot behind and beyond the barber shop – and in the old days Jeff would say, with a certain note of pride in his voice, that The Woman had sold as many as two dozen eggs in a day to the summer visitors.

But what with reading about Amalgamated Asbestos and Consolidated Copper and all that, the hens began to seem pretty small business, and, in any case, the idea of two dozen eggs at a cent apiece almost makes one blush. I suppose a good many of us have felt just as Jeff did about our poor little earnings. Anyway, I remember Jeff telling me one day that he could take the whole lot of the hens and sell them off and crack the money into

Chicago wheat on margin and turn it over in twenty-four hours. He did it too. Only somehow when it was turned over it came upside down on top of the hens.

After that the hen house stood empty and The Woman had to throw away chicken feed every day, at a dead loss of perhaps a shave and a half. But it made no difference to Jeff, for his mind had floated away already on the possibilities of what he called "displacement" mining on the Yukon.

So you can understand that when the mining boom struck Mariposa, Jefferson Thorpe was in it right from the very start. Why, no wonder; it seemed like the finger of Providence. Here was this great silver country spread out to north of us, where people had thought there was only a wilderness. And right at our very doors! You could see, as I saw, the night express going north every evening; for all one knew Rockefeller or Carnegie or anyone might be on it! Here was the wealth of Calcutta, as the Mariposa Newspacket put it, poured out at our very feet.

So no wonder the town went wild! All day in the street you could hear men talking of veins, and smelters and dips and deposits and faults – the town hummed with it like a geology class on examination day. And there were men about the hotels with mining outfits and theodolites and dunnage bags, and at Smith's bar they would hand chunks of rock up and down, some of which would run as high as ten drinks to the pound.

The fever just caught the town and ran through it! Within a fortnight they put a partition down Robertson's Coal and Wood Office and opened the Mariposa Mining Exchange, and just about every man on the Main Street started buying scrip. Then presently young Fizzlechip, who had been teller in Mullins's Bank and that everybody had thought a worthless jackass before, came back from the Cobalt country with a fortune, and loafed round in the Mariposa House in English khaki and a horizontal hat, drunk all the time, and everybody holding him up as an example of what it was possible to do if you tried.

They all went in. Jim Eliot mortgaged the inside of the drug store and jammed it into Twin Tamagami. Pete Glover at the hardware store bought Nippewa stock at thirteen cents and sold it to his brother at seventeen and brought it back in less than a week at nineteen. They didn't care! They took a chance. Judge Pepperleigh put the rest of his wife's money into Temiskaming Common, and Lawyer Macartney got the fever, too, and put every cent that his sister possessed into Tulip Preferred.

And even when young Fizzlechip shot himself in the back room of the Mariposa House, Mr Gingham buried him in a casket with silver handles and it was felt that there was a Monte Carlo touch about the whole thing.

They all went in – or all except Mr Smith. You see, Mr Smith had come down from there, and he knew all about rocks and mining and canoes and the north country. He knew what it was to eat flour-baked dampers under the lee side of a canoe propped among the underbrush, and to drink the last drop of whiskey within fifty miles. Mr Smith had mighty little use for the north. But what he did do, was to buy up enough early potatoes to send fifteen carload lots into Cobalt at a profit of five dollars a bag.

Mr Smith, I say, hung back. But Jeff Thorpe was in the mining boom right from the start. He bought in on the Nippewa mine even before the interim prospectus was out. He took a "block" of 100 shares of Abbitibbi Development at fourteen cents, and he and Johnson, the livery stable-keeper next door, formed a syndicate and got a thousand shares of Metagami Lake at 3 1-4 cents and then "unloaded" them on one of the sausage men at Netley's butcher shop at a clear cent per cent. advance.

Jeff would open the little drawer below the mirror in the barber shop and show you all kinds and sorts of Cobalt country mining certificates – blue ones, pink ones, green ones, with outlandish and fascinating names on them that ran clear from the Mattawa to the Hudson Bay.

And right from the start he was confident of winning.

"There ain't no difficulty to it," he said, "there's lots of silver up there in that country and if you buy some here and some there you can't fail to come out somewhere. I don't say," he used to continue, with the scissors open and ready to cut, "that some of the greenhorns won't get bit. But if a feller knows the country and keeps his head level, he can't lose."

Jefferson had looked at so many prospectuses and so many pictures of mines and pine trees and smelters, that I think he'd forgotten that he'd never been in the country. Anyway, what's two hundred miles!

To an onlooker it certainly didn't seem so simple. I never knew the meanness, the trickery, of the mining business, the sheer obstinate deter-mination of the bigger capitalists not to make money when they might, till I heard the accounts of Jeff's different mines. Take the case of the Corona Jewel. There was a good mine, simply going to ruin for lack of common sense.

"She ain't been developed," Jeff would say. "There's silver enough in her so you could dig it out with a shovel. She's full of it. But they won't get at her and work her."

Then he'd take a look at the pink and blue certificates of the Corona Jewel and slam the drawer on them in disgust.

Worse than that was the Silent Pine, – a clear case of stupid incompetence! Utter lack of engineering skill was all that was keeping the Silent Pine from making a fortune for its holders.

"The only trouble with that mine," said Jeff, "is they won't go deep enough. They followed the vein down to where it kind o' thinned out and then they quit. If they'd just go right into her good, they'd get it again. She's down there all right."

But perhaps the meanest case of all was the Northern Star. That always seemed to me, every time I heard of it, a straight case for the criminal law. The thing was so evidently a conspiracy.

"I bought her," said Jeff, "at thirty-two, and she stayed right there tight, like she was stuck. Then a bunch of these fellers in the city started to drive her down and they got her pushed down to twenty-four, and I held on to her and they shoved her down to twenty-one. This morning they've got her down to sixteen, but I don't mean to let go. No, sir."

In another fortnight they shoved her, the same unscrupulous crowd, down to nine cents, and Jefferson still held on.

"They're working her down," he admitted, "but I'm holding her."

No conflict between vice and virtue was ever grimmer.

"She's at six," said Jeff, "but I've got her. They can't squeeze me."

A few days after that, the same criminal gang had her down further than ever.

"They've got her down to three cents," said Jeff, "but I'm with her. Yes, sir, they think they can shove her clean off the market, but they can't do it. I've boughten in Johnson's shares, and the whole of Netley's, and I'll stay with her till she breaks."

So they shoved and pushed and clawed her down – that unseen nefarious crowd in the city – and Jeff held on to her and they writhed and twisted at his grip, and then . . .

And then – well, that's just the queer thing about the mining business. Why, sudden as a flash of lightning, it seemed, the news came over the wire to the Mariposa Newspacket, that they had struck a vein of silver in the Northern Star as thick as a sidewalk, and that the stock had jumped to seventeen dollars a share, and even at that you couldn't get it! And Jeff stood there flushed and half-staggered against the mirror of the little shop, with a bunch of mining scrip in his hand that was worth forty thousand dollars!

Excitement! It was all over the town in a minute. They ran off a news extra at the Mariposa Newspacket, and in less than no time there wasn't standing room in the barber shop, and over in Smith's Hotel they had three extra bar-keepers working on the lager beer pumps.

They were selling mining shares on the Main Street in Mariposa that afternoon and people were just clutching for them. Then at night there was a big oyster supper in Smith's caff, with speeches and the Mariposa band outside.

And the queer thing was that the very next afternoon was the funeral of young Fizzlechip, and Dean Drone had to change the whole text of his Sunday sermon at two days' notice for fear of offending public sentiment.

But I think what Jeff liked best of it all was the sort of public recognition that it meant. He'd stand there in the shop, hardly bothering to shave, and explain to the men in the arm-chairs how he held her, and they shoved her, and he clung to her, and what he'd said to himself – a perfect Iliad – while he was clinging to her.

The whole thing was in the city papers a few days after with a photograph of Jeff, taken specially at Ed. Moore's studio (upstairs over Netley's). It showed Jeff sitting among palm trees, as all mining men do, with one hand on his knee, and a dog, one of those regular mining dogs, at his feet, and a look of piercing intelligence in his face that would easily account for forty thousand dollars.

I say that the recognition meant a lot to Jeff for its own sake. But no doubt the fortune meant quite a bit to him too on account of Myra.

Did I mention Myra, Jeff's daughter? Perhaps not. That's the trouble with the people in Mariposa; they're all so separate and so different – not a bit like people in the cities – that unless you hear about them separately and one by one you can't for a moment understand what they're like.

Myra had golden hair and a Greek face and would come bursting through the barber shop in a hat at least six inches wider than what they wear in Paris. As you saw her swinging up the street to the Telephone Exchange in a suit that was straight out of the Delineator and brown American Boots, there was style written all over her, – the kind of thing that Mariposa recognised and did homage to. And to see her in the Exchange, – she was one of the four girls that I spoke of, – on her high stool with a steel cap on, – jabbing the connecting plugs in and out as if electricity cost nothing – well, all I mean is that you could understand why it was that the commercial travellers would stand round in the Exchange calling up all sorts of impossible villages, and waiting about so pleasant and genial! – it made one realise how naturally good-tempered men are. And then when Myra would go off duty and Miss Cleghorn, who was sallow, would come on, the commercial men would be off again like autumn leaves.

It just shows the difference between people. There was Myra who treated lovers like dogs and would slap them across the face with a banana skin to show her utter independence. And there was Miss Cleghorn, who was sallow, and who bought a forty cent Ancient History to improve herself: and yet if she'd hit any man in Mariposa with a banana skin, he'd have had her arrested for assault.

Mind you, I don't mean that Myra was merely flippant and worthless. Not at all. She was a girl with any amount of talent. You should have hear her recite "The Raven," at the Methodist Social! Simply genius! And when she acted Portia in the Trial Scene of the Merchant of Venice at the High School concert, everybody in Mariposa admitted that you couldn't have told it from the original.

So, of course, as soon as Jeff made the fortune, Myra had her resignation in next morning and everybody knew that she was to go to a dramatic school for three months in the fall and become a leading actress.

But, as I said, the public recognition counted a lot for Jeff. The moment you begin to get that sort of thing it comes in quickly enough. Brains, you know, are recognised right away. That was why, of course, within a week from this Jeff received the first big packet of stuff from the Cuban Land Development Company, with coloured pictures of Cuba, and fields of bananas, and haciendas and insurrectos with machetes and Heaven knows what. They heard of him, somehow – it wasn't for a modest man like Jefferson to say how. After all, the capitalists of the world are just one and the same crowd. If you're in it, you're in it, that's all! Jeff realised why it is that of course men like Carnegie or Rockefeller and Morgan all know one another. They have to.

For all I know, this Cuban stuff may have been sent from Morgan himself. Some of the people in Mariposa said yes, others said no. There was no certainty.

Anyway, they were fair and straight, this Cuban crowd that wrote to Jeff. They offered him to come right in and be one of themselves. If a man's got the brains, you may as well recognize it straight away. Just as well write him to be a director now as wait and hesitate till he forces his way into it.

Anyhow, they didn't hesitate, these Cuban people that wrote to Jeff from Cuba – or from a post-office box in New York – it's all the same thing because Cuba being so near to New York the mail is all distributed from there. I suppose in some financial circles they might have been slower, wanted guarantees of some sort, and so on, but these Cubans, you know, have got a sort of Spanish warmth of heart, that you don't see in business men in America, and that touches you. No, they asked no guarantee. Just send the money – whether by express order or by bank draft or cheque, they left that entirely to oneself, as a matter between Cuban gentlemen.

And they were quite frank about their enterprise – bananas and tobacco in the plantation district reclaimed from the insurrectos. You could see it all there in the pictures – the tobacco plants and the insurrectos – everything. They made no rash promises, just admitted straight out that the enterprise might realise 400 per cent. or might conceivably make less. There was no hint of more.

So within a month, everybody in Mariposa knew that Jeff Thorpe was "in Cuban lands" and would probably clean up half a million by New Year's. You couldn't have failed to know it. All round the little shop there were pictures of banana groves and the harbour of Habana, and Cubans in white suits and scarlet sashes, smoking cigarettes in the sun and too ignorant to know that you can make four hundred per cent. by planting a banana tree.

I liked it about Jeff that he didn't stop shaving. He went on just the same. Even when Johnson, the livery stable man, came in with five hundred dollars and asked him to see if the Cuban Board of Directors would let him put it in, Jeff laid it in the drawer and then shaved him for five cents, in the same old way. Of course, he must have felt proud when, a few days later, he got a letter from the Cuban people, from New York, accepting the money straight off without a single question, and without knowing anything more of Johnson except that he was a friend of Jeff's. They wrote most handsomely. Any friends of Jeff's were friends of Cuba. All money they might send would be treated just as Jeff's would be treated.

One reason, perhaps, why Jeff didn't give up shaving was because it allowed him to talk about Cuba. You see everybody knew in Mariposa that Jeff Thorpe had sold out of Cobalts and had gone into Cuban Renovated Lands – and that spread round him a kind of halo of wealth and mystery and outlandishness – oh, something Spanish. Perhaps you've felt it about people that you know. Anyhow, they asked him about the climate, and yellow fever and what the negroes were like and all that sort of thing.

"This Cubey, it appears, is an island," Jeff would explain. Of course, everybody knows how easily islands lend themselves to making money – "and for fruit, they say it comes up so fast you can't stop it." And then he would pass into details about the Hash-enders and the resurrectos and technical things like that till it was thought a wonder how he could know it. Still, it was realized that a man with money has got to know these things. Look at Morgan and Rockefeller and all the men that make a pile. They know just as much as Jeff did about the countries where they make it. It stands to reason.

Did I say that Jeff shaved in the same old way? Not quite. There was something even dreamier about it now, and a sort of new element in the way Jeff fell out of his monotone into lapses of thought that I, for one, mis-understood. I thought that perhaps getting so much money – well, you know the way it acts on people in the larger cities. It seemed to spoil one's idea of Jeff that copper and asbestos and banana lands should form the goal of his thought when, if he knew it, the little shop and the sunlight of Mariposa was so much better.

In fact, I had perhaps borne him a grudge for what seemed to me his perpetual interest in the great capitalists. He always had some item out of the paper about them.

"I see where this here Carnegie has give fifty thousand dollars for one of them observatories," he would say.

And another day he would pause in the course of shaving, and almost whisper: "Did you ever *see* this Rockefeller?"

It was only by a sort of accident that I came to know that there was another side to Jefferson's speculation that no one in Mariposa ever knew, or will ever know now.

I knew it because I went in to see Jeff in his house one night. The house – I think I said it – stood out behind the barber shop. You went out of the back door of the shop, and through a grass plot with petunias beside it and the house stood at the end. You could see the light of the lamp behind the blind, and through the screen door as you came along. And it was here that Jefferson used to sit in the evenings when the shop got empty.

There was a round table that The Woman used to lay for supper, and after supper there used to be a chequered cloth on it and a lamp with a shade. And beside it Jeff would sit, with his spectacles on and the paper spread out, reading about Carnegie and Rockefeller. Near him, but away from the table, was The Woman doing needlework, and Myra, when she wasn't working in the Telephone Exchange, was there too with her elbows on the table reading Marie Corelli – only now, of course, after the fortune, she was reading the prospectuses of Dramatic Schools.

So this night – I don't know just what it was in the paper that caused it – Jeff laid down what he was reading and started to talk about Carnegie.

"This Carnegie, I bet you, would be worth," said Jeff, closing up his eyes in calculation, "as much as perhaps two million dollars, if you was to sell him up. And this Rockefeller and this Morgan, either of them, to sell them up clean, would be worth another couple of million. . . ."

I may say in parenthesis that it was a favourite method in Mariposa if you wanted to get at the real worth of a man, to imagine him clean sold up, put up for auction, as it were. It was the only way to test him.

"And now look at 'em," Jeff went on. "They make their money and what do they do with it? They give it away. And who do they give it to? Why, to those as don't want it, every time. They give it to these professors and to this research and that, and do the poor get any of it? Not a cent and never will."

"I tell you, boys," continued Jeff (there were no boys present, but in Mariposa all really important speeches are addressed to an imaginary audience of boys) – "I tell you if I was to make a million out of this Cubey, I'd give it straight to the poor, yes, sir – divide it up into a hundred lots of a thousand dollars each and give it to the people that hadn't nothing."

So always after that I knew just what those bananas were being grown for.

Indeed after that, though Jefferson never spoke of his intentions directly, he said a number of things that seemed to bear on them. He asked me, for instance, one day, how many blind people it would take to fill one of these blind homes and how a feller could get ahold of them. And at another time he asked whether if a feller advertised for some of these incurables a feller could get enough of them to make a showing. I know for a fact that he got Nivens, the lawyers, to draw up a document that was to give an acre of banana land in Cuba to every idiot in Missinaba county.

But still – what's the use of talking of what Jeff meant to do? Nobody knows or cares about it now.

The end of it was bound to come. Even in Mariposa some of the people must have thought so. Else how was it that Henry Mullins made such a fuss about selling a draft for forty thousand on New York? And why was it that Mr Smith wouldn't pay Billy, the desk clerk, his back wages when he wanted to put it into Cuba?

Oh, yes; some of them must have seen it. And yet when it came, it seemed so quiet – ever so quiet – not a bit like the Northern Star mine and the oyster supper and the Mariposa band. It is strange how quiet these things look, the other way round.

You remember the Cuban Land frauds in New York – and Porforio Gomez shooting the detective, and him and Maximo Morez getting clear away with two hundred thousand? No, of course you don't; why, even in the city papers it only filled an inch or two of type and anyway the names were hard to remember. That was Jeff's money – part of it. Mullins got the telegram, from a broker or someone, and he showed it to Jeff just as he was going up the street with an estate agent to look at a big empty lot on the hill behind the town – the very place for these incurables.

And Jeff went back to the shop so quiet – have you ever seen an animal that is stricken through, how quiet it seems to move?

Well, that's how he walked.

And since that, though it's quite a little while ago, the shop's open till eleven every night now, and Jeff is shaving away to pay back that five hundred that Johnson, the livery man, sent to the Cubans, and —

Pathetic? tut! tut! You don't know Mariposa. Jeff has to work pretty late, but that's nothing – nothing at all, if you've worked hard all your lifetime. And Myra is back at the Telephone Exchange – they were glad enough to get her, and she says now that if there's one thing she hates, it's the stage, and she can't see how the actresses put up with it.

Anyway, things are not so bad. You see it was just at this time that Mr Smith's caff opened, and Mr Smith came to Jeff's Woman and said he wanted seven dozen eggs a day, and wanted them handy, and so the hens are back, and more of them, and they exult so every morning over the eggs they lay that if you wanted to talk of Rockefeller in the barber shop you couldn't hear his name for the cackling.

THE GAMBLER

Nkem Nwankwo

Nkem Nwankwo is one of Nigeria's leading contemporary writers and is rapidly gaining an international reputation both for himself and for his country's literature.

The following story entitled "The Gambler" is concerned

with the football pools, a popular form of gambling in West Africa and presumably a legacy of England's former colonial rule. It seems logical to Okoli Ede that if he invests £100 one week instead of his usual five shillings, he is certain to strike it rich. The range of the gambler's emotions is covered as thoroughly by this humble Nigerian post office clerk as by any Russian hussar out of the pages of Pushkin or Tolstoy.

A SMALL GROUP of tired men, most of them carrying football pools coupons, squatted or stood by the steps of a Lagos post office. The postal workers had all gone home for the midday break. It was yet some minutes before they were to resume but the waiting group, smarting from the sun, were restless.

"They no go come," said an old man, getting up from the stone he had made a seat. "They no go come."

"No mine am," said a lanky young man. "I sabe these post office people. They don suffer me three years but they no go suffer me again. My frend don teach me how I go play pools. Yes – no be small small money like that de win. No I go save big money and throw' am in my time." He glanced a challenge at the smilingly sceptic group. His clothes were shabby, his shoes down at heels but eyes were deadly optimistic.

"Yes," shouted the orator. "My frend Bay we de work with me last month no de work with me again. He throw in one hundred pounds, yes one hundred and he win thousands. Now I see am ride fine fine cars and carry fine fine women. You no see am." This last was directed at a shortish, self-effacing clerk standing by. "You no see am." The young orator had a way of converting anybody into an acquaintance with a glance.

"Perhaps," the man addressed said very cautiously, and glanced at the five-shilling note he meant to invest that week.

"Yes," said the orator, "I no go wait for this dam people. I go go for nother place." He smiled a companionable smile all round and straggled off.

As soon as he was gone the post office opened. The sturdy clerk of the five-shilling note dashed to the counter, and getting there first bought his postal order, registered his pools coupon and emerged feeling as he had felt for the past ten years that the world would be kind to him at last.

"One hundred pounds," he said to himself, remembering the fiery orator's words "Impossible". He smiled a smile of diffidence mixed with optimism. Some passers-by noted the smile and thinking it was for them returned it, but Okoli Ede nicknamed "Time up" by his friends of the Government department where he worked, did not notice. His thoughts were engaged in contemplating the vagaries of that new mysterious god football pools. He came to the bus stop and looked a little wistfully at a standing vehicle. He would have liked to go by it, his home was a mile away and the sun eagerly pricked his head, but his salary did not allow for casual expenses. He walked therefore and after sweating at the neck for some time came to his home, a small sooty room in the back yard of a rakish-angled building. The room had a tone of minimum convenience not of comfort. It was furnished with an iron bed, a table and a chair. A corner of it segregated with an old blanket served for kitchen.

Okoli Ede took off his workaday clothes; blue khaki shorts and white shirt, and changed into brown wrapper and singlet. Then he set about boiling water for his garri.

"No, impossible," he murmured to himself. He could not stop the train of thoughts set on by the orator. Mightn't there be something in it though? To gamble on a grand scale? But with one hundred pounds! Fifty perhaps . . .

The pot was aboil. Okoli Ede prepared his lunch, ate, washed up and then came to his table to work on his G.C.E. papers. That was the pervasive aspect of his life. He was always eager to get home to it and his nickname. "Time up" commemorated the haste with which he got away from the office at close of day.

But this time Okoli Ede could not concentrate. There was a restlessness inside him; bred of a mental conflict which was growing and spreading. Wasn't life ordinarily tedious. For five years he had been taking the G.C.E. and failing. Will he ever reach where he had all along aimed. A voyage to England. A law degree. Back to Nigeria. A prosperous car, long and American. Women. . . . Politics. More women. Ministerial office. More money than one could have need of . . . or would it not be better to gamble with everything. If one won. . . . In one jump the end achieved £75,000. Okoli Ede got up, excited by the overwhelming figure. He had always loved money. There was a time he lost a shilling, he went without his meal for the whole day to pay for that loss.

A reaction against optimism set in and Okoli Ede with a hiss of disapproval sat down hard and resumed his work. . . . But after some minutes the figure 75,000 persistently danced across his line of vision. He unlocked a drawer set in the table and slipped out a bank account book. He opened it. His assets stood at exactly £100. A coincidence? But it might be an omen. In the newspaper his stars for that week had said: "Do not be afraid to take a chance"; why should his credit stand at exactly the figure the young orator mentioned?

But one might fail even with a hundred pounds. Suppose he failed. He had responsibilities, his father and mother struggling against a perverse land which yearly failed to yield them enough to eat. Memories of that land had haunted him like an evil spectre forcing him to accumulate, to place a barrier between himself and want. Suppose he failed. He threw the accounts book inside the drawer and recommenced work. He must never again think of the mad scheme.

But he did think of it. Deep inside where the mind of men acted without awareness the conflict went on.

"I will not fail." Okoli Ede woke up the next morning with those words on his lips. "I will not fail." His nerves tingled, his body was all warm, his hands clammy with sweat, his throat constricted with excitement. With £100 it is impossible to fail. He jumped up and sought activity, anything that would prevent him from thinking, for to think is to hesitate and tremble. When Okoli Ede went to work that morning he carried with him his bank book; but he still had not the strength to tell himself what he wanted to do with it. Work was slack that day and when the chief clerk, bored with inactivity, left to chat with a pretty girl in the next section, Okoli Ede slipped out. The excitement was still on him. He walked hurriedly, he could not look himself in the face. The bank clerks divined his purpose and treated him with the insouciance reserved for those who withdrew rather than deposited.

That afternoon when he reached home he could not summon up life to boil water for his garri. He lay on his bed face down, exhausted with the strain, his mind torpid, unable to contemplate the terrible deed that would pitch him up or send him right down. Some force, some energy accumulated over the years had smoked off leaving only hope.

His mind was clearing now seeking points of contact with solid elements, boyhood memories. He remembered on a certain occasion being tempted to give his school fees to a money doubler. His father's friend had dragged him away by the ears. But this very day he had done it.

He slipped out of his pocket a wad of notes. Thirty pounds. The remains of five years' honey pot. Some instinct had prevented him from throwing in everything, he had remembered that he had to live until the fortune came. . . . He thought of the awed faces of the crowd at the post office when he had asked for a money order for seventy pounds. . . . And so he had fed the god twice in two days.

The morning sun flooded Okoli Ede's room revealing its dingy starkness, but fresh invigorating air came with it and gave out promises of a fuller more adventurous living. Okoli Ede was suddenly filled with a discontent and a shame for his stingy colourless way of living. When the money came – there was no doubt now that it would come – how would it look in that room. But no matter. It was wonderful what fresh paint, colourful curtains and a new carpet could do for a room. . . . A little bouncy, Okoli Ede went out to work. Afterwards he walked into a silver plush store and equipped himself for the role he was to play in a few days' time. Back home he sang and danced as he cleaned out his room. "Not bad," he said at last, stepping back and examining his handiwork; the almanacs covered the putrid parts of the wall and the curtains looked fetching. . . . With a pleasurable feeling of achievement which he had never known in all his thirty years he opened a leather box lying on the bright new carpet. Reverently he examined the contents: a made-to-measure two-piece suit, an up-to-date tie, black shoes, shirt – why not put them on now. Would that be a little pushing. Okoli Ede smiled with a little of his old diffidence. At last he was arrayed and trying to see himself in a small mirror, many things still lacked but some can wait. . . . He went to work the next day smartened, suited and stiff.

"Eh, 'Time up' don rise high," several clerks gathered, eager for banter.

"Na so!"

"Wetin be her name?"

"Why 'eeno tell us make we prepare?"

"I never know say ee has one."

"Whosai plenty-you no sabee them quiet ones. . . . Women die for 'am."

"Na waya O!"

The chief clerk looked up sharply and the clerks hustled to their places. That always inflated his dignity a little. He was a tall, thin man with museum-piece spectacles and the yellowing eyes of the drunkard. He peered suspiciously at Okoli Ede and remarked his suit. Then he looked furtively down at his own cigarette-ash-speckled bargain shirt and frowned. He would set down any clerk who got above himself. The office was not the place for show.

A thirst for experience, for pleasurable irresponsibility for secret sensation possessed Okoli Ede. His caution, rooted by upbringing, had not quite died, once or twice it had murmured from the deep recesses but Okoli Ede had pushed it down, after all one had to live, and with the coming fortune he was only living on his expectation. He entered a pub and for the first time in his life stared at the hired women, drank beer and listened to vigorous music – he would have liked to follow up and mingle with the whirling mass on the dance floor in riotous abandon, but timidity restrained him. He gulped more beer, his eyes glassed and his head swam. He rose to go. On his way a girl made eyes at him and his suit; but when he crawled near her she turned from him cold and proper. "Time will come. She will run after me," Okoli Ede consoled himself.

His change from steady modesty to recklessness gave neighbours matter for talk. But Okoli Ede did not heed brows or pointed whispers. He plunged violently into looseness borne on the crest of desire and hope.

The results of the football matches appeared on Sunday. Okoli Ede did not remember to buy the papers for he was suffering from the body's reaction to immoderate pleasure; the bowels moved funnily at painful intervals, the mouth was coated with spider webs, the eyes smarted, the legs were heavy.

The dividends were declared a few days later – £50,000 for top points. The excitement was too much for Okoli Ede. He had to walk the street to cool off. He wasn't afraid but his heart beat very loud.

While waiting, his craving for pleasure increased but there was no money to gratify it. Then one night he hired a girl. He woke very late in the morning and started dressing hastily. The girl woke, too, and when he wanted to pay her he was a shilling short. She made a point of it.

"Come tomorrow," said Okoli Ede roughly. "I no go come no time. You go pay me now." She was a hungry-looking waspish creature used to fights over pennies. Okoli Ede was afraid of her and of what the neighbours might say.

"If you no pay me you no go work," she grasped him. . . . "Or I go take this." She left him and dived for his new coat.

"No! No! Not that. Please make e take that," he gave her a tin of face powder . . . she considered, then threw the coat and powder contemptuously at him and stamped out, she would have preferred a fight – Okoli Ede was very late. The chief clerk, a little triumphant, watched him come in. He had had a difficult morning himself. A quarrel with his wife had left him as empty as a deflated football. The clerks had sensed his need to recover his prestige on somebody and were keeping out of his way.

"Na jus now 'ee de come," asked the chief clerk, darting a baleful glance at the dishevelled Okoli Ede.

"Yes," said the latter sullenly, going to his seat.

"You no hear me!" roared the chief clerk, his rage suddenly touched off. "If you no take time we go sack you . . . yes, sack you one time. . . . You come work when you like, eh. Abi you think you be a director . . . you think say na you alone sabe wear suit?"

This sally was too much for the other clerks. They roared and slapped their thighs and shouted, "Oga ejo – O!"

The plea only swelled the chief clerk and stimulated his tongue. "Look 'am!" he said. The clerks directed their several gazes at Okoli Ede who was standing scowling by his table.

"He no fit fill 'im belle and 'ee de wear suit. . . . No be your name be director or. . . ."

He did not go further. The clerks stifled their mirth and a hiss of amazement escaped them as they saw their chief's face a bewildered world of black-blue and spouts of blood.

Okoli Ede glared murderously for a moment, and assured that the bottle had made its mark, walked out of the office.

"Let them sack me," he shouted as he got home. "They don't know who I am . . . but they will."

He slumped on his wooden chair and put his head in his hands. He sat in that position all day. Evening had set in when he rose, still unsteady with passion. Just at that moment, a blue envelope crept through the aperture below the door.

"Who be that?" Okoli Ede shouted nervously.

"Na me."

"Who be you?"

No answer. Okoli Ede picked up the letter. Foreign postmark. The letter dropped twice from his shaking hands but he hastily picked it up each time. . . . He couldn't open it, for once opened the secret will no longer be a secret. Clutching the letter he lay on his bed and closed his eyes. Then he suddenly jumped up and in one swift movement tore it open and stared at it hard; his mind curiously enfeebled could not grasp the full meaning, but his body divining by reflex knew, and the heart thumped dumbly.

Ten shillings. Okoli Ede murmured at last with a dull voice. . . . Won. . . . Ten shillings. The thought circled on the wave of consciousness. Impossible – impossible, I spent a hundred – he would go and find out.

The pools people had representatives somewhere. . . . No, impossible. Ten shillings. It isn't true. But when he reached the streets his purpose started reflecting its futility. His legs didn't seem to belong to him.

Something must be done. . . . One can find a place where money was kept carelessly and steal. . . . He couldn't find another job and his parents and neighbours would have a poor opinion of him if he went home to farm. . . . If only there were no policemen around.

There was a deafening screech near Okoli Ede and suddenly a demoniac taxi careered wildly and halted near the pavement. The driver leapt out and came and towered angrily above him.

"Why 'ee no look wey 'ee de go?. . . You wan die?. . . If you wan die why 'ee no fall into lagoon there."

Okoli Ede didn't answer but walked on with the same mechanical gait.

"Oloriburuku, man of evil omen!" shouted the taxi-driver. "I no go kill you."

He walked back to his car and dashed away. Okoli Ede stood by the lagoon and watched the expanse of water calm and opalescent with the evening coloration. Far out to sea many many brightly coloured boats squatted like sated sea-monsters of old. Then a canoe with two pullers came by trailing close to the shore. The fishermen seemed pleased about something. They pulled with vigour lapping the invigorating evening breeze gratefully. . . . Then they broke into a song, anxious to drown their nagging fear of not being able to provide enough garri for their large families.

"They are happy," thought Okoli Ede, watching them until they had formed black specks that merged with the blue misty haze in the distance. Far in the west the sun had broken into little ridges that flamed like blood on fire. A little later the night with its usual formidable suddenness blotted out the day.

Okoli Ede looked around to make sure that no one was near, then spread his hands wide and went with the day.

MAMMON & CO. (2)

E. F. Benson

E. F. Benson obviously knew his stock market as well as he did his baccarat, and the following story from *Mammon & Co.* describes the innermost feelings of a stockmarket operator too accurately for the writer to have been no more than just a casual observer. Mr Alington plans to make a fortune out of manipulating the stock of one of the Australian gold mining companies that were all the rage in England in the 1890's. Those who were involved in the Great Australian Nickel Boom of ten years ago will note some uncomfortable parallels!

It is difficult for those who dwell on the level lands of sanity to understand the peaks and valleys of mania. To fully estimate the intolerable depression which ensues on the conviction that you have a glass leg, or the secret majesty which accompanies the belief that one is Charles I., is impossible to anyone who does not know the heights and depths to which such creeds conduct the holder. But the mania for speculation – as surely a madness as either of these – is easier of comprehension. Only common-sense of the crudest kind is required; if it is supposed that your country is on the verge of war, and you happen to know for certain that reassuring events will be made public to-morrow, it is a corollary to invest all you can lay hands on in the sunken consols in the certainty of a rise to-morrow. This is as simple as A B C, and your gains are only limited by the amount that you can invest. A step further and you have before you the enchanting plan of not paying for what you buy at all. Buy merely. Consols (of this you must be sure) will rise before next settling-day, and before next settling-day sell. And thus the secret of not taking up shares is yours.

But consols are a slow gamble. They may conceivably rise two points in a day. Instead of your hundred pounds you will have a hundred and two (minus brokerage), an inglorious spoil for so many shining sovereigns to lead home. But for the sake of those who desire to experience this fascinating form of excitement in less staid a manner there are other means supplied, and the chiefest and

289

choicest is mines. A single mining share which, judiciously bought, cost a sterling sovereign, may under advantageous circumstances be worth three or four in a week or two. How much more stirring an adventure! When we estimate this in hundreds and thousands, the prospect will be found to dazzle comparatively sober eyes.

IT WAS some eight weeks after Easter that Mr Alington decided to make the next move in the game of Carmel, a move which should be decisive and momentous. He would have preferred for certain reasons to put it off a little while yet, for he had much on his hands, but the balance on the whole inclined to immediate action. During the last four or five months he had done a considerable deal of business as a company-promoter, and at the present moment had some half-million of pounds engaged in other affairs than mines. Motor-cars in particular had much occupied him, and he was the happy possessor of many patents for noiseless tyres, automatic brakes, simpler steering-apparatus, and what not. He was a man of really large ideas where money was concerned, and a perfect godsend to patentees, for his policy was to buy up any invention concerning motors which possessed even the most modest merit, in the hopes that, say, in two years' time every motor-car that was built must probably carry one or more of the patents owned by him. He had, indeed, at the present moment in England not more than twenty thousand pounds which he could conveniently devote to the booming of Carmel, but there was lodged with Mr Richard Chavasse in Melbourne a sum of not less than fifty thousand pounds, with which it was his purpose to supply the "strong support in Australia," to the end that Carmel should rise rainbow-hued above the ruck of all other mines. Altogether his position was a good one, for the last six weeks had brought him from his manager the most excellent private accounts of the mine, which for the most part he had saved up till the booming began. Mr Linkwood also advised very strongly a fresh issue of shares. They had at present, for instance, only an eighty-stamp mill, whereas at the rate at which they were now getting gold out there was easily work for a mill of a hundred and fifty or two hundred stamps.

It was on this "strong support in Australia" by the convenient Mr Chavasse that Mr Alington chiefly relied; that at any rate should be the final touch. He intended first of all to make a large purchase of his own in England, ten thousand shares at least, and immediately publish encouraging news from the mine. This he would preface, as he had so often done before, by a wire to Mr Richard Chavasse, which in a few hours would bring forth the accustomed reply, "Strong support in Australia."

But though he would have preferred having a somewhat larger sum at his own disposal for the grand *coup*, he had reason for wishing to start the boom at once. Speculators had recovered from the scare of Carmel East and West, and already, before he had himself moved in the matter, the quotation for Carmel had risen from its lowest price of ten to eleven shillings up to sixteen. This was sufficient in his opinion to show that the public was already nibbling, for professional operators, he knew, were not entering this market, and this was the correct moment to give the fresh impetus. There had been a nineteen days' account just before Easter, which had made the market dull, but since then it had begun to show more vitality.

Other reasons also were his. He was beginning, for instance, to be a little nervous about the immediate success of his dealings in the motor trade. His patents were floated into companies, but in few instances only had the shares been well supported, and in more than one he had incurred a loss – recoverable no doubt in time – which even to a man of his means was serious. Worse than that, if this ill-success continued, it would not be the best thing for his name, and he was most anxious to get Carmel really a-booming while his prestige was still high. Again, many fresh mines had been started in Western Australia since the original flotation of the Carmel group, and his financial sense led him to distrust the greater part of them. Several had been grossly mismanaged from the first, some grossly misrepresented. Others he suspected did not exist at all, and he wished to hit the psychological moment when speculators were ready, as the improvement in Carmel shares had shown, to invest, and before they had seen too much of West Australian mines to make them shy. That moment he considered had come.

Accordingly he instructed his broker to make his own large purchase. This was ten days before settling day, and he hoped to sell out again before those ten days were passed. He had at first intended to purchase only ten thousand shares, but going over his scheme step by step, and being unable to see how it was possible, with this combination of satisfactory news from the mine, his own purchase, and Mr Chavasse's strong support in Australia, that the shares could fail to rise, he decided to purchase five thousand shares more than he could pay for. It was humanly impossible that the shares should not rise. Consequently on Thursday he telegraphed out to his manager to send a long cablegram embodying all the private news he had himself been receiving for two months back, to his broker, made his own purchase on Friday morning, and the same afternoon sent a cipher telegram to Mr Chavasse, telling him to invest the whole of his capital then lying at Melbourne Bank in Carmel, and another in cipher to the manager, bidding him wire "Strong support in Australia." Thus in twenty-four hours his *coup* was made, and he went back to his Passion music and his prints, to wait quietly for the news of the strong support in Australia. Already in a few hours after his own purchase, backed up as it was with the first of the favourable reports from the mine, the shares had risen three-eighths; the effect on the market, therefore, of the Australian support, he considered, level-headed man of business as he was, to be inevitable.

He was dining out that evening with Lord Haslemere, and was disposed in anticipation to enjoy himself. Lady Haslemere, it is true, was apt to be tedious when she talked about her own transaction in the City, and asked him whether the rise in some mine of which nobody had even heard was likely to continue, and was it not clever of her to have bought the shares at one and a half, for within a week they had risen to two and a sixteenth. She got the tip out of *Truth*. Mr Alington, however, had all the indifference of the professional in money matters to the scrannel operations of the amateur, and when in answer to a question of his it appeared that Lady Haslemere had only twenty shares in this marvellous mine, and had worked herself up into a perfect fever of indecision as to whether she should take her certain eleven pounds profit, or be very brave and fly at fourteen, he felt himself really powerless to understand her agitations.

This evening directly after dinner she collared and cornered him, and finance was in her eye.

"I want to have a serious financial talk with you," she said, "so we'll go into the other drawing-room, where we shall be alone. Come, Mr Alington."

Good manners insisted on obedience, but it was an ill-content financier who followed her. For Lady Devereux, who played Bach quite divinely, was among Lady Haslemere's guests, and even as he left the room to talk over his hostess's microscopic operations on the Stock Exchange, he saw her go across to the piano. It is true that he preferred a very large round sum of money of his own to half an hour of fugues and preludes, but he infinitely preferred half an hour of fugues and preludes to about seven and sixpence of Lady Haslemere's.

She lit a cigarette with a tremulous hand.

"I want to ask your advice very seriously," she said. "I put three hundred pounds into Carmel a week ago, and since then the shares have gone up a half. Now, what do you advise me to do, Mr Alington? Shall I sell out, or not? I don't want to make such a mess as poor dear Kit did. She really was *too* stupid! She took no one's advice, and lost most frightfully. Poor thing! she has no head. All her little nest-egg, she told me. But I mean to put myself completely into your hands. Do you expect Carmel will go higher?"

Mr Alington stroked the back of his head, and tried hard to look genial yet serious. But it was difficult. Lady Haslemere had closed the door between them and the next room, and he could hear faintly and regretfully those divine melodies on the Steinway grand. And here was this esteemed lady, who was quite as rich as anyone need be – certainly so rich as to be normally unconscious of the presence or absence of a fifty-pound note – consulting him gravely (she had let her cigarette go out in her anxiety) about these infinitesimal affairs. If she had had a fortune at stake, he would willingly have given her his very best attention, regretting only that Lady Devereux had chosen this moment for playing Bach; but to be shut off from that exquisite treat for a small sum affecting a woman who was not affected by small sums was trying.

"I can't undertake to advise you, Lady Haslemere," he said; "but I can tell you what I have done myself: I have bought twenty-five thousand shares in Carmel to-day, and have not the faintest intention of selling out to-morrow."

Lady Haslemere clasped her hands. This was a flash of lightning against her night-light.

"Good gracious! aren't you nervous?" she cried. "I shouldn't be able to eat or sleep. Twenty-five thousand – and they've gone up three-eighths to-day. Why, you've scored over nine thousand pounds since this morning!"

"About that – if I sold, that is to say, which I don't mean to do."

"And so you are going to chance the mine going still higher?"

"Certainly. I believe in it. I also believe the price will rise very considerably yet."

Lady Haslemere bit her lip; she was clearly summoning up all her powers of resolution, and Mr Alington for the moment felt interested. He was, as he might have told you, a bit of an observer. Whether or no Lady Haslemere won eleven pounds or fourteen he did not care at all, but that she should care so much was instructive. Then she struck her knee lightly with her fan.

"I shall not touch my three hundred," she said, and she turned on Mr

Alington a face portentous with purpose.

Mr Alington sat equally grave for a moment, but the corners of his mouth lost their sedateness, and at last they both broke out laughing.

"Oh, I know how ridiculous it must seem to you," said Lady Haslemere; "but if you have never earned a penny all your life, you have no idea how extraordinarily interesting it is to do so. You may think that it can't matter to me whether I gain ten pounds or lose twenty. But to gain it one's self – oh, that is the thing!"

Mr Alington smiled with peculiar indulgence. "Well, frankly, it is inexplicable to me," he said. "Now, if you were playing for a large stake I could understand it, though I seldom get excited myself. Well, that is what I am going to do; I am going to play for a very big stake indeed, and I confidently expect to turn up a natural. Have you anything more to ask me? – for if not, and you will allow me, I shall go and listen to Lady Devereux. I have been so much looking forward to hearing her play again."

Before long a baccarat table was made up, but he did not move from his place by the piano. Lady Devereux, a pretty, good-natured woman, who got on capitally with everybody except her husband, who, in turn, got on admirably with or without her, was delighted to go on playing to him, for she saw how real and how cultivated his enjoyment of her music was, and though she lost charmingly at baccarat, she really preferred playing even to one appreciative listener. She had an excellent memory, her taste was his, and the two wandered long in the enchanted land of early melody.

At last she rose, and with her Mr Alington.

"I need not even thank you," he said; "for you know, I believe, what it has been to me. You are going to play? Baccarat for Bach! Dear lady, how shocking! I think I shall go home. I do not want to disturb the exquisite memories. I shall remember this evening."

He stood for a moment with her hand in his. His face looked like the representation of some realistic saint in bad stained glass.

"Good-night," he said. "And I, too, go and daub myself in actualities. But at soul I am no realist."

It was a fine summer evening, fresh and caressing to the diner-out, and he walked back from Berkeley Street slowly, with the musician ascendant over the financier.

Mr. Alington had all the coolness in action which ensures success in most human pursuits, from the art of war to the art of making money, and the absence of which postulates a corresponding inefficiency in all practical undertakings. He never lost his head, nor got either frightened or *exalté* when he was at his work; but the intervals, after he had committed himself to some course of action, and before that action had produced its fruits, were sometimes tense periods to him. He went, no doubt, at forced draught when the great *coups* were being made, and after he had taken his headlong excursions Nature demanded a readjustment, and his fibres were relaxed. These periods of relaxation he usually tided over by the indulgence of his artistic tastes, which he used as a man of less fine sensibilities might use morphia or alcohol. But to-night the fugues and preludes so deftly exhibited by Lady Devereux seemed only temporarily efficacious. For a while they moved him, but he had not been home an hour when the effect wore off and left him, financially speaking, staring wide-awake.

Again and again he reviewed the natural effect of what he had done, the normal behaviour of the market towards the events which should be developed next day. Already the prices of Carmel were rising; tomorrow would come the announcement of strong support from Australia, and later in the day the more specific news that Mr Richard Chavasse – that hard-headed operator – had bought to the extent of fifty thousand pounds. Logically, for the money-market is as subject to logical conclusions as any set of syllogisms, its prices must leap. News of the most satisfactory description would continue to arrive from the mine; in a day or two, in a week at the outside, the shares should stand at not less than four to five – no feverish price, but well warranted, so thought Mr Alington, by its inherent excellence. There was no doubt there would be some slight fall owing to realizations, but that, so he imagined, would be only a temporary reaction. By settling-day, ten days from now, his twenty-five thousand shares bought in England should be worth more than four times their present value; his fifty thousand pounds invested by Mr Richard Chavasse something over two hundred thousand. After that a firm good-bye to clamorous gold-getting.

He strolled backwards and forwards in his room, now stopping to look for a moment at one of his beloved prints, now lighting a cigarette or sipping a little mild whisky-and-soda. How admirably, he reflected, had his Carmel group hitherto turned out! How alluring had been his board of directors, how convincing to the public mind of the security of a scheme to which hereditary legislators lent their honoured names! Already more than one new board had copied his example, but it had been a great thing to be first in the field; the novelty of the idea was half its success.

But now his noble colleagues might go hang, for all he cared; they had served their turn and been his bell-wethers to the public. Jack Conybeare, he knew, had followed him in this last Carmel speculation, investing largely; he was a shrewd fellow, so thought Alington, and would have made a good business man had not the onus of hereditary obligations borne him elsewhere; and if he himself had been intending to start new companies, he would not have been sorry to have him again on his board – no mere name this time, but a man likely to be of practical use.

Yes; indeed he had struck a vein! Though he believed that ninety per cent. of success is due to effort and wisdom, he had got, like most speculators, a secret faith in that "tide in the affairs of men." It was impossible not to believe in strokes of luck; if things showed a general tendency to prosper, it was well to put many things in hand at once. The stars or some occult influence happened to be favourable just then; in the remote, conjectured heavens there was a conjunction of planets of notable benignity to you; it was your chance; the line was clear; hurry, hurry, while it lasted! In the same way one had at other times to work with sobbing steps through a mire of ill-luck. Perversity for the moment characterized the universe; inanimate objects were malign; sheathed, hooded presences waited to clutch you. Nothing went right; the images of the gods were set awry; ominous mutterings were heard (not fancied) from the shrine. Then was the time to venture little, not to ride unmanageable horses, not to use new silk umbrellas, to go gently, neither praising nor complaining, for fear of further provoking the blind forces that strike; above all, not to think to repair ill-luck by wild strokes. In the nature of this world things would come round; a calm, dewy dawn would break on the low-roofed night. Wait!

Next morning came a very favourable report from the mine, and about mid-day the news of the strong support in Australia. The price had been opened at a little over thirty shillings, the mine was eagerly inquired for, and for a couple of hours it rose steadily, and as it rose seemed to get more and more in demand. Then one of those strange periodical madnesses which sometimes affect that shrewd body took possession of the Stock Exchange. Everything else was neglected; it seemed that the whole world contained only one thing worth buying, and that shares in Carmel. Men bought and sold, and bought and sold again; now for half an hour would come a run of realizations, and the price would sink like a back-drawing wave in a swiftly advancing tide; but in another hour that was forgotten; the tide had risen again, covering the lost ground, and those who had realized were cursing their premature prudence, and bought again.

Steady-going, unemotional operators lost their heads and joined in the wild skying of Carmel without a shred of justification, only hoping that they would find everyone else a shade madder than they, and that they would clear out on the top. Men sold at three and a half, bought again at four, sold at four and a half, and were not yet content. Nobody quite knew what was happening, except that they feverishly desired shares in Carmel, and that those shares were getting every moment more expensive. Bears who had sold ten minutes before came tumbling over each other to secure their shares before they had gone up out of sight, and having got them, as likely as not turned bulls and bought again, on the chance of Carmel going higher, though half an hour ago they had sold in the hope of its going lower. All day this went on, and about an hour before the closing of the market Alington, reading the tape record at his club, saw that the shares stood at five and a half – higher than he had ever hoped they would go in a week.

For a moment he hesitated. If he chose, there was now within his grasp all that he had been playing for. A hansom to the City; two careful words to his broker, for the unloading must be done very swiftly; then to his music and his baronetcy. In an hour the market would close till Monday, for Saturday was a holiday; but before Monday, on the other hand, would come fresh news from the mine. He debated with himself intently for a moment, and as he waited the tape ticked under his hand.

"Carmel," it spelled out, "five and five-eighths, five and three-quarters."

That was enough. For to-day nothing could stop the rise. There would be time to sell on Monday morning.

He called for a hansom; he was going to spend from Friday till Monday in the country, and not having more than enough time to catch the train, drove straight to Waterloo, where his valet would meet him with his luggage.

Mr Alington had never felt more at peace with himself, or in more complete harmony with his environment (a crucial test of happiness), than when he drove off to Waterloo from the doors of the Beaconsfield Club, of which he had lately become a member, after reading the last quotation of Carmel. All his life he had been working towards the consummation which was now practically his. His desire was satisfied, he had enough. A few forms only still remained to be put through, and he would be finally quit of all markets. On Monday morning his broker would sell for him every share he held in Carmel. On Monday morning, too, would that shrewd operator, Mr Richard Chavasse, follow, as if by telepathic sympathy, the workings of Mr Alington's mind, arriving at the same just conclusions, and close with the offer made him by the Varalet Company in Paris for all the patents he owned in the motor business *en bloc* – at a considerable sacrifice, it is true – completed his financial career.

These thoughts passed through his brain in a gentle glow of intimate pleasure, as his hansom went briskly towards Waterloo. He was going to spend this Friday till Monday with Mrs Murchison, in her charming house on the Winchester downs, where the invigorating unused air would make more temperate this really tropical weather. A terrific heat-wave, from a positively scalding sea, had drowned London these last few days; the city had been a burning fiery furnace, and the consolation of being cast there, of having got there unwillingly, was denied him, for the flames had been of his own self-seeking. He might, indeed, as soon as he had made the *grand coup*, three days ago, have left London, and waited for the inevitable result in cool retirement, but this retreat from the scene of action had been morally impossible to him. Never before, as far as he remembered, had an operation so taken hold of him; never before had the tickings of the tape, or the call-whistle of his telephone, been of so breathless an urgency. Exciting as had often been the satisfaction with which he had watched the climbing of a quotation from twos into threes, or threes into fours, he could not recollect a restlessness so feverish as that with which he had watched the rise of Carmel. For this had been the *comble* of all: the rise of the price meant to him a perfect freedom from all future rises. To see Carmel quoted above five had been equivalent to his emancipation from all that should hereafter touch the nerves. Yet here was one weak spot. He had seen the quotation of over five and a half ticked out by the tape, yet he had not instantly sold. The old Adam in his case, as in so many others, had inconveniently and inconsistently survived. He had not been able to resist the temptation of wanting to be richer than he truly wanted to be. But in order to cut himself off from any such weakness in the future, he immediately pushed open the trap-door, and told his driver to stop at the nearest telegraph-office, and ten minutes after he had taken his final step, wiring both to his broker in London, and in cipher to Mr Chavasse, at Melbourne, to sell out on Monday morning.

The deal was beyond doubt. At last and at last! This crippling of his life was over; he was free from the necessity of money-making, free also, thank God! from the desire. He no longer wanted more than he certainly had.

How much can be said of how few!

His inward happiness seemed reflected in all sorts of small external ways. His horse was fast, his driver nimble at picking an unsuspected way, and the porters at Waterloo, miraculously recovered from the paralysis of the brain induced by Ascot week, not only were in accord as to the platform from which his train would start, but, a thing far more rare and precious, were one and all perfectly correct in their information.

To Mr Alington, though his nature was far removed from the cynical, this seemed almost too good to be true, till, in his benignant strolls up and down the line of carriages, he met his hostess, Mrs Murchison. She was feeling the heat acutely, but was inclined to be talkative.

"So you've come by the early train," she said. "Well, I call that just friendly, and it's the early bird that catches the train, Mr Alington, and here we are. But the heat is such that if I was wicked and died this moment, I fancy I should send for a thicker mantle, and that's a chestnut. Lady Haslemere comes down by the four something, which slips a carriage at Winchester – or is it five? – which I think perilous. They cast you adrift, the Lord knows where, for I inquired about it, without engine, and if you haven't got an engine, where are you? A straw hat – that's just what we are going to be; a straw-hat party, like Lady Conybeare and the tea-gowns, and dinner in the garden."

"That will be delicious," said Mr Alington after his usual pause. "Dinner out of doors is the only possible way of feeding without the impression of being fed. I always. . . ."

"Well, that's just beautifully put," interrupted Mrs Murchison. "You get so much all-fresco out of doors. And that's what I missed so much in my last visit to America, where I stopped a fortnight nearly. The set-banquet, with all the ceremonial of the Barmecides, like what Mr Murchison rejoices in, and the colour he turns over his dinner, seems to me an utter nihilism of the flow of soul. Why, there's Lady Haslemere! So she's caught the early bird too."

Lady Haslemere, according to her invariable habit, only arrived at the station one minute before the starting of the train, in a great condition of fuss, but she pressed Mr Alington's hand warmly.

"You were quite right," she said: "I didn't sell out two days ago, and, oh! the difference to me. I have just this moment sold at five and three-quarters. Only think!"

"I congratulate you heartily," said Mr Alington, with a smile of kind indulgence; "I too am going to sell on Monday morning."

A shade of vexation crossed Lady Haslemere's face.

"Do you think it will go higher again?" she asked.

"A shade, very likely. But possibly it may react a little. I was in two minds myself as to whether I should sell to-day."

Lady Haslemere's brow cleared.

"Oh, well, one can't always sell out at the very top," she said; "but it will be annoying to me if it goes to six. Two hundred and forty times five shillings. Ye-s."

"I think you have done very well," said Mr Alington, with just a shade of reproof in his voice.

Mrs Murchison's house stood high on the broad-backed down, to the south of the town, and up at this height there was a wonderful freshness in the air, and the heat was without the oppressiveness of London. A vast stretch of rolling country spread out on every side, and line upon line of hills followed each other like great waves into the big distance. Though the drought had been so severe, the reservoirs of the sub-lying chalk had kept the short, flower-starred grass still green, and the long-continued heat had not filched from it its exquisite and restful colour.

Alington took off his hat and let the wind lift his rather scanty hair. It was an extreme pleasure to him to get out from the overheated stagnation of London streets into this unvitiated air, and he wondered at the keenness of his enjoyment. He had never been a great lover of the country, but it seemed to him to-day as if a heavy accumulation of years had been lifted off him, disclosing capacities for enjoyment which none, himself perhaps least of all, had suspected could be his. He gently censured himself in this regard. He had made a mistake in thus stifling and shutting up so pure and proper a source of pleasure. He would certainly take himself to task for this, and put himself under the tuition of country sights and sounds.

They had tea under the twinkling shade of a pine copse at the end of the lawn, and presently after Mr Alington again took his straw hat, with the design of a stroll in the fresh cool of the approaching evening. The two ladies preferred to enjoy it in inaction, waiting for the arrival of the adventurous slip-carriage guests, about whose fate Mrs Murchison reiterated her anxiety.

So Mr Alington, secretly not ill-pleased, started alone. He was about half-way down the drive, when he met a telegraph-boy going towards the house, and, in his expansive, kindly manner, detained him a moment with a few simple questions as to his name and age. Finally, just as he turned to walk on, he asked him for whom he was delivering a telegram, and the boy, drawing it out of his pouch, showed him the address.

Mr Alington opened it slowly, wondering, as he had often wondered before, why the envelope was orange and the paper pink. It was from his brokers, and very short; but he looked for some considerable time at the eight words it contained:

Terrible panic in Carmels. Shares unnegotiable. Wire instructions.

At first he read it quite blankly; it seemed to him that the words, though they were simple and plain enough, conveyed nothing to his mind. Then suddenly a huge intense light, hot and dazzling beyond description, appeared to have been uncovered somewhere in his brain, and the words burned and blinded him. He let the pink paper fall, bowing and sidling on the gravel of the drive, then stooped down with a curious groping manner and picked it up again. He put it neatly back inside the envelope, and asked the boy for a form, on which he scribbled a few words.

"Do nothing," he wrote. "I will come up immediately."

He gave the boy a shilling, waving away the change, and then, going to the grassy bank that bounded the drive, he sat down. Except for the moment, when his brain, no doubt instantaneously stunned, refused to tell him the meaning of the words, it had been absolutely composed and alert. The telegram gave no hint as to the cause of this panic, but without casting about for other possibilities, he put it down at once to his one weak point, Mr Chavasse. That determined, he gave it no further thought, but wondered idly and without much interest what he felt. But this was beyond him. He had no idea what he felt, except that he was conscious of a slight qualm of sickness, so slight and so purely physical, to all seeming, that he would naturally have put it down, had it not appeared simultaneously with this news, to some small error of diet. Otherwise his brain, though perfectly clear and capable of receiving accurate impressions, was blank. There was a whisper of fir-trees round him, and little points of sunlight flickered on the yellow gravel of the drive as the branches stirred in the wind. Lady Haslemere's voice sounded thin and high from the lawn near – he had always remarked the unpleasant shrillness of her tones – and his straw hat had fallen off. He was conscious of no dismay, no agony of regret that he had not sold out two hours ago, no sense of disaster.

He sat there five minutes at the outside, and then went back to the lawn. The ladies looked up in surprise at the quickness of his return, but neither marked any change in his sleek features nor uncertainty in his step. His voice, too, when he spoke, was neither hurried, unsteady, nor differently modulated.

"Mrs Murchison," he said, "I have just received the worst news about – about a venture of mine, which is of some importance. In fact, there has been, I fear, a great panic on the Stock Exchange over Carmel. May I be driven back to the station at once? It is necessary I should return to London. It is a great regret to me to miss my visit. Lady Haslemere, I congratulate you on your promptitude in selling."

The London evening papers that day were full of the extraordinary scenes that had taken place on the Stock Exchange. Before the opening of the market that morning Carmel had been eagerly inquired for, owing to the activity produced by the very extensive purchases on the day before, and an hour before mid-day news had been cabled from Australia that there was very strong support in the market there for the same, Mr Richard Chavasse alone having purchased fifty thousand pounds' worth of the shares. Closely following on this came news from the mine itself: the last crushing had yielded five ounces to the ton, and a new, unsuspected reef had been struck. The combination of these causes led to one of the most remarkable rises in price ever known. The market (so said one correspondent) completely lost its head, and practically no business was done except by the mining brokers. The shares that day had started a little above thirty shillings, and by four o'clock they had reached the astounding figure of £5 12s 6d. A well-known broker who had been interviewed on the subject said that never in the course of a long experience had he known anything like it. Sober, steady dealers, in his own words, went screaming, raving mad. A boom in Westralian gold, it is true, had long been expected, but nothing could account for this extraordinary demand. No doubt the fact that Mr Alington had purchased largely the day before had prepared the way for it, for he was considered among mining operators the one certain man to follow. But the sequel to this unparalleled rise was even more remarkable. Buying, as had been stated, was much stimulated by the news of strong support in Australia (indeed, it was this that had been the signal for the rush); but about four o'clock, when the shares were at their highest, and some considerable realizations were being made, though the buying still went on, a sudden uneasiness was manifested. This was due to the fact that the telegram announcing the strong support in Australia was contradicted by another and later one, saying that the market in Carmel was absolutely inactive. Upon this, first a general distrust of telegrams from the mine itself was manifested, and then, literally in a few minutes, a panic set in, as unaccountable as the previous rise; business came to a standstill, for in half an hour everyone was wanting to sell Carmel, and buyers could not be found. A few of the heaviest plungers cleared out, with thousands to their credit, but the majority of holders were caught. The shares became simply unnegotiable. The market closed on a scene of the wildest confusion, and when the Exchange was shut the street became impassable. To a late hour a mob of excited jobbers continued trying to sell, and just before going to press came a report that Mr Alington, who had left town that day, but suddenly returned, was picking up all the shares he could lay hands on at a purely nominal figure. Settling-day, it would be remembered, occurred next week. A committee of the Stock Exchange was going to investigate the matter of the false telegram.

Kit and Jack had come down to Goring that day to join Toby and his wife there. Kit was steadily gaining strength, but this evening, being a little tired, she had gone to bed before dinner, and now, dinner being just over, Lily had left the others to see how she was. Neither Jack nor Toby was given to sitting over wine, and as soon as Lily went upstairs, they removed into the hall to smoke. The evening paper had just come in, and Jack took it up with some eagerness, for his stake in Carmel was a large one. He read through the account of what had taken place quite quietly, and leaned back in his chair thinking. Unlike Lady Haslemere, a few nights ago, he did not let his cigarette go out. At length he spoke.

"I expect I have gone smash, Toby," he said. He threw him over the paper. "Read the account of what happened to-day on the Stock Exchange," he added.

Toby did not reply, but took the paper.

"The only thing to be thankful for is that I didn't sell out just before the panic," remarked Jack.

Toby read on in silence till he had finished it.

"Why?" he asked.

"Because it would look as if I had known that the first telegram was false. What extraordinary nerve Alington must have! Do you see that he has been buying every share he can lay hands on?"

"I don't understand about the first telegram," said Toby.

"Nor do I, thank God!"

He took a turn up and down the room in silence.

"Extremely annoying," he said, with laudable moderation; "and I can't imagine what has happened, or who is responsible for the first cable.

Alington cannot have caused it to be sent merely to make the market active, for it was certain to be contradicted."

A man came into the room with a telegram on a salver, and handed it to Jack.

"Reply paid, my lord," he said.

Jack turned it over in his hand without opening it, unable to make the effort. Then he suddenly tore it open, and unfolded the thin pink sheet. It was from Alington.

Can you meet me to-morrow morning at my rooms, St James's Street?

He scribbled an affirmative, and gave it back to the man.

"I shall have to go up to-morrow," he said to Toby; "Alington wants me to meet him in London; I shall go, of course. What a blessing one is a gentleman, and doesn't scream and swear! Now, not a word to anyone; it may not be as bad as it looks."

Jack started off early next morning, and drove straight to Alington's rooms. Sounds of piano-playing came from upstairs, and this somehow gave him a sense of relief. "People *in extremis* do not play pianos," he said to himself, as he mounted the stairs. Alington got up as soon as he came in.

"I am glad you were able to come," he said; "it was expedient – necessary almost – that I should see you, my dear Conybeare."

"What has happened?" asked Jack.

Mr Alington took a telegram from his pocket, and handed it to him.

"The unexpected – it always does: this, in fact."

Jack took it and read:

Chavasse left for England by P. and O. yesterday.

"You don't understand, my dear Conybeare, do you?" he said. "It is a very short story, and quite a little romance in its way."

And, in a few words, he told Jack the story of the burglary, Chavasse's confession, and his employment of the man as an independent operator in Australia.

"I make no doubt what has occurred," he said. "The man has drawn out the somewhat considerable balance I left at Melbourne for him to invest when ordered, and has taken it off with him. He has also, I expect, got hold of his own confession – a clever rogue."

"But the telegram?" asked Jack. "Who sent the telegram about the strong support in Australia?"

Mr Alington opened his mild eyes to their widest.

"I, my dear fellow!" he said; "at least, of course I caused it to be sent. As usual, two days ago, I despatched one cipher telegram to this valet of mine, telling him to invest, and another to my manager telling him to wire, 'Strong support in Austalia.' He did as I told him; Chavasse did not. That is all."

Jack was silent a moment, but it did not take him long to grasp the whole situation, for it was very simple.

"And what next?" he said.

Alington shrugged his shoulders.

"Unless the shares go up again before next settling-day, I shall almost certainly be bankrupt," he said.

"Then why, if the papers were correctly informed, did you go on buying last night?"

"Because I could get Carmel dirt cheap," he said. "If they go up, I am so much the richer; if they do not, I am done in any case. This unfortunate contretemps about my foolish valet does not effect the value of the mine. The gold is there just the same."

"But nobody will believe that," put in Jack.

"For the present, as you say – for the immediate present – they will not realize it. They will think themselves lucky to part with their shares enormously below their value. My fortune depends on how soon they realize it."

"There will be an inquiry into the matter?"

"Undoubtedly. Bogus telegrams are not officially recognised by the Stock Exchange."

Alington was certainly at his best, so thought Jack, when things happened. His sleek, unhurried respectability, a little trying and conventional at ordinary times, though unaltered in itself, became admirable, a rare manifestation of self-control. No flurried quickening marked his precise, unhurried sentences; they remained just as leisurely as ever. As in the days when Carmel East and West was behaving in so mercurial a manner, though so consonantly with his wishes, so now, when the greater coup had struck so backhandedly against himself, he did not cease to be imperturbably calm and lucid. Though without breeding in the ordinary sense of the word, he had to a notable extent that most characteristic mark of breeding, utter absence of exaltation in unexpected prosperity and complete composure in disaster. There was nothing affected about him; he was, as always, unimpulsive master of himself, and this, which in the social mill seemed a lack of animation, in the mill of adversity became a thing to respect.

"But what do you suppose they will find out at the inquiry?" asked Jack.

"Ah, you need not fear the inquiry in the least. That will not touch your salary as director, which is the sort of thing which I see you have on your mind. No. What would perhaps be serious for you is, if I became bankrupt. Then, it is true, my private accounts where your salary figures would be made public. The surest means of avoiding that is that shares should go up again before settling-day. It is with this view I am buying now."

Toby was sitting in the smoking-room of the Bachelors' Club some weeks later on a hot evening in July. The window was open, and the hum of London came booming in soft and large. It was nearly midnight, and the tide of carriages had set westward from the theatres, and was flowing fast. The pavements were full, the roadway was roaring, the season was gathered up for its final effort. Now and then the door opened, and a man in evening-dress would lounge in, ring for a whisky and soda, and turn listlessly over the leaves of an evening paper or exchange a few remarks with a friend. As often as the door opened Toby looked up, as if expecting someone.

It had already struck midnight half an hour ago when Jack entered. He looked worried and tired, and by the light of a match for his cigarette, which he lit as he crossed the room to where Toby was sitting, the lines round his eyes, noticed and kindly commiserated a few months before by Ted Comber, seemed deeper and more harshly cut. He threw himself into a chair by Toby.

"Drink?" asked the other.

"No, thanks."

Toby was silent a moment.

"I'm devilish sorry for you, Jack," he said at length. "But I see by the paper that it is all over."

"Yes; they finished with me this afternoon. Alington will have another week of it. Jove! Toby, for all his sleekness and hymn-singing, he is an iron fellow! He's got some fresh scheme on hand, and he's going about it with all his old quiet energy, and asked me to join him; but I told him I'd had enough of directorships. But there's a strong man for you! He is knocked flat, he picks himself up and goes straight on."

He took up the paper, and turned to the money-market.

"And here's the cruel part of it all," he said, "for both of us: Carmel is up to four pounds again. If they had only given him another month, he would have been as rich as ever, instead of having to declare bankruptcy; and I – well, I should have had a pound or two more. Lord! on what small things life depends!"

ANYTHING
GOES

THE FATALIST

Mikhail Lermontov

Poet and novelist, Mikhail Lermontov was one of those romantic and impassioned Russian characters who was as ready to use his pistol as his pen. He was a great admirer of Byron and Pushkin and when Pushkin was killed in a duel, he published an elegy with political overtones which led to his arrest and imprisonment. Banished to a line regiment fighting in the Caucasus, Lermontov managed to complete his masterpiece *A Hero of Our Times* before being killed himself in a duel with a brother officer.

The following story taken from a collection called *The Heart of the Russian*, is concerned with predestination and tells how a man gambled with his own life to prove his point – and lost. The romanticism, however, is tempered by the ending which demonstrates a touch of typical Russian cynicism.

I ONCE HAPPENED to spend a couple of weeks in a Cossack village on our left flank. A battalion of infantry was stationed there; and it was the custom of the officers to meet at each other's quarters in turn and to play cards in the evening.

On one occasion – it was at Major S—'s – finding our game of Boston not sufficiently absorbing, we threw the cards under the table and sat on for a long time, talking. The conversation, for once in a way, was interesting. The subject was the Mussulman tradition that a man's fate is written in heaven, and we discussed the fact that it was gaining many votaries, even amongst our own countrymen. Each of us related various extraordinary occurrences, *pro* or *contra*.

"What you have been saying, gentlemen, proves nothing," said the old major. "I presume there is not one of you who has actually been a witness of the strange events which you are citing in support of your opinions?"

"Not one, of course," said many of the guests. "But we have heard of them from trustworthy people." . . .

"It is all nonsense!" someone said. "Where are the trustworthy people who have seen the Register in which the appointed hour of our death is recorded?. . . And if predestination really exists, why are free will and reason granted us? Why are we obliged to render an account of our actions?"

At that moment an officer who was sitting in a corner of the room stood up, and, coming slowly to the table, surveyed us all with a quiet and solemn glance. He was a native of Servia, as was evident from his name.

The outward appearance of Lieutenant Vulich was quite in keeping with his character. His height, swarthy complexion, black hair, piercing black eyes, large but straight nose – an attribute of his nation – and the cold and melancholy smile which ever hovered around his lips, all seemed to concur in lending him the appearance of a man apart, incapable of reciprocating the thoughts and passions of those whom fate gave him for companions.

He was brave; talked little, but sharply; confided his thoughts and family secrets to no one: drank hardly a drop of wine; and never dangled after the young Cossack girls, whose charm it is difficult to realise without having seen them. It was said, however, that the colonel's wife was not indifferent to those expressive eyes of his; but he was seriously angry if any hint on the subject was made.

There was only one passion which he did not conceal – the passion for gambling. At the green table he would become oblivious of everything. He usually lost, but his constant ill success only aroused his obstinacy. It was related that, on one occasion, during a nocturnal expedition, he was keeping the bank on a pillow, and had a terrific run of luck. Suddenly shots rang out. The alarm was sounded; all but Vulich jumped up and rushed to arms.

"Stake, *va banque*!" he cried to one of the most ardent gamblers.

"Seven," the latter answered as he hurried off.

Notwithstanding the general confusion, Vulich calmly finished the deal – seven was the card.

By the time he reached the cordon a violent fusillade was in progress. Vulich did not trouble himself about the bullets or the sabres of the Chechenes, but sought for the lucky gambler.

"Seven it was!" he cried out, as at length he perceived him in the cordon of skirmishers who were beginning to dislodge the enemy from the wood; and going up to him, he drew out his purse and pocket-book and handed them to the winner, notwithstanding the latter's objections on the score of the inconvenience of the payment. That unpleasant duty discharged, Vulich dashed forward, carried the soldiers along after him, and, to the very end of the affair, fought the Chechenes with the utmost coolness.

When Lieutenant Vulich came up to the table, we all became silent, expecting to hear, as usual, something original.

"Gentlemen!" he said – and his voice was quiet though lower in tone than usual – "gentlemen, what is the good of futile discussions? You wish for proofs? I propose that we try the experiment on ourselves: whether a man can of his own accord dispose of his life, or whether the fateful moment is appointed beforehand for each of us. Who is agreeable?"

"Not I. Not I," came from all sides.

"There's a queer fellow for you! He does get strange ideas into his head!"...

"I propose a wager," I said in jest.

"What sort of wager?"

"I maintain that there is no such thing as predestination," I said, scattering on the table a score or so of ducats – all I had in my pocket.

"Done," answered Vulich in a hollow voice. "Major, you will be judge. Here are fifteen ducats, the remaining five you owe me, kindly add them to the others."

"Very well," said the major; "though, indeed, I do not understand what is the question at issue and how you will decide it!"

Without a word Vulich went into the major's bedroom, and we followed him. He went up to the wall on which the major's weapons were hanging, and took down at random one of the pistols – of which there were several of different calibres. We were still in the dark as to what he meant to do. But, when he cocked the pistol and sprinkled powder in the pan, several of the officers, crying out in spite of themselves, seized him by the arms.

"What are you going to do?" they exclaimed. "This is madness!"

"Gentlemen!" he said slowly, disengaging his arm. "Who would like to pay twenty ducats for me?"

They were silent and drew away.

Vulich went into the other room and sat by the table; we all followed him. With a sign he invited us to sit round him. We obeyed in silence – at the moment he had acquired a certain mysterious authority over us. I stared fixedly into his face; but he met my scrutinising gaze with a quiet and steady glance, and his pallid lips smiled. But, notwithstanding his composure, it seemed to me that I could read the stamp of death upon his pale countenance. I have noticed – and many old soldiers have corroborated my observation – that a man who is to die in a few hours frequently bears on his face a certain strange stamp of inevitable fate, so that it is difficult for practised eyes to be mistaken.

"You will die to-day!" I said to Vulich.

He turned towards me rapidly, but answered slowly and quietly:

"May be so, may be not." . . .

Then, addressing himself to the major, he asked:

"Is the pistol loaded?"

The major, in the confusion, could not quite remember.

"There, that will do, Vulich!" exclaimed somebody. "Of course it must be loaded, if it was one of those hanging on the wall there over our heads. What a man you are for joking!"

"A silly joke too!" struck in another.

"I wager fifty rubles to five that the pistol is not loaded!" cried a third.

A new bet was made.

I was beginning to get tired of it all.

"Listen," I said, "either shoot yourself, or hang up the pistol in its place and let us go to bed."

"Yes, of course!" many exclaimed. "Let us go to bed."

"Gentlemen, I beg of you not to move," said Vulich, putting the muzzle of the pistol to his forehead.

We were all petrified.

"Mr Pechorin," he added, "take a card and throw it up in the air."

I took, as I remember now, an ace of hearts off the table and threw it into the air. All held their breath. With eyes full of terror and a certain vague curiosity they glanced rapidly from the pistol to the fateful ace, which slowly descended, quivering in the air. At the moment it touched the table Vulich pulled the trigger . . . a flash in the pan!

"Thank God!" many exclaimed. "It wasn't loaded!"

"Let us see, though," said Vulich.

He cocked the pistol again, and took aim at a forage-cap which was hanging above the window. A shot rang out. Smoke filled the room; when it cleared away, the forage-cap was taken down. It had been shot right through the centre, and the bullet was deeply embedded in the wall.

For two or three minutes no one was able to utter a word. Very quietly Vulich poured my ducats from the major's purse into his own.

Discussions arose as to why the pistol had not gone off the first time. Some maintained that probably the pan had been obstructed; others whispered that the powder had been damp the first time, and that, afterwards, Vulich had sprinkled some fresh powder on it; but I maintained that the last supposition was wrong, because I had not once taken my eyes off the pistol.

"You are lucky at play!" I said to Vulich . . .

"For the first time in my life!" he answered, with a complacent smile. "It is better than 'bank' and 'shtoss.' "

"But, on the other hand, slightly more dangerous!"

"Well? Have you begun to believe in predestination?"

"I do believe in it; only I cannot understand now why it appeared to me that you must inevitably die to-day!"

And this same man, who, such a short time before, had with the greatest calmness aimed a pistol at his own forehead, now suddenly fired up and became embarrassed.

"That will do, though!" he said, rising to his feet. "Our wager is finished, and now your observations, it seems to me, are out of place."

He took up his cap and departed. The whole affair struck me as being strange – and not without reason. Shortly after that, all the officers broke up and went home, discussing Vulich's freaks from different points of view, and, doubtless, with one voice calling me an egoist for having taken up a wager against a man who wanted to shoot himself, as if he could not have found a convenient opportunity without my intervention.

I returned home by the deserted byways of the village. The moon, full and red like the glow of a conflagration, was beginning to make its appearance from behind the jagged horizon of the house-tops; the stars were shining tranquilly in the deep, blue vault of the sky; and I was struck by the absurdity of the idea when I recalled to mind that once upon a time there were some exceedingly wise people who thought that the stars of heaven participated in our insignificant squabbles for a slice of ground, or some other imaginary rights. And what then? These lamps, lighted, so they fancied, only to illuminate their battles and triumphs, are burning with all their former brilliance, whilst the wiseacres themselves, together with their hopes and passions, have long been extinguished, like a little fire kindled at the edge of a forest by a careless wayfarer! But, on the other hand, what strength of will was lent them by the conviction that the entire heavens, with their innumerable habitants, were looking at them with a sympathy, unalterable, though mute! . . . And we, their miserable descendants, roaming over the earth, without faith, without pride, without enjoyment, and without terror – except that involuntary awe which makes the heart shrink at the thought of the inevitable end – we are no longer capable of great sacrifices, either for the good of mankind or even for our own happiness, because we know the impossibility of such happiness; and, just as our ancestors used to fling themselves from one delusion to another, we pass indifferently from doubt to doubt, without possessing, as they did, either hope or even that vague though, at the same time, keen enjoyment which the soul encounters at every struggle with mankind or with destiny.

These and many other similar thoughts passed through my mind, but I did not follow them up, because I do not like to dwell upon abstract ideas – for what do they lead to? In my early youth I was a dreamer; I loved to hug to my bosom the images – now gloomy, now rainbow-hued – which my restless and eager imagination drew for me. And what is there left to me of all these? Only such weariness as might be felt after a battle by night with a phantom – only a confused memory full of regrets. In that vain contest I have exhausted the warmth of soul and firmness of will indispensable to an active life. I have entered upon that life after having already lived through it in thought, and it has become wearisome and nauseous to me, as the reading of a bad imitation of a book is to one who has long been familiar with the original.

The events of that evening produced a somewhat deep impression upon me and excited my nerves. I do not know for certain whether I now believe in predestination or not, but on that evening I believed in it firmly. The proof was startling, and I, notwithstanding that I had laughed at our forefathers and their obliging astrology, fell involuntarily into their way of thinking. However, I stopped myself in time from following that dangerous road, and, as I have made it a rule not to reject anything decisively and not to trust anything blindly, I cast metaphysics aside and began to look at what was beneath my feet. The precaution was well-timed. I only just escaped stumbling over something thick and soft, but, to all appearance, inanimate. I bent down to see what it was, and, by the light of the moon, which now shone right upon the road, I perceived that it was a pig which had been cut in two with a sabre . . . I had hardly time to examine it before I heard the sound of steps, and two Cossacks came running out of a byway. One of them came up to me and enquired whether I had seen a drunken Cossack chasing a pig. I informed him that I had not met the Cossack and pointed to the unhappy victim of his rabid bravery.

"The scoundrel!" said the second Cossack. "No sooner does he drink his fill of *chikhir* than off he goes and cuts up anything that comes in his way. Let us be after him, Eremeich, we must tie him up or else" . . .

They took themselves off, and I continued my way with greater caution, and at length arrived at my lodgings without mishap.

I was living with a certain old Cossack under-officer whom I loved, not only on account of his kindly disposition, but also, and more especially, on account of his pretty daughter, Nastya.

Wrapped up in a sheepskin coat she was waiting for me, as usual, by the wicket gate. The moon illumined her charming little lips, now turned blue by the cold of the night. Recognizing me she smiled; but I was in no mood to linger with her.

"Good night, Nastya!" I said, and passed on.

She was about to make some answer, but only sighed.

I fastened the door of my room after me, lighted a candle, and threw myself on the bed; but, on that occasion, slumber caused its presence to be awaited longer than usual. By the time I fell asleep the east was beginning to grow pale, but I was evidently predestined not to have my sleep out. At four o'clock in the morning two fists knocked at my window. I sprang up.

"What is the matter?"

"Get up – dress yourself!"

I dressed hurriedly and went out.

"Do you know what has happened?" said three officers who had come for me, speaking all in one voice.

They were deadly pale.

"No, what is it?"

"Vulich has been murdered!"

I was petrified.

"Yes, murdered!" they continued. "Let us lose no time and go!"

"But where to?"

"You will learn as we go."

We set off. They told me all that had happened, supplementing their story with a variety of observations on the subject of the strange pre-destination which had saved Vulich from imminent death half an hour before he actually met his end.

Vulich had been walking alone along a dark street, and the drunken Cossack who had cut up the pig had sprung out upon him, and perhaps would have passed him by without noticing him, had not Vulich stopped suddenly and said:

"Whom are you looking for, my man?"

"You!" answered the Cossack, striking him with his sabre; and he cleft him from the shoulder almost to the heart. . . .

The two Cossacks who had met me and followed the murderer had arrived on the scene and raised the wounded man from the ground. But he was already at his last gasp and said these three words only – "he was right!"

I alone understood the dark significance of those words: they referred to me. I had involuntarily foretold his fate to poor Vulich. My instinct had not deceived me; I had indeed read on his changed countenance the signs of approaching death. . . .

. . . After all that, it would hardly seem possible to avoid becoming a fatalist? But who knows for certain whether he is convinced of anything or not? And how often is a deception of the senses or an error of the reason accepted as a conviction!. . . I prefer to doubt everything. Such a disposition is no bar to decision of character; on the contrary, so far as I am concerned, I always advance more boldly when I do not know what is awaiting me. You see, nothing can happen worse than death – and from death there is no escape.

On my return to the fortress I related to Maksim Maksimych all that I had seen and experienced: and I sought to learn his opinion on the subject of predestination.

At first he did not understand the word. I explained it to him as well as I could, and then he said, with a significant shake of the head:

"Yes, sir, of course! It was a very ingenious trick! However, these Asiatic pistols often miss fire if they are badly oiled or if you don't press hard enough on the trigger. I confess I don't like the Circassian carbines either. Somehow or other they don't suit the like of us: the butt end is so small, and any minute you may get your nose burnt! On the other hand, their sabres, now – well, all I need say is, my best respects to *them*!"

Afterwards he said, on reflecting a little:

"Yes, it is a pity about the poor fellow! The devil must have put it into his head to start a conversation with a drunken man at night! However, it is evident that fate had written it so at his birth!"

I could not get anything more out of Maksim Maksimych; generally speaking, he had no liking for metaphysical disputations.

THE STAKE

Saki

Another story by Saki, "The Stake" shows that the compulsive gambler will not only bet *on* anything but will always find something to bet *with*.

"Ronnie is a great trial to me," said Mrs Attray plaintively. "Only eighteen years old last February and already a confirmed gambler. I am sure I don't know where he inherits it from; his father never touched cards, and you know how little I play – a game of bridge on Wednesday afternoons in the winter, for threepence a hundred, and even that I shouldn't do if it wasn't that Edith always wants a fourth and would be certain to ask that detestable Jenkinham woman if she couldn't get me. I would much rather sit and talk any day than play bridge; cards are such a waste of time, I think. But as to Ronnie, bridge and baccarat and poker-patience are positively all that he thinks about. Of course I've done my best to stop it; I've asked the Norridrums not to let him play cards when he's over there, but you might as well ask the Atlantic Ocean to keep quiet for a crossing as expect them to bother about a mother's natural anxieties."

"Why do you let him go there?" asked Eleanor Saxelby.

"My dear," said Mrs Attray, "I don't want to offend them. After all, they are my landlords and I have to look to them for anything I want done about the place; they were very accommodating about the new roof for the orchid house. And they lend me one of their cars when mine is out of order; you know how often it gets out of order."

"I don't know how often," said Eleanor, "but it must happen very frequently. Whenever I want you to take me anywhere in your car I am always told that there is something wrong with it, or else that the chauffeur has got neuralgia and you don't like to ask him to go out."

"He suffers quite a lot from neuralgia," said Mrs Attray hastily. "Anyhow," she continued, "you can understand that I don't want to offend the Norridrums. Their household is the most rackety one in the county, and I believe no one ever knows to an hour or two when any

317

particular meal will appear on the table or what it will consist of when it does appear."

Eleanor Saxelby shuddered. She liked her meals to be of regular occurrence and assured proportions.

"Still," pursued Mrs Attray, "whatever their own home life may be as landlords and neighbours they are considerate and obliging, so I don't want to quarrel with them. Besides, if Ronnie didn't play cards there he'd be playing somewhere else."

"Not if you were firm with him," said Eleanor; "I believe in being firm."

"Firm? I am firm," exclaimed Mrs Attray; "I am more than firm – I am farseeing. I've done everything I can think of to prevent Ronnie from playing for money. I've stopped his allowance for the rest of the year, so he can't even gamble on credit, and I've subscribed a lump sum to the church offertory in his name instead of giving him instalments of small silver to put in the bag on Sundays. I wouldn't even let him have the money to tip the hunt servants with, but sent it by postal order. He was furiously sulky about it but I reminded him what happened to the ten shillings that I gave him for the Young Men's Endeavour League 'Self-Denial Week'."

"What did happen to it?" asked Eleanor.

."Well, Ronnie did some preliminary endeavouring with it, on his own account, in connection with the Grand National. If it had come off, as he expressed it, he would have given the League twenty-five shillings and netted a comfortable commission for himself; as it was, that ten shillings was one of the things the League had to deny itself. Since then I've been careful not to let him have a penny piece in his hands."

"He'll get round that in some way," said Eleanor with quiet conviction; "He'll sell things."

"My dear, he's done all that is to be done in that direction already. He's got rid of his wrist-watch and his hunting flask and both his cigarette cases, and I shouldn't be surprised if he's wearing imitation gold sleeve links instead of those his Aunt Rhoda gave him on his seventeenth birthday. He can't sell his clothes, of course, except his winter overcoat, and I've locked that up in the camphor cupboard on the pretext of preserving it from moth. I really don't see what else he can raise money on. I consider that I've been both firm and farseeing."

"Has he been at the Norridrums lately?" asked Eleanor.

"He was there yesterday afternoon and stayed to dinner," said Mrs Attray. "I don't quite know when he came home, but I fancy it was late."

"Then depend on it he was gambling," said Eleanor, with the assured air of one who has few ideas and makes the most of them. "Late hours in the country always mean gambling."

"He can't gamble if he has no money and no chance of getting any," argued Mrs Attray; "even if one plays for small stakes one must have a decent prospect of paying one's losses."

"He may have sold some of the Amherst pheasant chicks," suggested Eleanor; "they would fetch about ten or twelve shillings each, I dare say."

"Ronnie wouldn't do such a thing," said Mrs Atrray; "and anyhow I went and counted them this morning and they're all there. No," she continued, with the quiet satisfaction that comes from a sense of pains-taking and merited achievement, "I fancy that Ronnie had to content himself with the rôle of onlooker last night, as far as the card-table was concerned."

"Is that clock right?" asked Eleanor, whose eyes had been straying relentlessly towards the mantelpiece for some little time; "lunch is usually so punctual in your establishment."

"Three minutes past the half-hour," exclaimed Mrs Attray; "cook must be preparing something unusually sumptuous in your honour. I am not in the secret; I've been out all the morning, you know."

Eleanor smiled forgivingly. A special effort by Mrs Attray's cook was worth waiting a few minutes for.

As a matter of fact, the luncheon fare, when it made its tardy appearance, was distinctly unworthy of the reputation which the justly treasured cook had built up for herself. The soup alone would have sufficed to cast a gloom over any meal that it had inaugurated, and it was not redeemed by anything that followed. Eleanor said little, but when she spoke there was a hint of tears in her voice that was far more eloquent than outspoken denunciation would have been, and even the insouciant Ronald showed traces of depression when he tasted the rognons Saltikoff.

"Not quite the best luncheon I've enjoyed in your house," said Eleanor at last, when her final hope had flickered out with the savoury.

"My dear, it's the worst meal I've sat down to for years," said her hostess; "that last dish tasted principally of red pepper and wet toast. I'm awfully sorry. Is anything the matter in the kitchen, Pellin?" she asked of the attendant maid.

"Well, ma'am, the new cook hadn't hardly time to see to things properly, coming in so sudden. . . ." commenced Pellin by way of explanation.

319

"The *new* cook!" screamed Mrs Attray.

"Colonel Norridrum's cook, ma'am," said Pellin.

"What on earth do you mean? What is Colonel Norridrum's cook doing in my kitchen – and where is *my* cook?"

"Perhaps I can explain better than Pellin can," said Ronald hurriedly; "the fact is, I was dining at the Norridrums' yesterday, and they were wishing they had a swell cook like yours, just for today and tomorrow, while they've some gourmet staying with them; their own cook is no earthly good – well, you've seen what she turns out when she's at all flurried. So I thought it would be rather sporting to play them at baccarat for the loan of our cook against a money stake, and I lost, that's all. I have had rotten luck at baccarat all this year."

The remainder of his explanation, of how he had assured the cooks that the temporary transfer had his mother's sanction, and had smuggled the one out and the other in during the maternal absence, was drowned in the outcry of scandalized upbraiding.

"If I had sold the woman into slavery there couldn't have been a bigger fuss about it," he confided afterwards to Bertie Norridrum, "and Eleanor Saxelby raged and ramped the louder of the two. I tell you what, I'll bet you two of the Amherst pheasants to five shillings that she refuses to have me as a partner at the croquet tournament. We're drawn together, you know."

This time he won his bet.

ARIGATO

Richard Condon

American writer, Richard Condon, believes that the novelist should set out primarily to entertain his audience, and the success of *The Manchurian Candidate* both as a book and as a film shows that he practices exactly what he preaches. His later novel, *A Talent for Loving*, has won him an even greater following and confirms his reputation as one of the most entertaining of contemporary novelists.

In *Arigato*, Richard Condon has created in Captain Richard Huntington, a man irresistible to women, a dedicated *bon viveur* and a compulsive gambler, one of the most attractive characters in modern fiction. In this passage from the novel, the Captain, already practically a ruined man thanks to his gambling, still cannot resist the challenge of a bet over dinner. . . .

JUAN FRANCOHOGAR was waiting just inside the door at the Splendide as the chocolate-colored Rolls drove up. He stowed his small satchel behind the seat and got into the car.

"Did you rest?" the Captain asked.

"Yes," the assured, bass voice said. "I bathed with a free product which is provided by the hotel. I thought the patron before me had left it behind but when I telephoned the concierge he said it was a service of the hotel. It softens the water, the box says. It was all right."

"I am very interested to see the wines they have chosen for tonight."

"You may not agree, sir, but the wines will be right. A little showmanly but precisely right."

"I hope there's none of that damned pink champagne like last year."

"Oh, one mustn't think about champagne. There will be serious wines."

"It is a very important night for me, Juan. More for me than for you, perhaps, because you are an artist and you know you belong here. I am a spectator."

Francohogar chuckled. "You are the greatest taster a cook ever had, sir. You made tonight possible. I did it, but you made it possible." He polished a red apple with a large handkerchief. They stared at the road leading west out of Bordeaux toward the manifestation of the soul of a nation, even if that soul happened to be gluttonous, which was as solemn as the trooping of the colors on the Queen's birthday, the merger of two gigantic conglomerates by the Mafia in North America, or the wedding anniversary of Princess Grace in Monaco: the soul, that which from, or, as in this case, into which, all blessings flowed.

The French television crews which would cover the event would number more than thirty. The French press would deploy photographers by the dozen, reporters, researchers, experts, fashion writers, fixers and beyond all else, the food critics. The national radio would find new unctions of language. Thirteen hundred vintners would sob themselves to sleep that night because only six French wines, one cognac and one liqueur had been chosen.

Although he greeted Otardi with warmth, asked for his wife, Emilie, and his daughters, Hortense, Denise, and Françoise, the Captain did not get out of the car to enter the restaurant where the other great cooks were assembling and preparing. He drove back to the hotel and bathed, leaving Francohogar in Otardi's kitchens to conjugate their joint glory.

While he was bathing the telephone rang. The telephone was in the bedroom thirty feet away. Mumbling about the unfairness of a system which could insist that it be answered at once, into a darkness of purpose or identity, he stumbled across the vast space to the phone, dripping.

Wrapped in a huge towel he said, into the telephone, "Hello?"

"Colin?"

"Yes. Who is this?"

"Uncle Jim."

"Uncle Jim? Are you here for the cook-out?"

"I'm in Washington. At the White House."

"Ah. Yes. Of course. My best to the President."

"He's on the road. Say, this is a fine connection. You sound as if you are in the same room." Uncle Jim always said that.

"How's – uh – Daddy? Uncle Pete? The boys?"

"Fine. All fine, Colin. Colin – we're all flying to London in the morning."

"Marvellous."

"It's not really so gosh darned marvellous. We're sort of a lynch mob, I guess."

"Who're you lynching?"

"Well – as a matter of fact – you. Can you be at Farm Street by six o'clock tomorrow evening?"

"Me? Why me?"

"We'll explain everything at the meeting. Can you be there?"

"This is most unusual, Jim. I mean – it is only fair that you give me some *inkling*. . . ."

"Can you be there, Colin?"

"Of course I can be there, but. . . ."

"See you at six. Don't take any wooden chewing gum." Uncle Jim disconnected.

The Captain suddenly began to feel his head coming to a point. This was the most pressure they had ever applied. The five men had not been in the same room at the same time, in London, since he and Bitsy had been married. He began to need to gamble to lessen the tension.It was the only way he could get out of the vice. He couldn't stand it if he had to wait until six o'clock the next evening to find out what was so serious for Jim to refer to a lynch mob and to refuse to say what or why. He began to put calls through to Bitsy but she was either out or she was not answering the telephone.

Captain Huntington did not show the face tics he had earned, or the pain and weakness of the duodenal ulcers his endlessly conflicted life had him deserving. He stared at the wall as he sat on the edge of the bed in the towel. His handsome face seemed to have been composed of angular blocks which, had they been alphabet blocks might have spelled out words which he would dread to read. He stood up slowly; a tall man with the ecstatic carriage naval officers have been taught. He swanned into rooms regardless of all shocks, chin properly cocked, shoulders level, backline at true vertical. He wondered how long his watery legs would support him, whether he could make it back to the tub. His wife was getting ready to tell him that life was over. Life without her was nothing he really wanted. He would have achieved a unique suicide using roulette wheels, some dice, and many hundreds of decks of cards.

He was relieved that he and Chezfrance would be dining with John Bryson, a vastly-game periodical gambler, the Captain's sort of company. Bryson should be vastly game, the Captain thought ruefully. He was always winning.

They had decided it would be too uncomfortable to try to jam into the bar at Otardi so they met for an aperitif in the bar in the Splendide. The Captain had not seen Bryson since the banker's last summer holiday. He was looking very fit. He was brash, sardonic and about twenty years older than Chezfrance or Captain Huntington. He was an art patron who had been married four times. He was a Pittsburgh banker who was very, very rich and who was an amused rather than an anguished gambler perhaps because of having so much money it didn't matter a damn whether he won or lost. He loved to gamble for high stakes but, being a good banker, would not gamble in his home country: not at bridge, not at Vegas, not anywhere but in the stock market or during his six weeks annual holiday in Europe where he would gamble on anything including fondling the bottoms of newly-introduced wives while he stared into the eyes of their husbands and grated on about Renoir or the Common Market, stating each or any topic wrong because he didn't feel he was on holiday to educate.

He was a tall, almost white-haired man who wore heavy hornrimmed glasses. Chezfrance was a small, blond man who had overlarge teeth which gave him the impression of a small boy walking around with a mouthful of water. Everyone was glad to see each other again and Bryson stood them to a bottle of Dom Perignon '61 and got on with the business of conversation.

"Nixon's a short-term plunger," Bryson said in answer to the Captain's question of "how is everything?" "We'll be able to buy the goddam country for ten cents on the dollar again, just like in '32, if that little son-of-a-bitch gets reelected. I'm all for him."

"I understand – there is a rumor," Chezfrance said, "that someone will cook the fish with a red wine sauce tonight. Had you heard this?"

"I only know what Francohogar will cook," the Captain said.

"What the hell is wrong with cooking fish in red wine?" Bryson asked. "If cooks as good as these guys tonight say cook red wine with fish then where's a better authority."

"I did not say it would happen," Chezfrance replied. "I only said I heard it would happen."

"As John says – why not?" the Captain agreed mildly.

"Like to bet on that? Like to bet me a thousand pounds that not only will they serve fish in red wine but that the press will flip?"

"You're on."

"Which side of the bet am I taking?"

"You are betting me one thousand pounds that there will be no fish in red wine tonight and therefore the press will not flip."

"Got it." Bryson made a note with a gold pencil in a check-book, but on the back of a check.

"I think we should be on our way, gentlemen," Chezfrance said. "This is not a dinner we would want to be late for." They finished the wine and got to their feet. The Captain felt relief from the pressure which Bitsy had only begun to apply for the first time since he knew that she had discovered the disappearance of the Watteau.

It took them only twenty minutes to get within fifty yards of Otardi's then twenty minutes more to make it to the door through the excitement of crowds, lights, cars and police. The French become inordinately excited at the sight of a Rolls Royce adding together its probable cost with the probable income tax it would require that its owner pay, under the French system. International events were rated by the number of Rolls journalists had been able to spot at such galas. The fact that this Rolls was chocolate, had its top down to reveal extremely rich looking men in black ties and boiled shirts, and wore Hong Kong license plates brought burst after burst of genuinely admiring applause from the crowds on either side as the car inched through.

Inside the restaurant it seemed as if le Tout Paris, le Tout Bordeaux, le Tout Cannes and le Tout St Moritz had come spinning in out of a giant centrifuge of couturiers, coiffeures, masseuses, parfumeurs, joailliers and les tailleurs du mode Anglais. The three men kissed cheeks, pressed hands, admired, appreciated, were in turn admired and appreciated and were conducted by Otardi himself (because Captain Huntington was the only individual sponsor of one of the Ten Master Cooks of France since perhaps Monsieur le Prince or a few Rothschilds) to an elegantly placed table for three where they could see the beautiful ladies and the hungry gentlemen and yet be able to look through the long, wide plate glass screen into the kitchen itself where the great men were even then at work.

"Jesus," Bryson said, "I came all the way from Pittsburgh for this and I thought I was going to meet some new French broads."

"Comment?" Chezfrance said.

"Always the same broads. They travel in a pack and only at night."

The Captain had opened the menu and was staring with no little awe at what he had wrought. The billing was cold and clear. Between Paul Bocuse, Collonges au Mont d'Or and Jean-Pierre et Paul Haeberlin, Illhaeusern, stood Juan Francohogar, Huntington Fine Wines (London).

"You really have the knack don't you, Captain," Bryson said.

"The impossible dream," the Captain murmured, still staring.

"Your boy must be a pretty good cook."

"I assure you, Monsieur Bryson –" Chezfrance began but Bryson was intent on building a bet.

"Francohogar is a great artist," Chezfrance persisted to say.

"You think so, too, Captain?"

The Captain smiled at him dreamily. "You've been saying that yourself, John, for the past three years."

"Bet your ass," Bryson said. "I would know this particular cook's work blindfolded in the bottom of a coal mine sniffling with a head cold."

"No."

"Why no?"

"You have no palate and he's only making one dish out of eleven and each other dish will be fit for the gods. "

"Will you give me ten to one?"

"Eight to one."

"Should be ten. Make it nine."

"Eight."

"What are you betting, gentlemen?" Chezfrance asked.

"I am betting that I can tell which one of the dishes we'll eat tonight will be cooked by Francohogar," said Bryson.

"Formidable!"

"One thousand pounds," Bryson said. "Eight to one."

"Done." The Captain marked the wager down inside the elaborate four page menu.

The large room, overpacked with shrillness, seemed to have bales of smoke like so much organdy floating in mid-air over the heads of the diners, enraging 23.7 percent to whom a Kubeb smoked in a parking lot behind the restaurant could endanger the enjoyment of the food.

Otardi, his face contorted with outrage, ran through the diners snatching cigarettes and cigars from the hands and mouths of Philistines and flinging them into a container a small *commis* carried. He stood on a chair. He announced, "The windows will now be opened to clear the filthy smoke from this room. Anyone who dishonors me by smoking before the cognac is served will be escorted from my restaurant." He stood down to tumultuous applause.

There was a feeling of excitement, of movement. Sommeliers burst into the room carrying magnums of wine. Simultaneously the diners who had already memorized the menu looked down at it and read again, showing intense interest. The wine was listed:

> Dom Perignon Rosé 1959
> Puligny-Blagny 1961
> Chateau Canon 1955
> Taittinger 1964
> Cognac Pellison 1929
> China-China

"Looks like I won me a thousand pounds, Captain," Bryson said, trying not to grin.

"You did?"

"No fish in red wine on this menu."

The Captain glanced down at the listing of the food to be offered.

"Indeed, you have, John. But look at this balance. It is flawless! Did Otardi compose this? It is so elegant and refined, it has such exquisite counterpoint of texture and flavor and scent and sight!" The three men stared downward reverentially. Otardi, working as Beethoven, had written a score for the great artists beyond that glass wall to bring to vibrant harmonies: Beluga caviar – "If I know Otardi it will be sterlet," Chezfrance breathed; Dieppe turbot in golden mustard sauce; a saddle of veal with a daring onion sauce, it had to be delicate for such flesh, it had to *pique*, it had to marry and never to dominate; there would be Basque rice and a courgettes au gratin – simplicity throughout, genius throughout, always *balance*, the Captain marvelled. After that came a sorbet Dom Perignon to clear the mouth for some quail in aspic then les fromages sompteux followed by small cakes, glazed fruit, petits fours.

Bryson lost by choosing the *Selle de Veau* as the dish Francohogar had cooked. Wrong. He had cooked the fish. "Who the hell ever heard a letting a Basque cook fish, for Christ's sake?" Bryson said. The Captain picked up a thousand pounds when he doubted that the Dom Perignon Rosé was 1959. Otardi was summoned and admitted that a freight problem had delayed things but that the menus had been printed and Moët had been gracious enough to fly in the '61. "Anyone could tell the difference," he added, "but so far yours is the first complaint, Captain Huntington."

"I detest champagne rosé," the Captain said. "I should have preferred Raspberry Soda '72."

The Captain picked up a surprise two thousand pounds when Bryson doubled his bet to recover and bet that China-China would have an apricot brandy base blended with armagnac because he had had it at the French Embassy in '34 when that son-of-a-bitch Roosevelt had been in the White House. When the dinner was over the Captain was feeling wondrously relieved, felt little apprehension about what Bitsy might be planning for him the next afternoon, and wondrously lucky. After they had congratulated Francohogar and his colleagues and the Captain had posed for a few pictures with his cook and had said a few felicitous words concerning *la belle France*, acme of civilization, into the television cameras, thus also making the front pages of *Le Monde*, *Le Figaro* and *France-Soir* (. . . . "for my ladies and my gentlemen of France, all over France, it is as your great President Pompidou said on the last day of the year 1971 –" in French the Captain's voice was stridently Gallic, "you are among the most respected and happy people in the world and why hide it." The Captain's voice was strong. "Your President's reasons proving that you were the happiest and most respected people were to the point – but incomplete. He told you that it was because of the visits paid to France by the Peking government, by the Soviet chief, Leonid Brezhnev, the Summit meeting with President Nixon and France's settlement of the monetary crisis – and he is right! But I say to you that France is what France is, whatever France is, because of the greatest of great arts which we have witnessed here tonight") they departed for the casino at Arcachon, some forty miles to the west, where the Captain lost thirty two thousand pounds; a sum which he did not have.

His clothes were damp with the sweat of fear; any hound would have veered away from him to avoid the stench of hopelessness he emanated. He arose from his seat at the chemmy table with all surface correctness and good cheer and carelessly tossed five hundred francs to the croupier who bowed low to him and continued the play.

The Captain wandered off across the high stakes room. He remained cheerfully correct until he reached an alcove which was the backgammon corner where so few people played that it would not be there the following season. He dropped into a chair and lowered his face into his hands. He felt rather than heard the chair being moved across the table from him. He looked up, composing himself. It was John Bryson.

"Feeling down, Captain?"

"Beastly headache," the Captain explained.

"Hell, why not, the way you're losing."

"Yes. Well, excuse me, John. I must pop off in search of an asprin or two." He did not move because he felt that the only courteous thing would be for Bryson to move because it had been made clear that he was presently intruding.

"How about a little backgammon?" Bryson said.

"No, thank you, John. The desperate fact is, I am flat broke." That should certainly not come as news to Bryson who had won most of it.

"Hell," Bryson said, "I don't want to play for money."

"What else can one play with?"

"Thought you might like to play for your cook."

"My *cook*?" The Captain was not only incredulous, he was offended.

"He sure is one helluva cook, Captain."

"It would be barbaric for a man to wager his cook."

"Maybe where you come from." Bryson took out a wallet which was fat enough to be holding several dozen frankfurters. He began to toss large banknotes on the backgammon board. "Suppose you just let me give you a credit of two thousand pounds against your cook."

"Two thousand pounds? The man is my friend."

"Jessa same I suppose you have a written contract with him?"

The Captain nodded. Then he stared down at the impossible sums of money; money which, if he could wager it well could stall the terrible confrontation with Bitsy and her family. He began to sweat. Chezfrance came up.

"Are you all right, Colin?" he asked.

The Captain nodded. "I'm fine, I think. But I bet a little too heavily and I am a bit worried now that if the casino gets to the bank before you do the check I gave you for the order this afternoon won't be much good at all."

"I will cancel the order, Colin."

"Thank you."

"How about it, Captain?"

"The bet you suggest would be utterly out of the question," the Captain said hoarsely. "However, for a credit of fifty thousand pounds I'll play you for my building in Farm Street."

"What the hell would I ever want another building for?"

"Frankly, John, I don't intend that you shall win." It was a pathetic line, delivered from behind sand-bags of self-delusion. The Captain had never started any gambling play without knowing he would win while secretly hoping he would lose.

"We'll just see about that, Captain," Bryson said, grinning. He picked up the dice cup and began to shake it.

By the time the gamblers got back to the Splendide at two forty-five, Juan Francohogar had checked out and had returned on the night plane to London. There would be no other planes out of Bordeaux, the concierge said, until ten minutes to ten the next morning.

"Hell, Captain," Bryson said, "I got the bank's Gulfstream II over here with me so's I don't have to get hung up on airports and baggage. Come on, we'll shake the crew outta bed and get on up to London right now. I just hate it when you're this depressed."

"You are really very kind, John," the Captain said.

The Grumman was almost ready when they got there and they passed the short waiting time by having a good breakfast in the cabin.

"Fine looking craft," Captain Huntington said, chewing Irish bacon with French eggs.

"Yes, she is. She has a good old sixty-eight foot wingspan and two Rolls

Royce Spey Mk511–8 jet engines that will cruise us along at five ninety."

"What's the range?"

"Just about four thousand. We fly right in outta Allegheny County Airport into Paris. I just step outta the bar at the Holiday Inn – they make a helluva hamburger – and into the old Gulfstream and there I am. How's about we have dinner tonight?"

"I have a very, very important meeting tonight."

"Thought you had something heavy on your mind. How about lunch today then?"

"Lunch will be fine."

"Where?"

"If you can let's make it at Tiberio in Queen Street. It's so nearby to Bitsy's and to Yvonne's."

"One-fifteen."

The Captain nodded. He took a deep breath. "Bitsy and her entire family have called a meeting at Farm Street at six o'clock this evening."

Bryson was impressed. "All of them?"

"Yes. They come over for a good meal every now and then. But tonight – at seven o'clock – I will come face-to-face with an old opponent, Commander Uto Fujikawa of the Imperial Japanese Navy."

Bryson's eyebrows went up. "I didn't know you were old enough to be in the Pearl Harbor war."

"No, no, no! For the past eight years Commander Fujikawa and I have been re-fighting all the battles of the Pacific by mail. I keep this big tactical board at Yvonne's to work out all the maneuvers. In all that time we've never met."

"Everyone to his own taste, as the man said when he kissed the cow," Bryson shrugged.

They had arranged to air freight the Captain's car in the morning. In London, Bryson's Rolls was at the airport to drive the Captain to Yvonne's house in Charles Street.

The Captain let himself into the hushed house silently then moved along the hall and went down the stairs to the kitchen to have a glass of milk and to try to get his terrible predicament sorted out. When he opened the heavy door to the large refrigerator the trick of light made it seem as if he were robbing a bank vault then the yehudi went on and revealed the inside of the fridge. As he removed a bottle of milk, the overhead lights in the kitchen went on. The Captain turned toward the click of the switch. Wearing a bulky bathrobe and looking more rugged than his countryman,

Paolino Uzcudin, Francohogar stood in the doorway. He had a tall, *toque blanche* cook's hat on above his nightdress.

"Do you sleep in that hat?" the Captain asked reflexively.

"I am greatly excited," Francohogar said, showing all the excitement of a sea turtle basking in the sun. "I would not be able to sleep until you came home."

"Mademoiselle is all right?" There was sudden panic in the Captain's voice.

"Oh, yes."

"Then what happend?"

"I wanted to show my deep appreciation for all you have done for me. If I did not accomplish this I would never feel that you knew how grateful I am."

"Accomplished what?"

"Do you recall mentions in histories of gourmandise of the exalted *Pâté de Banquier Henri Emmet*?"

"Well, yes. Of course."

"Have you ever tasted it?"

"No. Of course not."

"The *Pâté de Banquier Henri Emmet* in all the time since its discovery in 1868, in Marton, Department of Seine et Loire, has been capable of being made by only three cooks. The *Pâté de Banquier Henri Emmet* is such a *pâté* that it requires six and a quarter days to make and if the precise balance of its thirty-two ingredients is disturbed, everything is ruined."

"I know. I know."

"Tonight there are four cooks who have made it."

"Juan!"

"I have not only made it but I have advanced it by two taste factors and have made it seven percent lighter and easier to digest."

"*Juan!*"

"I did this before we left for the gala yesterday – for six days before – only that you could know the extent of the appreciation I feel for what you have done for me." He moved stolidly to the kitchen counter. With three hand movements he pulled the cork out of a bottle of wine. "Chateau Palmer '55," he said. He lifted a white porous cloth which covered a large *pâté en croûte*. He took up a sharp knife, cut three equal-size portions rapidly, hesitated, then cut a fourth.

Captain Huntington was seating himself at the kitchen table, tying a large white napkin around his neck. The great cook set a plate before him which held three slices of the *paté*. "Taste!" he commanded.

The Captain sipped the wine. He disregarded the silver beside the plate and picked up a slice of the *pâté* and bit into it. He chewed thoughtfully. Francohogar chewed abstractedly, leaning forward. The Captain swallowed then quickly sipped more wine. He took a larger bite of the *pâté*.

"Alors?"

Captain Huntington looked up at his cook with tears glistening in his eyes. "You have done it," he said.

"Did you sense the two additional taste factors?" he pressed.

The Captain nodded, deeply moved. Tears were now rolling down his cheeks. "You have added one pasilla *chili*," he said brokenly, "and the juices of a Belgian gherkin."

Francohogar's face became as a great searchlight, beaming all over the room.

With a choked voice the Captain said, "On the day you bring me the greatest *paté* the world will ever know, on the day after you reached the summit with the greatest cooks of France – a terrible thing has happened."

"What has happened? Madame is all right?"

"Madame is all right, but I have lost you at backgammon to a man from Pittsburgh."

"What is Pittsburgh?"

The Captain arose with the plate of *pâté* and the wine. He walked to the counter next to the shocked cook and set them down. He kissed Francohogar on both cheeks, ceremonially, but he was unable to speak. He wept as he picked up the food and wine and walked off into the darkened building.

A PIECE OF PIE

Damon Runyon

A newspaper man through and through, Damon Runyon had already achieved a national reputation as a sports writer before breaking into literature with his humorous and affectionate short stories of the guys and dolls of New York's underworld. Their success was such that his style is recognized as having had a lasting influence on American language and the word "Runyonese" has entered the vocabulary.

Most of the characters in Damon Runyon's stories are always ready to lay a bet on any proposition, and in "A Piece of Pie," Horsey thinks he has a certain winner when he plans to match Nicely Nicely Jones against Joel Duffle in an eating contest. . . .

ON BOYLSTON STREET, in the city of Boston, Mass., there is a joint where you can get as nice a broiled lobster as anybody ever slaps a lip over, and who is in there one evening partaking of this tidbit but a character by the name of Horse Thief and me.

This Horse Thief is called Horsey for short, and he is not called by this name because he ever steals a horse but because it is the consensus of public opinion from coast to coast that he may steal one if the opportunity presents.

Personally, I consider Horsey a very fine character, because any time he is holding anything he is willing to share his good fortune with one and all, and at this time in Boston he is holding plenty. It is the time we make the race meeting at Suffolk Down, and Horsey gets to going very good, indeed, and in fact he is now a character of means, and is my host against the broiled lobster.

Well, at a table next to us are four or five characters who all seem to be well-dressed, and stout-set, and red-faced, and prosperous-looking, and who all speak with the true Boston accent, which consists of many ah's and very few r's. Characters such as these are familiar to anybody who is ever in Boston very much, and they are bound to be politicians, retired cops, or contractors, because Boston is really quite infested with characters of this nature.

I am paying no attention to them, because they are drinking local ale, and talking loud, and long ago I learn that when a Boston character is engaged in aleing himself up, it is a good idea to let him alone, because the best you can get out of him is maybe a boff on the beezer. But Horsey is in there on the old Ear-ie, and very much interested in their conversation, and finally I listen myself just to hear what is attracting his attention, when one of the characters speaks as follows:

"Well," he says, "I am willing to bet ten thousand dollars that he can outeat anybody in the United States any time."

Now at this, Horsey gets right up and steps over to the table and bows and smiles in a friendly way on one and all, and says:

"Gentlemen," he says, "pardon the intrusion, and excuse me for billing in, but," he says, "do I understand you are speaking of a great eater who resides in your fair city?"

Well, these Boston characters all gaze at Horsey in such a hostile manner that I am expecting any one of them to get up and request him to let them miss him, but he keeps on bowing and smiling, and they can see that he is a gentleman, and finally one of them says:

"Yes," he says, "we are speaking of a character by the name of Joel Duffle. He is without doubt the greatest eater alive. He just wins a unique wager. He bets a character from Bangor, Me., that he can eat a whole window display of oysters in this very restaurant, and he not only eats all the oysters but he then wishes to wager that he can also eat the shells, but," he says, "it seems that the character from Bangor, Me., unfortunately taps out on the first proposition and has nothing with which to bet on the second."

"Very interesting," Horsey says. "Very interesting, if true, but," he says, "unless my ears deceive me, I hear one of you state that he is willing to wager ten thousand dollars on this eater of yours against anybody in the United States."

"Your ears are perfect," another of the Boston characters says. "I state it although," he says, "I admit it is a sort of figure of speech. But I state it all right," he says, "and never let it be said that a Conway ever pigs it on a betting proposition."

"Well," Horsey says, "I do not have a tenner on me at the moment, but," he says, "I have here a thousand dollars to put up as a forfeit that I can produce a character who will outeat your party for ten thousand, and as much more as you care to put up."

And with this, Horsey outs with a bundle of coarse notes and tosses it on the table, and right away one of the Boston characters, whose name turns out to be Carroll, slaps his hand on the money and says:

"Bet."

Well, now this is prompt action to be sure, and if there is one thing I admire more than anything else, it is action, and I can see that these are characters of true sporting instincts and I commence wondering where I can raise a few dibs to take a piece of Horsey's proposition, because of course I know that he has nobody in mind to do the eating for his side but Nicely-Nicely Jones.

And knowing Nicely-Nicely Jones, I am prepared to wager all the money I can possibly raise that he can outeat anything that walks on two legs. In fact, I will take a chance on Nicely-Nicely against anything on four legs, except maybe an elephant, and at that he may give the elephant a photo finish.

I do not say that Nicely-Nicely is the greatest eater in all history, but what I do say is he belongs up there as a contender. In fact, Professor D, who is a professor in a college out West before he turns to playing the horses for a livelihood, and who makes a study of history in his time, says he will not be surprised but what Nicely-Nicely figures one-two.

Professor D says we must always remember that Nicely-Nicely eats under the handicaps of modern civilization, which require that an eater use a knife and fork, or anyway a knife, while in the old days eating with the hands was a popular custom and much faster. Professor D says he has no doubt that under the old rules Nicely-Nicely will hang up a record that will endure through the ages, but of course maybe Professor D overlays Nicely-Nicely somewhat.

Well, now that the match is agreed upon, naturally Horsey and the Boston characters begin discussing where it is to take place, and one of the Boston characters suggests a neutral ground, such as New London, Conn., or Providence, R.I., but Horsey holds out for New York, and it seems that Boston characters are always ready to visit New York, so he does not meet with any great opposition on this point.

They all agree on a date four weeks later so as to give the principals plenty of time to get ready, although Horsey and I know that this is really unnecessary as far as Nicely-Nicely is concerned, because one thing about him is he is always in condition to eat.

This Nicely-Nicely Jones is a character who is maybe five feet eight inches tall, and about five feet nine inches wide, and when he is in good shape he will weigh upward of two hundred and eighty-three pounds. He is a horse player by trade, and eating is really just a hobby, but he is undoubtedly a wonderful eater even when he is not hungry.

Well, as soon as Horsey and I return to New York, we hasten to Mindy's restaurant on Broadway and relate the bet Horsey makes in Boston, and right away so many citizens, including Mindy himself, wish to take piece of the proposition that it is oversubscribed by a large sum in no time.

Then Mindy remarks that he does not see Nicely-Nicely Jones for a month of Sundays, and then everybody present remembers that they do not see Nicely-Nicely around lately, either, and this leads to a discussion of where Nicely-Nicely can be, although up to this moment if nobody sees Nicely-Nicely but once in the next ten years it will be considered sufficient.

Well, Willie the Worrier, who is a bookmaker by trade, is among those present, and he remembers that the last time he looks for Nicely-Nicely hoping to collect a marker of some years' standing, Nicely-Nicely is living at the Rest Hotel in West Forty-ninth Street, and nothing will do Horsey but I must go with him over to the Rest to make inquiry for Nicely-Nicely, and there we learn that he leaves a forwarding address away up on Morningside Heights in care of somebody by the name of Slocum.

So Horsey calls a short, and away we go to this address, which turns out to be a five-story walk-up apartment, and a card downstairs shows that Slocum lives on the top floor. It takes Horsey and me ten minutes to walk up the five flights as we are by no means accustomed to exercise of this nature, and when we finally reach a door marked Slocum, we are plumb tuckered out, and have to sit down on the top step and rest a while.

Then I ring the bell at this door marked Slocum, and who appears but a tall young Judy with black hair who is without doubt beautiful, but who is so skinny we have to look twice to see her, and when I ask her if she can give me any information about a party named Nicely-Nicely Jones, she says to me like this:

"I guess you mean Quentin," she says. "Yes," she says, "Quentin is here. Come in, gentlemen."

So we step into an apartment, and as we do so a thin, sickly looking character gets up out of a chair by the window, and in a weak voice says good evening. It is a good evening, at that, so Horsey and I say good evening right back at him, very polite, and then we stand there waiting for Nicely-Nicely to appear, when the beautiful skinny young Judy says:

"Well," she says, "this is Mr Quentin Jones."

Then Horsey and I take another swivel at the thin character, and we can see that it is nobody but Nicely-Nicely, at that, but the way he changes since we last observe him is practically shocking to us both, because he is undoubtedly all shrunk up. In fact, he looks as if he is about half what he is in his prime, and his face is pale and thin, and his eyes are away back in his head, and while we both shake hands with him it is some time before either of us is able to speak. Then Horsey finally says:

"Nicely," he says, "can we have a few words with you in private on a very important proposition?"

Well, at this, and before Nicely-Nicely can answer aye, yes or no, the beautiful skinny young Judy goes out of the room and slams a door behind her, and Nicely-Nicely says:

"My fiancée, Miss Hilda Slocum," he says. "She is a wonderful character. We are to be married as soon as I lose twenty pounds more. It will take a couple of weeks longer," he says.

"My goodness gracious, Nicely," Horsey says. "What do you mean lose twenty pounds more? You are practically emaciated now. Are you just out of a sick bed, or what?"

"Why," Nicely-Nicely says, "certainly I am not out of a sick bed. I am never healthier in my life. I am on a diet. I lose eighty-three pounds in two months, and am now down to two hundred. I feel great," he says. "It is all because of my fiancée, Miss Hilda Slocum. She rescues me from gluttony and obesity, or anyway," Nicely-Nicely says, "this is what Miss Hilda Slocum calls it. My, I feel good. I love Miss Hilda Slocum very much," Nicely-Nicely says. "It is a case of love at first sight on both sides the day we meet in the subway. I am wedged in one of the turnstile gates, and she kindly pushes on me from behind until I wiggle through. I can see she has a kind heart, so I date her up for a movie that night and propose to her while the newsreel is on. But," Nicely-Nicely says, "Hilda tells me at once that she will never marry a fat slob. She says I must put myself in her hands and she will reduce me by scientific methods and then she will become my ever-loving wife, but not before.

"So," Nicely-Nicely says, "I come to live here with Miss Hilda Slocum and her mother, so she can supervise my diet. Her mother is thinner than Hilda. And I surely feel great," Nicely-Nicely says. "Look," he says.

And with this, he pulls out the waistband of his pants, and shows enough spare space to hide War Admiral in, but the effort seems to be a strain on him, and he has to sit down in his chair again.

"My goodness gracious," Horsey says. "What do you eat, Nicely?"

"Well," Nicely-Nicely says, "I eat anything that does not contain starch, but," he says, "of course everything worth eating contains starch, so I really do not eat much of anything whatever. My fiancée, Miss Hilda Slocum, arranges my diet. She is an expert dietitian and runs a widely known department in a diet magazine by the name of *Let's Keep House.*"

Then Horsey tells Nicely-Nicely of how he is matched to eat against this Joel Duffle, of Boston, for a nice side bet, and how he has a forfeit of a thousand dollars already posted for appearance, and how many of Nicely-Nicely's admirers along Broadway are looking to win themselves out of all their troubles by betting on him, and at first Nicely-Nicely listens with great interest, and his eyes are shining like six bits, but then he becomes very sad, and says:

"It is no use, gentlemen," he says. "My fiancée. Miss Hilda Slocum, will never hear of me going off my diet even for a little while. Only yesterday I try to talk her into letting me have a little pumpernickel instead of toasted whole wheat bread, and she says if I even think of such a thing again, she will break our engagement. Horsey," he says, "do you ever eat toasted whole wheat bread for a month hand running? Toasted?" he says.

"No," Horsey says. "What I eat is nice, white French bread, and corn muffins, and hot biscuits with gravy on them."

"Stop," Nicely-Nicely says. "You are eating yourself into an early grave, and, furthermore," he says, "you are breaking my heart. But," he says, "the more I think of my following depending on me in this emergency, the sadder it makes me feel to think I am unable to oblige them. However," he says, "let us call Miss Hilda Slocum in on an outside chance and see what her reactions to your proposition are."

So we call Miss Hilda Slocum in, and Horsey explains our predicament in putting so much faith in Nicely-Nicely only to find him dieting, and Miss Hilda Slocum's reactions are to order Horsey and me out of the joint with instructions never to darken her door again, and when we are a block away we can still hear her voice speaking very firmly to Nicely-Nicely.

Well, personally, I figure this ends the matter, for I can see that Miss Hilda Slocum is a most determined character, indeed, and the chances are it does end it, at that, if Horsey does not happen to get a wonderful break.

He is at Belmont Park one afternoon, and he has a real good thing in a jump race, and when a brisk young character in a hard straw hat and eyeglasses comes along and asks him what he likes, Horsey mentions this good thing, figuring he will move himself in for a few dibs if the good thing connects.

Well, it connects all right, and the brisk young character is very grateful to Horsey for his information, and is giving him plenty of much-obliges, and nothing else, and Horsey is about to mention that they do not accept much-obliges at his hotel, when the brisk young character mentions that he is nobody but Mr McBurgle and that he is the editor of the *Let's Keep House* magazine, and for Horsey to drop in and see him any time he is around his way.

Naturally, Horsey remembers what Nicely-Nicely says about Miss Hilda Slocum working for this *Let's Keep House* magazine, and he relates the story of the eating contest to Mr McBurgle and asks him if he will kindly use his influence with Miss Hilda Slocum to get her to release Nicely-Nicely from his diet long enough for the contest. Then Horsey gives Mr McBurgle a tip on another winner, and Mr McBurgle must use plenty of influence on Miss Hilda Slocum at once, as the next day she calls Horsey up at his hotel before he is out of bed, and speaks to him as follows:

"Of course," Miss Hilda Slocum says, "I will never change my attitude about Quentin, but," she says, "I can appreciate that he feels very bad about you gentlemen relying on him and having to disappoint you. He feels that he lets you down, which is by no means true, but it weighs upon his mind. It is interfering with his diet.

"Now," Miss Hilda Slocum says, "I do not approve of your contest, because," she says, "it is placing a premium on gluttony, but I have a friend by the name of Miss Violette Shumberger who may answer your purpose. She is my dearest friend from childhood, but it is only because I love her dearly that this friendship endures. She is extemely fond of eating," Miss Hilda Slocum says. "In spite of my pleadings, and my warnings, and my own example, she persists in food. It is disgusting to me but I finally learn that it is no use arguing with her.

"She remains my dearest friend," Miss Hilda Slocum says, "though she continues her practice of eating, and I am informed that she is phenomenal in this respect. In fact," she says, "Nicely-Nicely tells me to say to you that if Miss Violette Shumberger can perform the eating exploits I relate to him from hearsay she is a lily. Good-bye." Miss Hilda Slocum says. "You cannot have Nicely-Nicely."

Well, nobody cares much about this idea of a stand-in for Nicely-Nicely in such a situation, and especially a Judy that no one ever hears of before, and many citizens are in favour of pulling out of the contest altogether. But Horsey has his thousand-dollar forfeit to think of, and as no one can suggest anyone else, he finally arranges a personal meet with the Judy suggested by Miss Hilda Slocum.

He comes into Mindy's one evening with a female character who is so fat it is necessary to push three tables together to give her room for her lap, and it seems that this character is Miss Violette Shumberger. She weighs maybe two hundred and fifty pounds, but she is by no means an old Judy, and by no means bad-looking. She has a face the size of a town clock and enough chins for a fire escape, but she has a nice smile and pretty teeth, and a laugh that is so hearty it knocks the whipped cream off an order of strawberry shortcake on a table fifty feet away and arouses the indignation of a customer by the name of Goldstein who is about to consume same.

Well, Horsey's idea in bringing her into Mindy's is to get some kind of line on her eating form, and she is clocked by many experts when she starts putting on the hot meat, and it is agreed by one and all that she is by no means a selling-plater. In fact, by the time she gets through, even Mindy admits she has plenty of class, and the upshot of it all is Miss Violette Shumberger is chosen to eat against Joel Duffle.

Maybe you hear something of this great eating contest that comes off in New York one night in the early summer of 1937. Of course eating contests are by no means anything new, and in fact they are quite an old-fashioned pastime in some sections of this country, such as the South and East, but this is the first big public contest of the kind in years, and it creates no little comment along Broadway.

In fact, there is some mention of it in the blats, and it is not a frivolous proposition in any respect, and more dough is wagered on it than any other eating contest in history, with Joel Duffle at 6 to 5 favourite over Miss Violette Shumberger all the way through.

This Joel Duffle comes to New York several days before the contest with the character by the name of Conway, and requests a meet with Miss Violette Shumberger to agree on the final details and who shows up with Miss Violette Shumberger as her coach and adviser but Nicely-Nicely Jones. He is even thinner and more peaked-looking than when Horsey and I see him last, but he says he feels great, and that he is within six pounds of his marriage to Miss Hilda Slocum.

Well, it seems that his presence is really due to Miss Hilda Slocum herself, because she says that after getting her dearest friend Miss Violette Shumberger into this jackpot, it is only fair to do all she can to help her win it, and the only way she can think of is to let Nicely-Nicely give Violette the benefit of his experience and advice.

But afterward we learn that what really happens is that this editor, Mr McBurgle, gets greatly interested in the contest, and when he discovers that in spite of his influence, Miss Hilda Slocum declines to permit Nicely-Nicely to personally compete, but puts in a pinch eater, he is quite indignant and insists on her letting Nicely-Nicely school Violette.

Furthermore we afterward learn that when Nicely-Nicely returns to the apartment on Morningside Heights after giving Violette a lesson, Miss Hilda Slocum always smells his breath to see if he indulges in any food during his absence.

Well, this Joel Duffle is a tall character with stooped shoulders, and a sad expression, and he does not look as if he can eat his way out of a tea shoppe, but as soon as he commences to discuss the details of the contest, anybody can see that he knows what time it is in situations such as this. In fact, Nicely-Nicely says he can tell at once from the way Joel Duffle talks that he is a dangerous opponent, and he says while Miss Violette Shumberger impresses him as an improving eater, he is only sorry she does not have more seasoning.

This Joel Duffle suggests that the contest consist of twelve courses of strictly American food, each side to be allowed to pick six dishes, doing the picking in rotation, and specifying the weight and quantity of the course selected to any amount the contestant making the pick desires, and each course is to be divided for eating exactly in half, and after Miss Violette Shumberger and Nicely-Nicely whisper together a while, they say the terms are quite satisfactory.

Then Horsey tosses a coin for the first pick, and Joel Duffle say heads and it is heads, and he chooses, as the first course, two quarts of ripe olives, twelve bunches of celery, and four pounds of shelled nuts, all this to be split fifty-fifty between them. Miss Violette Shumberger names twelve dozen cherry-stone clams as the second course, and Joel Duffle says two gallons of Philadelphia pepper-pot soup as the third.

Well, Miss Violette Shumberger and Nicely-Nicely whisper together again, and Violette puts in two five-pound striped bass, the heads and tails not to count in the eating, and Joel Duffle names a twenty-two pound roast turkey. Each vegetable is rated as one course, and Miss Violette Shumberger asks for twelve pounds of mashed potatoes with brown gravy. Joel Duffle says two dozen ears of corn on the cob, and Violette replies with two quarts of lima beans. Joel Duffle calls for twelve bunches of asparagus cooked in butter, and Violette mentions ten pounds of stewed new peas.

This gets them down to the salad, and it is Joel Duffle's play, so he says six pounds of mixed green salad with vinegar and oil dressing, and now Miss Violette Shumberger has the final selection, which is the dessert. She says pumpkin pie, two feet across, and not less than three inches deep.

It is agreed that they must eat with knife, fork or spoon, but speed is not to count, and there is to be no time limit, except they cannot pause more than two consecutive minutes at any stage, except in case of hiccoughs. They can drink anything, and as much as they please, but liquids are not to count in the scoring. The decision is to be strictly on the amount of food consumed, and the judges are to take account of anything left on the plates after a course, but not of loose chewings on bosom or vest up to an ounce,

The losing side is to pay for the food, and in case of a tie they are to eat it off immediately on ham and eggs only.

Well, the scene of this contest is the second-floor dining-room of Mindy's restaurant, which is closed to the general public for the occasion, and only parties immediately connected in the contest are admitted. The contestants are seated on either side of a big table in the center of the room, and each contestant has three waiters.

No talking and no rooting from the spectators is permitted, but of course in any eating contest the principals may speak to each other if they wish, though smart eaters never wish to do this, as talking only wastes energy, and about all they ever say to each other is please pass the mustard.

About fifty characters from Boston are present to witness the contest and the same number of citizens of New York are admitted, and among them is this editor, Mr McBurgle, and he is around asking Horsey if he thinks Miss Violette Shumberger is as good a thing as the jumper at the race track.

Nicely-Nicely arrives on the scene quite early, and his appearance is really most distressing to his old friends and admirers, as by this time he is shy so much weight that he is a pitiful scene, to be sure, but he tells Horsey and me that he thinks Miss Violette Shumberger has a good chance.

"Of course," he says, "she is green. She does not know how to pace herself in competition. But," he says, "she has a wonderful style. I love to watch her eat. She likes the same things I do in the days when I am eating. She is a wonderful character, too. Do you ever notice her smile?" Nicely-Nicely says.

"But," he says, "she is the dearest friend of my fiancée, Miss Hilda Slocum, so let us not speak of this. I try to get Hilda to come to see the contest, but she says it is repulsive. Well, anyway," Nicely-Nicely says, "I manage to borrow a few dibs, and am wagering on Miss Violette Shumberger. By the way," he says, "if you happen to think of it, notice her smile."

Well, Nicely-Nicely takes a chair about ten feet behind Miss Violette Shumberger, which is as close as the judges will allow him, and he is warned by them that no coaching from the corners will be permitted, but of course Nicely-Nicely knows this rule as well as they do, and furthermore by this time his exertions seem to have left him without any more energy.

There are three judges, and they are all from neutral territory. One of these judges is a party from Baltimore, Md., by the name of Packard, who runs a restaurant, and another is a party from Providence, R.I., by the name of Croppers, who is a sausage manufacturer. The third judge is an old Judy by the name of Mrs Rhubarb, who comes from Philadelphia, and once keeps an actors' boarding-house, and is considered an excellent judge of eaters.

Well, Mindy is the official starter, and at 8.30 p.m. sharp, when there is still much betting among the spectators, he outs with his watch, and says like this:

"Are you ready, Boston? Are you ready, New York?"

Miss Violette Shumberger and Joel Duffle both nod their heads, and Mindy says commence, and the contest is on, with Joel Duffle getting the jump at once on the celery and olives and nuts.

It is apparent that this Joel Duffle is one of these rough-and-tumble eaters that you can hear quite a distance off, especially on clams and soups. He is also an eyebrow eater, an eater whose eyebrows go up as high as the part in his hair as he eats, and this type of eater is undoubtedly very efficient.

In fact, the way Joel Duffle goes through the groceries down to the turkey causes the Broadway spectators some uneasiness, and they are whispering to each other that they only wish the old Nicely-Nicely is in there. But personally, I like the way Miss Violette Shumberger eats without undue excitement, and with great zest. She cannot keep close to Joel Duffle in the matter of speed in the early stages of the contest, as she seems to enjoy chewing her food, but I observe that as it goes along she pulls up on him, and I figure this is not because she is stepping up her pace, but because he is slowing down.

When the turkey finally comes on, and is split in two halves right down the middle, Miss Violette Shumberger looks greatly disappointed, and she speaks for the first time as follows:

"Why," she says, "where is the stuffing?"

Well, it seems that nobody mentions any stuffing for the turkey to the chef, so he does not make any stuffing, and Miss Violette Shumberger's disappointment is so plain to be seen that the confidence of the Boston characters is somewhat shaken. They can see that a Judy who can pack away as much fodder as Miss Violette Shumberger has to date, and then beef for stuffing, is really quite an eater.

In fact, Joel Duffle looks quite startled when he observes Miss Violette Shumberger's disappointment, and he gazes at her with great respect as she disposes of her share of the turkey, and the mashed potatoes, and one thing and another in such a manner that she moves up on the pumpkin pie on dead even terms with him. In fact, there is little to choose between them at this point, although the judge from Baltimore is calling the attention of the other judges to a turkey leg that he claims Miss Violette Shumberger does not clean as neatly as Joel Duffle does his, but the other judges dismiss this as a technicality.

Then the waiters bring on the pumpkin pie, and it is without doubt quite a large pie, and in fact it is about the size of a manhole cover, and I can see that Joel Duffle is observing this pie with a strange expression on his face, although to tell the truth I do not care for the expression on Miss Violet Shumberger's face, either.

Well, the pie is cut in two dead centre, and one half is placed before Miss Violette Shumberger and the other half before Joel Duffle, and he does not take more than two bites before I see him loosen his waistband and take a big swig of water, and thinks I to myself, he is now down to a slow walk, and the pie will decide the whole heat, and I am only wishing I am able to wager a little more dough on Miss Violette Shumberger. But about this moment, and before she as much as touches her pie, all of a sudden Violette turns her head and motions to Nicely-Nicely to approach her, and as he approaches, she whispers in his ear.

Now at this, the Boston character by the name of Conway jumps up and claims a foul and several other Boston characters join him in this claim, and so does Joel Duffle, although afterwards even the Boston characters admit that Joel Duffle is no gentleman to make such a claim against a lady.

Well, there is some confusion over this, and the judges hold a conference, and they rule that there is certainly no foul in the actual eating that they can see, because Miss Violette Shumberger does not touch her pie so far.

But they say that whether it is a foul otherwise all depends on whether Miss Violette Shumberger is requesting advice on the contest from Nicely-Nicely and the judge from Providence, R I., wishes to know if Nicely-Nicely will kindly relate what passes between him and Violette so they may make a decision.

"Why," Nicely-Nicely says, "all she asks me is can I get her another piece of pie when she finishes the one in front of her."

Now at this, Joel Duffle throws down his knife, and pushes back his plate with all but two bites of his pie left on it, and says to the Boston characters like this:

"Gentlemen," he says, "I am licked. I cannot eat another mouthful.

You must admit I put up a game battle, but," he says, "it is useless for me to go on against this Judy who is asking for more pie before she even starts on what is before her. I am almost dying as it is, and I do not wish to destroy myself in a hopeless effort. Gentlemen," he says, "she is not human."

Well, of course this amounts to throwing in the old napkin and Nicely-Nicely stands up on his chair, and says:

"Three cheers for Miss Violette Shumberger!"

Then Nicely-Nicely gives the first cheer in person, but the effort over-taxes his strength, and he falls off the chair in a faint as Joel Duffle collapses under the table, and the doctors at the Clinic Hospital are greatly baffled to receive, from the same address at the same time, one patient who is suffering from undernourishment, and another patient who is unconscious from over-eating.

Well, in the meantime, after the excitement subsides, and wagers are settled, we take Miss Violette Shumberger to the main floor in Mindy's for a midnight snack, and when she speaks of her wonderful triumph, she is disposed to give much credit to Nicely-Nicely Jones.

"You see," Violette says, "what I really whispered to him is that I am a goner. I whisper to him that I cannot possibly take one bite of the pie if my life depends on it, and if he has any bets down to try and hedge them off as quickly as possible.

"I fear," she says, "that Nicely-Nicely will be greatly disappointed in my showing, but I have a confession to make to him when he gets out of the hospital. I forget about the contest," Violette says, "and eat my regular dinner of pig's knuckles and sauerkraut an hour before the contest starts and," she says, "I have no doubt this tends to affect my form somewhat. So," she says, "I owe everything to Nicely-Nicely's quick thinking."

It is several weeks after the great eating contest that I run into Miss Hilda Slocum on Broadway and it seems to me that she looks much better nourished than the last time I see her, and when I mention this she says:

"Yes," she says, "I cease dieting. I learn my lesson," she says. "I learn that male characters do not appreciate anybody who tries to ward off surplus tissue. What male characters wish is substance. Why," she says, "only a week ago my editor, Mr McBurgle, tells me he will love to take me dancing if only I get something on me for him to take hold of. I am very fond of dancing," she says.

"But," I say, "what of Nicely-Nicely Jones? I do not see him around lately."

"Why," Miss Hilda Slocum says, "do you not hear what this cad does? Why, as soon as he is strong enough to leave the hospital, he elopes with my dearest friend, Miss Violette Shumberger, leaving me a note saying something about two souls with but a single thought. They are down in Florida running a barbecue stand, and," she says, "the chances are, eating like seven mules."

"Miss Slocum," I says, "can I interest you in a portion of Mindy's chicken fricassee?"

"With dumplings?" Miss Hilda Slocum says. "Yes," she says, "you can. Afterwards I have a date to go dancing with Mr McBurgle. I am crazy about dancing," she says.

THE BET

Anton Chekhov

In "The Bet," Chekhov tells the strange story of a young man who bets twenty years of his life against a fortune and how his sense of values is drastically changed during his long years of solitary confinement.

IT WAS a dark autumn night. The old banker was pacing from corner to corner of his study, recalling to his mind the party he gave in the autumn fifteen years ago. There were many clever people at the party and much interesting conversation. They talked among other things of capital punishment. The guests, among them not a few scholars and journalists, for the most part disapproved of capital punishment. They found it obsolete as a means of punishment, unfitted to a Christian State and immoral. Some of them thought that capital punishment should be replaced universally by life-imprisonment.

"I don't agree with you," said the host. "I myself have experienced neither capital punishment nor life-imprisonment, but if one may judge *a priori*, then in my opinion capital punishment is more moral and more humane than imprisonment. Execution kills instantly, life-imprisonment kills by degrees. Who is the more humane executioner, one who kills you in a few seconds or one who draws the life out of you incessantly, for years?"

"They're both equally immoral," remarked one of the guests, "because their purpose is the same, to take away life. The State is not God. It has no right to take away that which it cannot give back, if it should so desire."

Among the company was a lawyer, a young man of about twenty-five. On being asked his opinion, he said:

"Capital punishment and life-imprisonment are equally immoral; but if I were offered the choice between them, I would certainly choose the second. It's better to live somehow than not to live at all."

There ensued a lively discussion. The banker who was then younger and more nervous suddenly lost his temper, banged his fist on the table, and turning to the young lawyer, cried out:

"It's a lie. I bet you two millions you wouldn't stick in a cell even for five years."

"If that's serious," replied the lawyer, "then I bet I'll stay not five but fifteen."

"Fifteen! Done!" cried the banker. "Gentlemen, I stake two millions."

"Agreed. You stake two millions, I my freedom," said the lawyer.

So this wild, ridiculous bet came to pass. The banker, who at that time had too many millions to count, spoiled and capricious, was beside himself with rapture. During supper he said to the lawyer jokingly:

"Come to your senses, young man, before it's too late. Two millions are nothing to me, but you stand to lose three or four of the best years of your life. I say three or four, because you'll never stick it out any longer. Don't forget either, you unhappy man, that voluntary is much heavier than enforced imprisonment. The idea that you have the right to free yourself at any moment will poison the whole of your life in the cell. I pity you."

And now the banker pacing from corner to corner, recalled all this and asked himself:

"Why did I make this bet? What's the good? The lawyer loses fifteen years of his life and I throw away two millions. Will it convince people that capital punishment is worse or better than imprisonment for life. No, No! all stuff and rubbish. On my part, it was the caprice of a well-fed man; on the lawyer's pure greed of gold."

He recollected further what happened after the evening party. It was decided that the lawyer must undergo his imprisonment under the strictest observation, in a garden-wing of the banker's house. It was agreed that during the period he would be deprived of the right to cross the threshold, to see living people, to hear human voices, and to receive letters and newspapers. He was permitted to have a musical instrument, to read books, to write letters, to drink wine and smoke tobacco. By the agreement he could communicate, but only in silence, with the outside world through a little window specially constructed for this purpose. Everything necessary, books, music, wine, he could receive in any quantity sending a note through the window. The agreement provided for all the minutest details, which made the confinement strictly solitary, and it obliged the lawyer to remain exactly fifteen years from twelve o'clock of November 14th 1870 to twelve o'clock of November 14th 1885. The least attempt on his part to violate the conditions, to escape if only for two minutes before the time freed the banker from the obligation to pay him the two millions.

During the first year of imprisonment, the lawyer, as far as possible to judge from his short notes, suffered terribly with loneliness and boredom. From his wing day and night came the sound of the piano. He rejected wine and tobacco. "Wine," he wrote, "excites desires, and desires are the chief foes of a prisoner; besides, nothing is more boring than to drink good wine alone," and tobacco spoils the air in his room. During the first year the lawyer was sent books of light character; novels with a complicated love interest, stories of crime and fantasy, comedies, and so on.

In the second year the piano was heard no longer and the lawyer asked only for classics. In the fifth year, music was heard again, and the prisoner asked for wine. Those who watched him said that during the whole of that year he was only eating, drinking, and lying on his bed. He yawned often and talked angrily to himself. Books he did not read. Sometimes at nights he would sit down to write. He would write for a long time and tear it all up in the morning. More than once he was heard to weep.

In the second half of the sixth year, the prisoner began zealously to study languages, philosophy, and history. He fell on these subjects so hungrily that the banker hardly had time to get books enough for him. In the space of four years about six hundred volumes were bought at his request. It was while that passion lasted that the banker received the following letter from the prisoner: "My dear gaoler, I am writing these lines in six languages. Show them to experts. Let them read them. If they do not find one single mistake, I beg you to give orders to have a gun fired off in the garden. By the noise I shall know that my efforts have not been in vain. The geniuses of all ages and countries speak in different languages; but in them all burns the same flame. Oh, if you knew my heavenly

348

happiness now that I can understand them!'' The prisoner's desire was fulfilled. Two shots were fired in the garden by the banker's order.

Later on, after the tenth year, the lawyer sat immovable before his table and read only the New Testament. The banker found it strange that a man who in four years had mastered six hundred erudite volumes, should have spent nearly a year in reading one book, easy to understand and by no means thick. The New Testament was then replaced by the history of religions and theology.

During the last two years of his confinement the prisoner read an extraordinary amount, quite haphazard. Now he would apply himself to the natural sciences, then would read Byron or Shakespeare. Notes used to come from him in which he asked to be sent at the same time a book on chemistry, a text-book of medicine, a novel, and some treatise on philosophy or theology. He read as though he were swimming in the sea among the broken pieces of wreckage, and in his desire to save his life was eagerly grasping one piece after another.

II

The banker recalled all this, and thought:

"To-morrow at twelve o'clock he receives his freedom. Under the agreement, I shall have to pay him two millions. If I pay, it's all over with me. I am ruined for ever. . . .''

Fifteen years before he had too many millions to count, but now he was afraid to ask himself which he had more of, money or debts. Gambling on the Stock-Exchange, risky speculation, and the recklessness of which he could not rid himself even in old age, had gradually brought his business to decay; and the fearless, self-confident, proud man of business had become an ordinary banker, trembling at every rise and fall in the market.

"That cursed bet,'' murmured the old man clutching his head in despair . . . "Why didn't the man die? He's only forty years old. He will take away my last farthing, marry, enjoy life, gamble on the Exchange, and I will look on like an envious beggar and hear the same words from him every day: 'I'm obliged to you for the happiness of my life. Let me help you.' No, it's too much! The only escape from bankruptcy and disgrace — is that the man should die.''

The clock had just struck three. The banker was listening. In the house everyone was asleep, and one could hear only the frozen trees whining outside the windows. Trying to make no sound, he took out of his safe the key of the door which had not been opened for fifteen years, put on his overcoat, and went out of the house. The garden was dark and cold. It was raining. A keen damp wind hovered howling over all the garden and gave the trees no rest. Though he strained his eyes, the banker could see neither the ground, nor the white statues, nor the garden-wing, nor the trees. Approaching the place where the garden wing stood, he called the watchman twice. There was no answer. Evidently the watchman had taken shelter from the bad weather and was now asleep somewhere in the kitchen or the greenhouse.

"If I have the courage to fulfil my intention," thought the old man, "the suspicion will fall on the watchman first of all."

In the darkness he groped for the stairs and the door and entered the hall of the garden-wing, then poked his way into a narrow passage and struck a match. Not a soul was there. Someone's bed, with no bedclothes on it, stood there, and an iron stove was dark in the corner. The seals on the door that led into the prisoner's room were unbroken.

When the match went out, the old man, trembling from agitation, peeped into the little window.

In the prisoner's room a candle was burning dim. The prisoner himself sat by the table. Only his back, the hair on his head and his hands were visible. On the table, the two chairs, the carpet by the table open books were strewn.

Five minutes passed and the prisoner never once stirred. Fifteen years' confinement had taught him to sit motionless. The banker tapped on the window with his finger, but the prisoner gave no movement in reply. Then the banker cautiously tore the seals from the door and put the key into the lock. The rusty lock gave a hoarse groan and the door creaked. The banker expected instantly to hear a cry of surprise and the sound of steps. Three minutes passed and it was as quiet behind the door as it has been before. He made up his mind to enter.

Before the table sat a man, unlike an ordinary human being. It was a skeleton, with tightdrawn skin, with a woman's long curly hair, and a shaggy beard. The colour of his face was yellow, of an earthy shade: the cheeks were sunken, the back long and narrow, and the hand upon which he leaned his hairy head was so lean and skinny that it was painful to look upon. His hair was already silvering with grey, and no one who glanced at the senile emaciation of the face would have believed that he was only forty years old. On the table, before his bended head, lay a sheet of paper on which something was written in a tiny hand.

"Poor devil," thought the banker, "he's asleep and probably seeing millions in his dreams. I have only to take and throw this half-dead thing on the bed, smother him a moment with the pillow, and the most careful examination will find no trace of unnatural death. But, first, let us read what he has written here."

The banker took the sheet from the table and read:

To-morrow at twelve o'clock midnight, I shall obtain my freedom and the right to mix with people. But before I leave this room and see the sun I think it necessary to say a few words to you. On my own clear conscience and before God who sees me I declare to you that I despise freedom, life, health, and all that your books call the blessings of the world.

For fifteen years I have diligently studied earthly life. True, I saw neither the earth nor the people, but in your books I drank fragrant wine, sang songs, hunted deer and wild boar in the forests, loved women. . . . And beautiful women, like clouds ethereal, created by the magic of your poets' genius, visited me by night and whispered me wonderful tales, which made my head drunken. In your books I climbed the summits of Elbruz and Mont Blanc and saw from thence how the sun rose in the morning, and in the evening overflowed the sky, the ocean and the mountain ridges with a purple gold. I saw from thence how above me lightnings glimmered cleaving the clouds; I saw green forests, fields, rivers, lakes, cities; I heard syrens singing, and the playing of the pipes of Pan; I touched the wings of beautiful devils who came flying to me to speak of God. . . . In your books I cast myself into bottomless abysses, worked miracles, burned cities to the ground, preached new religions, conquered whole countries. . . .

Your books gave me wisdom. All that unwearying human thought created in the centuries is compressed to a little lump in my skull. I know that I am more clever than you all.

And I despise your books, despise all wordly blessings and wisdom. Everything is void, frail, visionary and delusive like a mirage. Though you be proud and wise and beautiful, yet will death wipe you from the face of the earth like the mice underground; and your posterity, your history, and the immortality of your men of genius will be as frozen slag, burnt down together with the terrestrial globe.

You are mad, and gone the wrong way. You take lie for truth and ugliness for beauty. You would marvel if by certain conditions there should suddenly grow on apple and orange trees, instead of fruit, frogs and lizards, and if roses should begin to breathe the odour of a sweating horse. So do I marvel at you, who have bartered heaven for earth. I do not want to understand you.

That I may show you in deed my contempt for that by which you live, I waive the two millions of which I once dreamed as of paradise, and which I now despise. That I may deprive myself of my right to them, I shall come out from here five minutes before the stipulated term, and thus shall violate the agreement.

When he had read, the banker put the sheet on the table, kissed the head of the strange man, and began to weep. He went out of the wing. Never at any other time, not even after his terrible losses on the Exchange, had he felt such contempt for himself as now. Coming home, he lay down on his bed, but agitation and tears kept him long from sleep. . . .

The next morning the poor watchman came running to him and told him that they had seen the man who lived in the wing climbing through the window into the garden. He had gone to the gate and disappeared. Together with his servants the banker went instantly to the wing and established the escape of his prisoner. To avoid unnecessary rumours he took the paper with the renunciation from the table and, on his return, locked it in his safe.